MODERN
WARSHIP
Design and Development

Perhaps the most revolutionary naval
development of the postwar period has been the
surface-to-air missile, although at first nothing
short of a large cruiser could support a worthwhile
SAM battery. Here the second US guided missile
cruiser, USS *Canberra*, is helped into position for
the International Naval Review at Jamestown, 12
June 1957.

MODERN WARSHIP
Design and Development

By NORMAN FRIEDMAN
Hudson Institute New York

Drawings by John Roberts

CONWAY MARITIME PRESS/GREENWICH

To my wife Rhea

First published in Great Britain 1979
by
Conway Maritime Press Ltd
2 Nelson Road, Greenwich,
London SE10 9JB

ISBN 0 85177 147 5

Designed by Jon Blackmore
Printed in Great Britain by
Butler & Tanner Ltd, Frome

Contents

Acknowledgements

This book could not have been written without the kind assistance of many friends, particularly Norman Polmar, John Lewis, Joel Bloom, A D Baker III, Capt James W Kehoe USN, and August Billones. Others asked not to be named. For their comments and corrections, many thanks; the errors of fact and understanding are my own. For illustrations I am indebted to Dr Giorgia Arra, A D Baker III, Paul Beaver, Ken Brower, Robert Carlisle (US Navy Still Photo Branch), Stefano Cioglia, Earl Gray, Charles Haberlein (US Naval Historical Center), J A Jedrlinic, Len Pierce (Vosper Thornycroft Ltd), Norman Polmar and Dr Robert Scheina, to the British Ministry of Defence (Navy), the French Ministère de la Défense (Marine) and the Dutch Ministerie van Defensie (Marine), as well as to several companies, among them Boeing, British Aerospace, the British Hovercraft Corporation, the FMC Corporation, Israel Aircraft Industries, Italcantieri, the P & O Steam Navigation Co, the Plessey Co Ltd, C & S Taylor and Yarrow (Shipbuilders) Ltd; uncredited photos in the book are USN Official. Susan Wiedner of the Congressional and Public Affairs Office of the US Naval Sea Systems Command was extremely helpful in having several key illustrations cleared for publication. I must also thank the many personnel of the former US Naval Ship Engineering Center who helped me in my research on US destroyer and frigate design, which contributed markedly to the present volume, most notably Reuven Leopold, Charles Wiseman (now retired) and Mrs Mildred Grissom. I am grateful to my wife Rhea for her encouragement and assistance, both in reading early drafts and in the choice of photographs, not to mention her toleration of many dreary weekends.

Norman Friedman

Introduction

The modern warships of this book are surface combatants: frigates, destroyers and cruisers. 'Modern' denotes the post-1945 naval world. Although in the past all three types differed very considerably in role and in equipment, they have tended since World War II to merge into one type. More and more the categories of the past have come to denote only differences in size and in level of capability. The other major categories of postwar combatants – carriers, submarines, and fast attack craft – require separate treatment. The restriction to the post-1945 world is essential: 1945 was a great watershed in naval development, both tactical and technical. Although navies East and West differ considerably in their strategic and tactical ideas, and hence in the sorts of ships they have built, they share a common heritage arising out of the experience of World War II. All have faced in common a revolution in the naval environment, which separates the modern surface warship from its predecessor. The two may also share a common designator and even a common hull form, but not a common rationale or a common mode of operation.

The current range of warship designators reflects the postwar merging of what were once quite distinct categories. In this sense the present period of ferment in warship development recalls the 1860s, 1870s and 1880s, when a similar revolution was under way. During World War II the Royal Navy, for example, included among its ships destroyers intended for fleet operations (but often assigned to convoy protection), sloops, designed for coastal AA and ASW escort as well as minesweeping, corvettes and frigates, the last two entirely (at first) for ASW and distinguished only by size and performance. The destroyer force included some very small vessels ('Hunt' class) best described rather as fast AA frigates. After 1945 the corvettes and sloops were merged, quite logically, with the frigates. Cruisers were much larger ships; even when British destroyers attained cruiser dimensions (in the 'County' class and later in the *Bristol*), they retained their destroyer designations. At present the primary distinction appears to be that British destroyers are armed with area defense SAMs, whereas frigates are not. Both classes have about the same speed and endurance; it may be argued that destroyers are potentially self-supporting or that they are most effective in a task force which may be subject to heavy air attack. At the least this is not quite the distinction envisaged in 1945.

In the US Navy by way of contrast, there appeared destroyer escorts, essentially small destroyers for convoy escort; they were partly inspired by the British 'Hunt' class. There were also US frigates, patterned on the British type, and so close in characteristics as to be indistinguishable from the destroyer escorts; and there were lesser ASW craft ('patrol craft' and minesweepers) roughly equivalent to the British corvette. After the war the US Navy began to build a new class of super-destroyers for carrier task force screening duties; to distinguish them from the destroyers they were designated 'DL' rather than 'DD'. However, they were referred to as 'frigates'. They were cruiser-sized, but, unlike the earlier cruisers, they were not intended for independent operations; moreover, the US Navy had much larger ships in service which it called cruisers, so that a new designation seemed appropriate. The destroyer escorts retained their DE designator but became 'ocean escorts'; a coastal escort program never materialized. There were also 'escort destroyers' (DDE), destroyers converted to improve their ASW qualities and so roughly equivalent to the British 'Weapon' class; for a time they were described as 'destroyer escorts' and considered the true successors of the wartime DEs, given improvements in submarine performance. The whole system became unpopular as the Soviets began to designate their own DL-sized ships 'cruisers' and so appeared extremely formidable in fleet-to-fleet comparisons. Moreover, outside the United States the entire English-speaking world meant a rather limited ship when it said 'frigate'. Matters came to a head when a new Ocean Escort, which became the current *Perry*, was designated a 'patrol frigate' (PF), in the same series of hull numbers which had included the wartime frigates and a series of postwar corvette-sized ASW ships for foreign customers. In June 1975, all Ocean Escorts became frigates (FF, or FFG if armed with area defense SAMs), as in the Royal Navy. The former frigates, for the most part, became cruisers. However, the earliest missile frigates, which were smaller than some destroyers, became missile destroyers (DDG). Only the old destroyer designation survived untouched.

This system of categories is far from universal. France, for example, never had a destroyer category. Before World War II she had *torpilleurs* (torpedo boats), which in other navies would be considered destroyers) and *contre-torpilleurs* (torpedo boat killers, or super-destroyers) for fleet operations, as well as *avisos* (literally despatch boats) for colonial operations and trade route defense. In the early 1950s the French very logically classed their new ships as *escorteurs*, either *d'escadre* (of the fleet, therefore destroyers) or of convoys. The former were later redesignated *torpilleurs*, and when the French resumed construction of ships for colonial operations they were styled *avisos-escorteurs*. As in the United States, the French styled their new missile task force escorts *frégates* (frigates). However, when these ships became too expensive the French adopted the old designation *corvette*, which had, in the days of sail, denoted a ship below the frigate class. Now the new coastal escorts are rated *avisos*. None of these designators refers to much more than relative size.

The Soviet system is somewhat more functional. As in the West, the Soviets began with traditional designations. However, they invented new ones when they adopted ship-to-ship missiles on a large scale, such as 'rocket cruiser' (RKR) for the 'Kyndas'. At present most Soviet warships are designated ASW ships, divided by size into ASW cruisers (such as *Kiev* and *Moskva*), and then large ('bolshoi') and small ASW ships. A 'Krivak', for example, is a large ASW ship (BPK) – as is a 'Kara' class 'cruiser'. One Soviet category which has no Western counterpart is the SKR, a coast guard ship. Such ships are often styled 'frigates' or 'escorts' in the West ('Rigas'), but the Soviet designation reveals their role.

The present work continues the pattern of a previous book, *Battleship Design and Development,* and deals with the compromises of warship design, but shifts its focus to the present. Unfortunately the security restrictions imposed by all major navies make it difficult to present sufficient data to permit the reader to estimate the detailed characteristics of most modern warships. For example, the United States Navy is extremely secretive concerning the performance of its nuclear warships, although it is alone among major Western navies in permitting the publication of weight breakdowns of its conventional ones. Despite such restrictions, it is possible, in the chapters which follow, to give a qualitative picture of the considerations which shape modern warships. Some particular cases can be discussed in detail. The author is fortunate to have been able to study the postwar evolution of US warships in considerable detail, using official source materials. Most importantly, in the US case it was often possible to discover the alternatives rejected and the reasons given at the time. The post-1945 evolution of other navies cannot be examined in anything like the same detail – this holds for weapon development as well as for the design of the ships themselves. It is hoped that the US bias which has resulted has not upset the balance of this account too greatly.

For all the world's navies, the postwar period began with a continuation of earlier classes of warships. Here the light cruiser *Sverdlov* lies at anchor for the Coronation Review of the Fleet at Spithead, 10 June 1953. Although of postwar construction, *Sverdlov* class vessels, like many of their contemporaries, were modified versions of ships laid down before the outbreak of World War II. *(CPL)*

Western navies spent the years immediately after 1945 completing ships of their war programs, which reflected some of the continuing changes in the roles of navies. The large British *Daring* class destroyers, for example, were equipped both with classical destroyer weapons – guns and torpedoes – and with Squid, a powerful ahead-throwing ASW weapon far superior to the wartime depth charge. Much of the transformation was subtle: Squid required a specialized depth-finding sonar, not shown in any above-water view, and ASW required expanded electronics, such as the HF/DF which caps *Dainty's* foremast in this 21 November 1960 photograph. Unlike contemporary US destroyers, this ship has no large air search radar, only Type 293 Target Indication. The familiar British UHF D/F antenna, which somewhat resembles a candlestick, appears both on the port yardarm and, unusually, on a stub mast aft. *(CPL)*

A few navies continued to order 'traditional' warships. The Venezuelan *Nueva Esparta*, when completed, was almost covered in twin 40mm guns, but only two of these were left after her Seacat system was installed. The missile system is visible, with its director, forward of No 3 gunhouse, and Hedgehog can be seen abreast the bridge, in this September 1970 photograph. The ship is unusual in having two air search radars, an L-band SPS-12 (US) at the masthead and an S-band AWS-2 (British) further down; the latter probably functions as a surface search set, with the small waveguide set just below the SPS-12 operating for navigation. The arrays of small dipoles at the yardarm ends are for tactical radio communication – their length suggests UHF operation.

CHAPTER ONE

A Revolution in Naval Affairs

Every warship is a compromise, ultimately between the desires of the naval staff which orders it and the economic limits set by the government buying it. What distinguishes post-1945 warships from their predecessors is the terms of compromise, set by a new regime of naval tactics and technology. The moving force has been the rise of modern electronics, which buys both increased weapon effectiveness and much increased weapon range. The latter development sharply reduces the value of tactical speed – modern surface warships tend to be slower than their predecessors. Moreover, many function more as sensor platforms within a task force than as individual combatants. This role has become extremely important – communications within task forces have nowadays become so effective that, for example, one ship can operate as a radar platform for another.

SOME FUNDAMENTAL DESIGN
CONSIDERATIONS

Naval electronics is now almost the dominant factor in warship cost; by the late 1960s it was commonly said that ship steel was the least expensive element of the cost of a new destroyer. The important question was how much armament, and, even more, what sort of command and control system, the ship was to carry. That is why the *Spruance*, at 7000 tons virtually the equivalent of a prewar light cruiser, is relatively inexpensive for her size. Moreover, within a weapon system, fire control was quite often far more expensive than the weapon itself. For example, in 1961 the US Navy attempted to design a new austere escort, with some minimal missile armament, for convoy protection in mid-ocean. It was assumed that the cost of a Tartar battery was proportional to the number of missiles carried (ie, to the complexity of missile launcher and magazine); those concerned with the new design thought they could cut costs very considerably by adopting an austere twelve-missile launcher in place of the conventional forty. What they never reckoned with was that Tartar itself, whether installed in a magazine of twelve missiles or forty, required the same fire control computer, and the same search and guidance radars. They only realized their error when the Bureau of Ships cost estimates appeared. The rest of the story carries a similar point. Other requirements developed during the design were an improved (SQS-26 rather than -23) sonar and 1500 miles' more endurance; it appears that those who drew up the Characteristics for this ship had in mind a less expensive development of the *Charles F Adams* class missile destroyer, which could not be built in sufficient numbers to replace the large fleet of World War II hulls. In fact the combination of a much larger sonar and a one-third increase in endurance considerably increased the size of the hull, adding 500 tons even though 300 had been saved by the adoption of a new pressure-fired boiler. The cost goal was $25 million (1959 values), but the final estimate came out at $38 million, all due to electronics (sonar and unanticipated remaining Tartar costs) and added hull size (sonar and ship endurance). In the end the endurance and sonar seemed more important than the low cost, and the 'austere' destroyer became the *Belknap* class missile cruiser. Its destroyer origin shows in its 5in gun; its high cost made the more effective Terrier system seem well worth while.

At least until the advent of integrated circuits, electronics always carried with it the requirement for large numbers of technicians; every advance increases their number, hence the required complement of a ship. Moreover, technicians are more expensive than the average sailor; in any case, at least in the West, the general improvement in the standard of living since 1945 has made arduous sea duty less and less attractive. Since 1970 in particular, the need to reduce costs has led to more and more automation: both gas turbine powerplants and lightweight gun mounts are to some extent examples of this trend. The need to keep trained technicians has led to constant pressure, at least in the West, to improve habitability, which in turn means to accept larger and larger ships. Many of the pressures are indirect. For example, a demand for more headroom leads in turn to more space between decks and therefore to a deeper hull; but that hull, wrapped around the same volume of equipment, would have too small a beam to be stable. Therefore the ship must grow as a whole, even when reductions in the number of weapons allow for some economy in complement. The relatively low cost of ship steel makes roominess, which in turn makes for crew comfort, relatively inexpensive. Unfortunately, some critics of modern

The US Navy ended World War II with a large, modern destroyer fleet; it was impossible to convince Congress to replace it with ships better adapted to postwar conditions, and the navy spent the 1950s in the unhappy knowledge that most of its destroyers would wear out at the same time. The Fleet Rehabilitation and Modernization (FRAM) program was an attempt to forestall this problem; one of its products, the destroyer *Rowan*, is shown here (April 1965). In effect, the capability in anti-air warfare, except for an air search radar, was given up in favor of ASW and shore bombardment. There were three separate ASW systems on board: the lightweight torpedo (Mk 32 tubes in 'B' position), ASROC (amidships, with reloads abreast the hangar aft), and a drone helicopter (DASH).

warship design, who are used to the very crowded vessels of the past, assume that costs are proportional to hull size, and consider modern Western warships extravagant 'pleasure yachts'.

If a ship designed to, say, 1956 habitability standards is redesigned for greater habitability without any change in weapons or sensors, relatively little cost is imposed, and there may even be a bonus in seakeeping performance. However, the larger ship will appear grossly underarmed by comparison with her forebears, and her designers will feel strong pressures to accommodate more and more weapons and sensors, regardless of the cost these may impose, indeed, regardless of the inefficiency of cramming them together. The inexpensive extra ship steel then serves only as a magnet for very expensive equipment, and all present express themselves as depressed by the spiralling cost of ships. The only cure for this disease is strong design discipline, easy to prescribe but very difficult to apply. Recent US practice offers one example. The *Spruance* specification called for the weapon and sensor suit of a 3000-ton frigate in a 7000-ton hull, to provide high endurance and good rough-weather high speed performance (for carrier escort) as well as the potential for later conversion to an anti-aircraft (AAW) missile configuration. All that empty space must have been tempting, but the design of the ship was out of the Navy's hands, at Litton – and Litton found it easy to stick to its original mandate.

Litton's experience is reminiscent of a remark made two decades earlier by William Gibbs, the naval architect. In response to Navy complaints that new destroyers were not fast enough, Gibbs commented that ship steel was relatively inexpensive and that he could easily buy speed with ship length – if only the Navy would agree to avoid driving up cost by filling that extra length with weapons. In practice, the Navy enforced a kind of design discipline by driving down displacement, at the cost, however, of seakeeping and speed performance. This approach was useful before the advent of modern electronics and particularly of modern missiles, because warships were generally 'weight-critical': a hull sufficiently large to create enough displacement to carry the weights of all ship components could easily accommodate them, since they were relatively dense.

Electronic components and missile systems are anything but dense. Electronic systems are light, and they require space around them for access. Missiles are far lighter, per unit volume, than were the guns and shells they have replaced and modern warships generally lack the single densest component of the ships of the past, armor. A ship can be thought of as the sum of its components: hull, machinery, armament, command-and-control (including sensors), and lesser items. Most modern surface combatants are

The heavy gun ships which had formed the core of fleets before World War II were reduced to supporting roles, but their large accommodations made them useful as flagships. Here the cruiser *Los Angeles* is shown in Hawaii, 26 August 1961. She had been converted to fire the Regulus strategic missile from a new sponson on her fantail, visible here by its shadow; guidance was by the SPQ-2 radar atop her mainmast, with missile acquisition by the SPS-12 air search radar which had been installed in place of her after main battery director – an alteration which in itself says a great deal about the changing relative roles of gun and missile. Her flagship status is shown by the variety of radio antennas which sprout from hull and turrets; her foremast has been reinforced to support a long-range (SPS-37A) air search radar. ECM gear occupies the platform on her second funnel, with a jamming transmitter in the little hut.

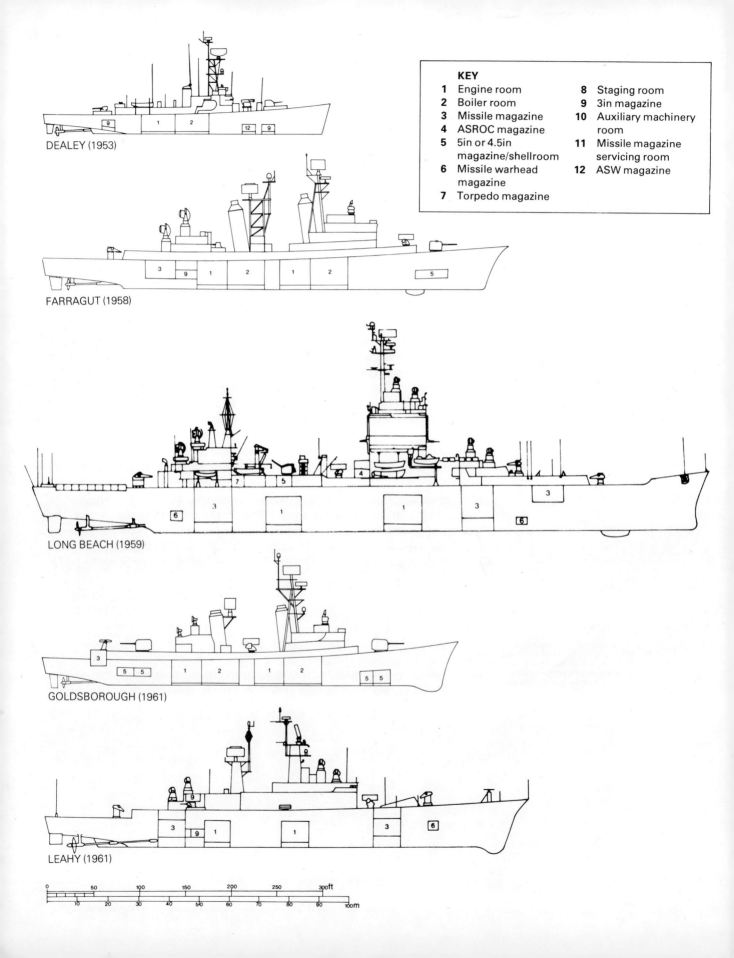

KEY

1 Engine room
2 Boiler room
3 Missile magazine
4 ASROC magazine
5 5in or 4.5in magazine/shellroom
6 Missile warhead magazine
7 Torpedo magazine
8 Staging room
9 3in magazine
10 Auxiliary machinery room
11 Missile magazine servicing room
12 ASW magazine

DEALEY (1953)

FARRAGUT (1958)

LONG BEACH (1959)

GOLDSBOROUGH (1961)

LEAHY (1961)

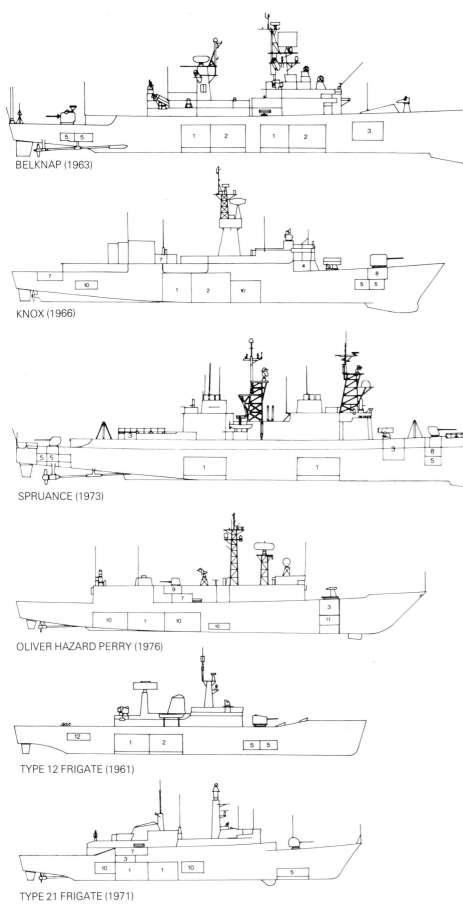

BELKNAP (1963)

KNOX (1966)

SPRUANCE (1973)

OLIVER HAZARD PERRY (1976)

TYPE 12 FRIGATE (1961)

TYPE 21 FRIGATE (1971)

These comparative profiles of a selection of postwar naval vessels show only magazines and engine rooms, but note that in the steam-powered ships there are also boiler rooms, of roughly the same length, consuming additional centerline space. In the nuclear cruiser *Long Beach*, clear space above the reactor, which is presumably somewhere between the engine rooms, is required to permit access to reactor fuel rods for refueling. The location right aft of the second 5in/54 in the *Spruance* precludes its replacement by the much larger 8in/55 Mk 71; space forward of it is reserved for later mounting of a Mk 26 missile launching system (planned refit for AAW). The small above-decks missile magazine is for Sea Sparrow, not yet fitted. *Spruance*'s ASROC installation is unique in that the magazine is *below* the mount, not abaft it. This arrangement was adopted in view of plans ultimately to replace ASROC with a multi-purpose Mk 26. There are no ASROC reloads in earlier cruisers (CGN9, CG16) but the *Belknaps* (CG26 class) carry up to twenty ASROCs in their missile magazines forward; this is larger than the 40-missile magazine in the *Leahy* (CG16). Finally, the *Belknap* drawing shows her refitted with quadruple Harpoon SSM cannisters aft, as well as two Vulcan-Phalanx guns.

Compared to modern destroyers, frigates – both British and US – do not show any dispersion of engine rooms which would guarantee the survival of their propulsion in the event of a torpedo hit: compare the Type 21, for example with the US *Spruance*. The *Leander* and the Type 21 are roughly similar in size, but differ markedly in internal arrangement. The requirement for two separate auxiliary machinery spaces in the gas turbine Type 21 is a consequence of the fact that without steam there can be no turbo-generators – separate generating powerplants are required. The location of the missile magazine far from the Seacat launcher emphasizes the point defense character of this weapon. Note, too, the location of the special torpedo magazine near both the Mk 32 tubes and the helicopter, an arrangement reminiscent of the *Knox* class.

volume- rather than weight-critical: there is not enough space in the hull to accommodate everything its displacement can (and must) carry, and so a great deal is packed into a bulky superstructure, which may sometimes appear as a forecastle almost the length of the hull itself. Volume criticality shows in the bulky superstructures of modern warships, and, indirectly, in the way in which essential weapon control systems such as computers have to be packed into these vulnerable spaces. Hull dimensions are often fixed by the need to support weights in the ship, and the excess volume requirement flows over into the superstructure. However, in some cases the ship is also *length*-critical: everything must be packed in along the centerline.

In each case, the way to reduce ship cost is generally to reduce the quantity in which she is critical, which used to be displacement. Now it is often length, and the British Type 42 is a good example of a minimum-length ship. Her length aft of the superstructure is dominated by a helicopter pad, whose size is fixed by the size of the helicopter she operates. Then there is a hangar, again fixed in size, a missile guidance radar, radar masts and uptakes, bridgework (with a second missile guidance radar on top), and, forward of the bridge, her missile launcher. The distance between the launcher and the bridge is set by blast considerations, and probably the length of the bow forward of this is set by seakeeping (launcher wetness) requirements. The minimum-length design philosophy is evidenced by the position of the 4.5in gun so far foward as to be probably rather wet, and that of the helicopter pad so far aft as to be in a region of considerable ship motion: better practice might have set the pad forward of the after quarter-length. Even so, helicopter facilities account for a very large fraction of a ship's length. Writing in 1962, a Canadian naval officer remarked that only with the advent of large frigate-borne helicopters had ships become truly length-critical. Prior to that date, the main consideration in destroyer and frigate length was often powering: it is far easier to drive a long rather than a short ship through the sea at a given speed.

Most navies were unable to join the missile revolution, at least not immediately. That did not make them uninterested in anti-aircraft warfare; cruisers were splendid platforms for task force radars. This is the Dutch cruiser *De Zeven Provincien*. Her 6in guns, built by Bofors, were capable of anti-aircraft fire at long range, and her radars were suitable for fighter control as well as for gunlaying. Reading from forward to aft, they are: M-45 (57mm director), ZW-01 (navigation radar), M-25 (6in fire control, atop her bridge), VI-01 ('orange peel' height-finder), DA-02 (target indicator), LW-01 (air search, on mainmast), and then M-25 and M-45 again. All were of Dutch manufacture. The guns were all Bofors types; the secondary weapon, of 57mm caliber, was also employed by the French Navy. *(Naval Historical Department, RNethN)*

A major factor in the trend towards length-critical ships is that weapons and sensors are generally mounted on the centerline, for maximum effectiveness, thereby assuming high reliability. The overwhelming Western trend in a period of greater and greater unit cost is to cut the number of individual weapons, launchers and sensors, in the name of quality over quantity. It courts disaster in action, since a ship can take only a very few hits. The need for clear arcs for search radar in any case implies that only one or two can be fitted. Their vulnerability in battle is so much greater than that of fire control systems and weapons as to justify such a philosophy. For example, radars which must be mounted high in a ship can be disabled if fragments cut their waveguides. On the other hand, the single launcher or sensor faces dangers other than those posed by enemy attack. It may, for example, require maintenance at an awkward moment, or it may simply jam. For example, in an anti-aircraft action off Vietnam in 1972, a US frigate had only one (out of two) guidance radars available; the other lacked spare parts. The ship was fortunate that her full designed multiple-target capability – which required both radars – was not being tested.

All of these trends are somewhat less pronounced in the Soviet Navy. Unlike Western navies, the Soviet fleet tends to do its maintenance at shore bases; major assemblies are removed, and sent back to the factory. Such a system minimizes the need for trained technicians at sea, and is appropriate to a navy chronically short of experienced manpower. It permits the use of smaller crews, which in turn make ships smaller. Soviet standards of habitability are also lower than those in Western navies, which is appropriate to a society in which civilian life is generally harsher than it is in the West. To some extent the Soviets, at least in the past, have insured against the failure of critical equipment simply by duplicating it. This is not without its costs; for example, a ship with two air search radars only one of which operates at any one time will have significant blind spots, although it will have one air search set available if the other fails at sea.

GUNS OR MISSILES?

A fundamental change shared by all navies is the rise of self-propelled missiles, which alter the relationship between the power of the weapon and the demands that weapon places on the ship launching it. Self-propulsion eliminates both recoil effects on a ship and, generally, the need for elaborate launching equipment (ie, heavy guns); the first self-propelled missiles – torpedoes – could be fired from very small craft indeed and yet could carry the explosive equivalent of the largest shells. Another way to describe the relation between ship and missile is to say that the balance in investment has shifted from a relatively inexpensive round fired from an expensive weapon provided with an elaborate system of fire control, to the opposite, an extremely expensive individual round requiring, often, very little in the way of a fixed investment in launcher or in fire control, the latter depending upon the extent to which the missile is self-guiding as well as self-propelled. It follows that the missile is far larger than the equivalent gun round (although modern missile ranges are such that the equivalent guns would be rather hard to find) and hence that if it is carried in anything like substantial quantities it requires elaborate reloading gear.

Thus for missions in which one or a few very accurate shots suffice, missiles provide quite small ships with the firepower equivalent of the capital ships of the past. For example, during much of the battleship era it was assumed that only 5 to 10 per cent of rounds fired at a moving target

France also completed all-gun cruisers after 1945; her *De Grasse*, shown here at Jamestown in 1957, had been laid down as a conventional cruiser before the war, but was completed instead as an anti-aircraft ship for task force operations. The French Navy developed its own twin 5in/54 semi-automatic dual-purpose gun, which armed two cruisers and the *Surcouf* class fleet destroyers; it was designed to use available US 5in/54 ammunition. This twin mount achieved a rate of fire roughly equivalent to that of the contemporary US automatic single (Mk 42) mount, but at a high cost in personnel. The smaller gunhouses are for Bofors 57mm guns, also used in other contemporary French warships. *De Grasse* had the usual pair of air search radars: a two-dimensional air search set on her foremast (DRBV-23) and a height-finder (DRBI-10) on a stump abaft her funnel – presumably this had been set low to reduce corrosion due to smoke. The Dutch preferred to set their radars very high, and to bring down their smoke pipes; their designs, in fact, foreshadowed the later US 'macks'.

would hit. Thus a battleship carrying 100 rounds per gun might actually make no more than 5 or 10 hits per gun, even were she to exhaust her ammunition. In practice such a ship might fire up to forty salvoes in an engagement, for perhaps 20 to 40 hits. On the other hand, many manufacturers of anti-ship missiles such as Exocet claim hit probabilities as high as 75 per cent, so that the same 20 to 40 hits would require only 25 to 50 weapons. The converted US heavy cruisers of the *Albany* class carried 102 Talos, a weapon considerably heavier than Exocet, on about one-third the displacement of a classical battleship. Moreoover, terminal homing ensured a high degree of accuracy for Talos well beyond classical battleship ranges: in 1968, for example, a US missile cruiser (*Long Beach*) shot down two MiG fighters over Vietnam at ranges beyond 65 miles, and one variant of the Talos anti-aircraft missile was intended specifically for attacks on North Vietnamese radar positions. Nor need every missile warship be huge: US frigates of the *Perry* class can, if they carry no anti-aircraft missiles, accommodate 40 Harpoon anti-ship weapons, each of which can carry roughly the equivalent of a 10in shell to a range of 60 or 70 miles, with highly accurate radar terminal homing.

All this smacks of charlatanism: surely there is some price to be paid, especially as the reader will have noticed the resurgence of the medium-calibre gun in several navies of late. Perhaps the most important factor is the high cost per round associated with the missile. For some applications no single round, however accurate, can suffice. For example, in fire support in an amphibious operation, what is important is a combination of area destruction and continuous fire to keep the defenders neutralized. Both tasks require large numbers of individual projectiles, and at least the second carries little requirement for accuracy. This argument was the principal reason for American development of the lightweight 8in gun: when it became clear in the early 1960s that the cruisers then providing US Marines with their heavy fire support would soon have to be retired, development began on a weapon which could be mounted either in a new generation of amphibious support ship (the abortive LFS) or aboard a destroyer or (then) frigate. Ironically, in the past few years the development of laser-guided artillery shells has offered the promise of missile accuracy with the low per-round cost of guns. However, the missiles still possess formidable advantages in warhead weight (compared to launcher weight) and in range; rocket-assisted projectiles can improve matters with respect to range, but they reduce warhead weight still further. Finally, any shell must be strong enough to withstand the shock of firing, and so, compared to a missile, it has a relatively limited capacity for explosive.

APPARENT POWER AND REAL QUALITIES

The missile is characteristic of the transition, in modern warships, from what used to be the most visible warship attributes to generally invisible ones. For example, it used to be possible to gauge the fighting power of a ship by counting her guns. Now, however, there may be only a single missile launcher, the effectiveness of which depends upon such invisible qualities as the electronics within the missiles, themselves hidden below decks, and the efficacy of the fire control system, itself not clearly on view. Even with missiles in view, invisible qualities dominate: the nature of the missile fuel, the logic of the guidance system, the subtleties of missile aerodynamics. Even missiles which are externally quite similar may have very different qualities. For example, the Standard missile, which resembles the second

Top The great revolution in modern warship design is away from 'weight-criticality' towards volume and length limitations, a point well illustrated by the converted missile cruiser *Oklahoma City*, shown here in January 1976. The entire bulky deckhouse aft is required for her missile magazine system (Talos); just how far aft these structures extend is suggested by the small size of her helicopter landing pad. Her internal volume could not accommodate this kind of structure. Forward, she had to lose one of her two triple 6in turrets to accommodate flagship facilities, again a massive consumer of internal volume (communications spaces, computer spaces, conference facilities, etc).

Middle For a time after 1945 it appeared that traditional weight-critical warship design would continue to be feasible. Warships *looked* less well armed not because of the rise of electronics but rather beacuse of the rise of automation in their weapons. For example, the US *Forrest Sherman* class destroyers (of which *Barry* is shown, about 1960) had only three 5in guns rather than the six of their predecessors. However, they were of the far more powerful 54cal type, and each automated mount could fire more than twice as fast as the earlier single semi-automatic gun, ie somewhat faster than the earlier standard twin mount. The *Forrest Sherman*s did, however, sacrifice torpedo armament (four fixed tubes replaced the former trainable quintuple mount) and two single rapid-fire 3in/50s. They gained enormously in seakeeping (as indicated by their high freeboard forward), in sustained speed, and in range. By 1960 there had been further modifications: *Barry* shows a clipper bow and bow anchor, installed to clear a new bow sonar, and her former fixed tubes have been replaced by two small trainable triple tubes for lightweight ASW torpedoes. One unusual feature of the design was the placement of the fire control directors: the Mk 68 aft is for 5in control, the Mk 56 forward for 3in control with a secondary 5in capability.

Bottom The French *Surcouf*s make an interesting comparision with the *Forrest Sherman*s: their twin 5in/54 mounts are at least nominally equivalent to the single US 5in/54s, and the French Navy treatcd its twin 57mm (2.25in) gun in very much the same way as the US Navy treated its rapid-fire 3in/50. Both classes of ship were of about the same size, although the French employed a forecastle hull of traditional form, based on a prewar design, and differed from the Americans in providing a very powerful torpedo battery – six long (ASW and anti-ship) and six short (ASW only) torpedoes, the latter apparently with reloads stowed in the small deckhouse just abaft the tubes. The unit here, *Cassard*, was photographed on 2 July 1960. The radars are: at the foremast, the P-band air search mattress DRBV-20; and atop the mainmast, a two-beam S-band set, DRBV-11, apparently with dual air and surface search functions.

stage of the Terrier missile which used to arm most American missile frigates (now classed as missile cruisers), outperforms the latter, more impressive-looking weapon; the frigates are to be rearmed with a two-stage version of even higher performance. The only way to know even the theroetical performance of a missile is to carry out quite elaborate calculations. Worse, because the weapon is not ballistic, the precise definition of its performance is open to question, whereas the performance of a gun can be estimated from a combination of the weight and shape of its shell and its muzzle velocity. Nor can the performance of the missile once it has approached its target be guessed very easily, owing to the variety of modern warheads and the sophistication of their fuzing systems. It is not that calculation is futile, but rather that the easy intuitive characterizations of the past no longer apply.

The distinction between visible and invisible attributes is not entirely new. In the battleship era, for example, much of the armor protection of a ship might be classed under those invisible attributes making for sterling battle performance but a poor press. Many modern warships, particularly those built in the West, seem naked (especially of weapons) in comparison with their forebears, and are criticized as such. However, that nakedness is often the sign not of a perverse desire among modern naval architects to build yachts rather than warships, but of the growing requirement for such invisible features as expanded computer facilities, which, in effect, improve the effect of every round fired; of silencing, for better acoustic performance; and of better seakeeping performance. Once more, as in the battleship era, some smaller navies find it better to buy ships which are apparently more heavily armed and which do indeed seem to be better buys – in peacetime. However, their failings are wartime failings: insufficient numbers of personnel inadequately housed, who cannot keep the ship operating around the clock in a hostile area; a lack of reloads; a suit of radars and sonars which in itself limits the performance of the apparently impressive weapons aboard; or even a lack of silencing which advertises the presence of the ship to every submarine for fifty miles around.

One very common comparison is between the apparently heavily armed Soviet fleet and its apparently naked Western contemporaries. The Soviets design their ships with weapons which make the minimum possible demands upon the interior of the hull: for example, where there are magazines below decks, these are relatively compact, and many weapons are mounted in box launchers above decks. Although such a choice of weapons makes for an impressive appearance, it also makes for a crowded deck, and for relatively small arcs of fire for each weapon. Alternatively, one might say that the Soviets have preferred many weapon systems and many launchers for each, on reliability grounds: better to be able to fire off half the missiles when one launcher misfires, than to lose all when the single sophisticated system jams. Such a philosophy would certainly accord well with Soviet practice in radar installation. Systems which affect basic hull design to only a small degree permit the designer to accept large changes in weapon characteristics at a relatively late stage of ship design, a consideration which may well have been important in cases where the Soviets developed concurrently a ship and the missiles she was to carry – a very important time-saver in the case of a planned economy. Several Western missile ship designs were bedevilled by late changes in the weapons they were to carry.

In the mid-1950s it appeared to the US Navy that a SAM could be developed to replace the 5in/54 gun on a 'one-for-one' basis; in effect, later units of the *Forrest Sherman* class could be re-ordered as guided missile destroyers. The result was the *Charles F Adams* class – *Robinson* is shown, on 23 April 1963 – which turned out to require rather more in the way of redesign, and consequently rather more cost growth, than had been expected. In the course of the design ASROC was adopted; it replaced the former large-caliber fixed torpedo tubes, which had been intended to fire both anti-ship and anti-submarine torpedoes.

The *Dewey* class missile frigates represent an evolution parallel to that of the *Charles F Adams* program. The first US destroyers designed after 1945 grew so large that they were reclassified as frigates (*Mitscher* class); they in turn were to have been succeeded by a class with four 5in/54s and two twin 3in/50s, as well as ASW weapons including torpedo tubes. Another design project envisaged the replacement of the two after 5in guns by a Terrier launcher, and it was this design which was ultimately ordered. Still later, ASROC was adopted; it replaced the originally envisaged No 2 5in gun. The 3in guns remained, but the expansion of the big quadruped radar mast forward of the second funnel precluded the fitting of any torpedo tubes other than the small triple type. This is *Luce*, in much her original configuration, on 26 February 1965. She was later redesignated a missile destroyer.

However, there is also another possibility. Historically, the Russians have never really understood the sea. Admiral Sergei Gorshkov has undoubtedly done a superb job of convincing his superiors about the virtues of a navy, and they have responded by buying him a series of what are certainly very expensive warships. It may well be that an important element in their own acceptance of this cost has been the impressive and aggressive appearance of the larger Soviet warships, which Gorshkov can describe as bargains (per unit of apparent firepower) in comparison to the 'yachts' of the West.

Visible and invisible attributes are not confined to an individual ship, because ships do not exist in a vacuum; rather, any one ship must always be considered in the context of a fleet and, beyond that, of a navy engaged in particular missions and provided not merely with ships but also with important shore-based assets. For example, many of the apparently naked warships of the United States Navy are more important as radar and sonar platforms than as missile launchers; their main batteries are actually the aircraft of the carriers with which they consort. Together, carrier and consorts are far more powerful than would be an assortment of purely surface warships of similar aggregate cost. The aircraft, however, are invisible: they are not mounted atop a frigate's radar mast, even though the frigate's radars are the key to a large part of their effectiveness.

Similarly, in the Soviet case, individual Soviet surface ships would probably have little chance of destroying a US task force equipped with defensive missiles, aircraft and ECM (electronic counter-measures). However, the Soviet surface ship is part of a strike organization which includes aircraft and submarines – and, quite invisibly to the average observer, a very large shore-based system intended merely to locate and track the task force so that the attack can be mounted in the first place. Indeed, a good part of the warfare between task force and strike force consists of attempts by the task force (and by other US units) to confuse the Soviet sea surveillance system.

Left For the Soviet Navy, the most important development of the postwar years has been the anti-ship missile. The big launcher shown here aboard a Soviet destroyer at a 1961 naval review fired the SSN-1 air-breathing missile ('Scrubber'); the ship is one of eight 'Krupny' class 'double-enders'. The enclosure atop the single rail is used to warm up the turbojet-propelled missile, which is credited with a range of about 100nm but is probably effective only out to the horizon, ie to about 25nm. The magazine behind the launcher reportedly holds ten missiles. The 'Krupnys' were the first vessels built by the Soviets from the keel up as missile ships, although it is likely that they were originally designed as conventional destroyers. They succeeded a group of four converted destroyers ('Kildin' class); the latter have only one launcher (aft) and are credited with a capacity of only four weapons. Most of these ships have had their SSN-1 missiles removed. (CPL)

Below The Chilean *Almirante Williams* shows several postwar trends, and an international suit of weapons and sensors. She was completed by Vickers in 1960, and followed the US move towards automated weapons: her automatic 4in guns are credited with 40 rounds per minute, and therefore presumably equate to earlier twin semi-automatic mounts such as the four twins of Canadian and Australian 'Tribal' class destroyers of similar size. The fire control installation was unusual for a destroyer in that it permitted the simultaneous engagement of two aerial targets, using fore and aft radar-equipped directors. There were also a pair of Dutch fire control radars (SGR-108) for the four single Bofors guns (Swedish) and the two Seacats (British) which replaced the two aftermost Bofors in a 1964 refit. As built, these ships had a quintuple bank of torpedo tubes amidships, but this had been removed by about 1971, when this photograph was taken; attention had shifted to ASW, symbolized by a pair of Squids (original) and a pair of triple US-type ASW torpedo tubes. Later, Exocets were added in the waist. The search radars are British commercial types, although the Marconi SNW-series air search antenna resembles US World War II types. However, the ESM gear atop the second funnel is (apparently) similar to US installations: fixed intercept antennas and radar direction-finders enclosed in radomes. Different antennas were required for the different frequency bands. (C & S Taylor)

This is an example of yet another invisible feature of the modern warship. So much of modern naval warfare is conducted by weapons guided by radar and sonar that attempts to counter both have become extremely important, sometimes more so than conventional forms of attack and defense. In the example of an anti-ship missile already mentioned, the hit probability was given as 75 per cent: on average three missiles out of a four-shot salvo can be expected to hit, and those weapons have quite likely been designed so that two or three have a high probability of destroying a ship. However, that is true only if the target ship meekly accepts its fate. Most modern warships have some point defense weapons, which may themselves eliminate some of the incoming weapons. There is also the dark art of ECM. An incoming radar-guided weapon looks for a large reflecting mass, which it thinks of as a ship, to hit. It is true that ships are good radar reflectors, but so are clouds of aluminum foil (chaff) – and such clouds are not too difficult to launch, given adequate warning. There are many other ways of deceiving an incoming missile radar, for example by repeating back its emissions with subtle alterations. A missile fooled by such deception devices is just as ineffective as one homing on chaff or one shot down by a defensive missile such as Seawolf. However, the ECM antenna is just one of several little domes scattered over a ship's superstructure, and does not give the impression of being a serious piece of defensive hardware. As radar and sonar grow in significance, devices to counter them become more and more important, and the 'soft' kills they engender begin to displace the classical 'hard' kill in which an incoming missile explodes (or its own launcher is destroyed). Somehow many observers feel that the soft kill is less of a kill; it is certainly less visible, and its potential is virtually invisible in peacetime.

Nuclear power has already transformed some US naval operations, and may do the same for the Soviets, if reports of a Soviet nuclear cruiser under construction at Leningrad are accurate. The *Long Beach,* shown here firing a Terrier in October 1961, was a deliberate attempt to press the new technology to its limits: an all-missile battery (to which two 5in guns were only later added), nuclear power, and very powerful phased-array radar.

CHAPTER TWO
Missions and Strategy

Perhaps the greatest shift in Western navies since 1945 has been in their role. Before World War II the objective of most naval tactics was the destruction of warships, or simply ships. Command of the sea was sought in order to permit the free movement of men and *matériel* between ports in friendly hands, and in order to blockade an enemy. Although warships might shell enemy positions, it was recognized that the ability of ships to attack land targets was at best limited; the ability of sea powers to attack land powers was considered insignificant. Although in theory the freedom of movement conferred by command of the sea would permit a sea power to mount attacks on the periphery of its land enemy (as the British attacked the Central Powers at Gallipoli in Turkey in 1915), in fact such operations were generally unprofitable; for example, during World War I the most important contribution of sea control to the land battle was probably that it permitted the rapid reinforcement of the Western Front, first by the British and later by the American Army.

Matters were very different in World War II. Carrier aircraft could strike deep inland, against traditional land as well as naval targets. Moreover, the development of amphibious forces made it possible for the sea powers – Japan, Britain, and the United States – to land troops at points of their choosing, against opposition. In fact, as Axis sea power faded in 1944–45, Britain and the United States turned more and more to the use of their navies for the *projection* of force against the land masses of their enemies: more and more the principal naval target was on land. By 1945, at least some naval strategists saw in nuclear weapons the ultimate instrument for projecting naval force. Very large carrier planes armed with such weapons could devastate the entire land mass of an enemy, even if there were no bases available for conventional strategic bombers. This was, in fact, the rationale for the abortive American super-carrier *United States,* and part of the justification for the succeeding ships of the *Forrestal* class. Of course, it was never fully accepted by advocates of land-based air power, but it was, for example, an important element in the decision, later revoked, to build a new generation of British carriers in the 1960s. In both Britain and the United States, then, an emphasis on carrier-borne strike operations decided the characteristics of several generations of surface combatants.

FIRE SUPPORT

The projection of power from the sea of course included amphibious operations, and these in turn required a considerable measure of fire support. In the United States, the decision to maintain a significant amphibious capability was linked to efforts to maintain significant numbers of heavy gun barrels afloat, to replace those which vanished with the surviving World War II cruisers. As early as 1961 analysts argued that something more than the destroyer 5in weapon would be required to deal with the heavier mobile coastal weapons commonly found in Communist states, and also to destroy beach fortifications*. As has been noted, the result of such considerations was the decision to provide for a lightweight 8in weapon in the new *Spruance*s. The postwar role of what had been major surface combatants in World War II, the battleships and cruisers, is noteworthy: no longer essential to carrier task force operations since their anti-aircraft weapons were of little value compared with the combination of ship-based missiles and carrier-based interceptors, these units were available for fire support missions, and indeed could be relatively lightly risked. The large war programs had provided them in considerable numbers, and many had seen only short war service. In addition, the war programs left the US Navy with very large numbers of heavily armed destroyers, whose 5in fire could supplement that of the larger ships. Only in the late 1950s did the Navy have to face the prospect of the mass obsolescence of these ships. The necessary program was delayed, first by attempts to evolve new anti-submarine warfare (ASW) technology for a new generation of destroyers, and then by the costs incurred by the war in Vietnam. When ships finally were built, both as the big destroyer escorts of the 1960s and then as the *Spruance*s, they were individually rather expensive, and they could not be laid down in the numbers which had resulted from relatively extravagant wartime programs. Thus although a *Spruance* with an 8in gun is in a nominal sense a replacement for some fraction of a heavy cruiser, in fact it is also one-thirtieth of the most potent US surface ASW force, and as such not particularly expendable. Individual ships are far more capable than their predecessors, but they are also far more expensive. Even though one ship may do the work of five older ones, it is doubtful whether she is five times as likely to survive, especially since weapons nowadays are far more potent than they used to be. However, the destruction of one of the older ships would have reduced net effectiveness by only one-fifth.

* This coincided with an increased US interest in limited war; previously it had been assumed that, in future wars, enemy shore fortifications would be dealt with by nuclear weapons. The Marines were never very happy with this concept, but Navy planners did not become interested in a new large-caliber gun before 1961. At that time, too, the demotion of war-built cruisers to the Reserve Fleet was just beginning.

Fire support in amphibious operations is a particularly good case in point because classically it has fallen to second-line warships, which a navy could afford to risk close to enemy shores. Perhaps the single most characteristic feature of modern navies is that most of them have scrapped their surviving World War II heavy ships, and as a result they no longer possess expendable ships suitable for fire support. The Soviet Navy, which still operates *Sverdlov* class gun cruisers, is unique in this respect, although these ships survive largely because the Soviet transition to modern types lagged behind the West's by about a decade. The surviving Soviet cruisers are surely beginning to wear out, and it is time for the Soviets to look for some alternative means of providing fire support for opposed landings – that they remain interested in such operations is made particularly evident by the appearance of their new amphibious transport, the *Ivan Rogov.*

THE CHANGING NATURE OF AIR DEFENSE

The projection of sea power was not unopposed in World War II, even after the Axis fleets had been very largely reduced to impotence. In Germany especially, stand-off weapons such as the radio-controlled FX 1400 glide bomb (which sank the Italian battleship *Roma*) and the Hs 293 guided missile were seen as an effective counter to Allied naval superiority. They were profound shocks both to the Royal Navy and to the US Navy, and led to efforts to develop guided missiles to attack the carriers of stand-off weapons before such weapons could be launched. In the United States, the importance of this effort was emphasized by the advent of the Kamikaze – in particular the jet-propelled Baka bomb, which could be dropped by a Japanese bomber out of anti-aircraft range. The primary shipborne effort to counter these threats was a series of anti-aircraft missiles known initially as 'Project Bumblebee', but later as Terrier and Talos. In view of the German successes with stand-off weapons, the Navy regarded an all-weather radar-guided stand-off missile as the most serious threat its carriers would have to face postwar. Although it appears that there was little or no hard information on Soviet interest in such weapons at the time, the US program was pressed forward, so that the products of 'Bumblebee' reached the Fleet in the mid-1950s.

This study did not constitute the whole of the Fleet Air Defense program of the time. That program included efforts to equip the Navy with carrier-based all-weather interceptors, with provision for carrier-controlled landing under most weather conditions, and also with a variety of airborne

For the Western navies, the single greatest task of the postwar period has been ASW against the new fast submarine. Both Britain and the United States produced interim fast ASW ships by converting some of the large number of fleet destroyers built in wartime: this is HMS *Relentless*, a Type 15 'full conversion', in December 1952. Of her ASW battery, only a pair of fixed tubes for ASW torpedoes is visible; two 'Limbos' aft are hidden by her superstructure. The tubes were specified for many British ASW ships, but apparently were not successful. *(CPL)*

radar pickets which could supplement or perhaps even supplant surface radar pickets for controlling the interceptors as well as for early warning for the missile ships. There were considerable trade-offs between carrier and carrier aircraft performance and surface escort requirements. For example, in 1945 the destroyer radar pickets were considered essential to carrier task force defense, as they provided early warning and air control facilities for sections of Combat Air Patrol (CAP) from the carrier. However, as carriers grew in size, and as their operating areas moved North in response to the Soviet threat, the destroyers were less and less capable of remaining with the carrier – their reduced speed, particularly in rough weather, was now considered a major liability. Meanwhile, the perfection of Airborne Early Warning (AEW) aircraft, exemplified now by the Grumman E-2, made it possible for carrier fighters to operate effectively in the absence of surface radar picket ships. Thus, where in the early 1950s the US Navy considered it necessary to convert twelve *Gearing* class destroyers to add to the twenty-four radar pickets of 1945, at the end of the decade most of these ships reverted to pure destroyer status upon their FRAM (Fleet Rehabilitation and Modernisation) refits. It must, of course, be admitted that by that time there were also, either in existence or under construction, a number of missile frigates, which had been designed specifically to accompany heavy carriers at high speed in bad weather, and that the requirements of guided missile control automatically met those of air control as well.

SOVIET THINKING

The Soviets, too, were impressed by the German successes, and they developed their own stand-off missile, which, like 'Bumblebee', reached an initial state of maturity by the late 1950s; at that time the US Navy considered Soviet naval bombers armed with these weapons the major threat to its carrier task forces. Thus, remarkably, both the stand-off missile and the weapons designed to counter it grew to maturity at about the same time, even though neither side seems to have taken much notice of the other. Indeed, no one in 1945 or even upon the death of Stalin in 1953 could reasonably have predicted that a few years later the probable major Soviet naval objective would be the destruction of Western carrier groups, or that the principal instrument for such a task would be the land-based naval bomber and its missile.

In 1945 the Soviet Union was a land power, and its leaders appear to have had little idea of the potentials of sea power, despite the many demonstrations which World War II had provided. In particular it now appears that Stalin wanted a blue-water navy primarily because he wanted the Soviet Union taken seriously as a world power, and he believed that a blue-water navy was a requisite of such status. He had begun to build such a fleet in the late 1930s, and in the 1940s he began once more, even building ships which are now known to have been modified versions of the prewar designs – the postwar *Sverdlov*, for example, is a modified *Chapaev* and the postwar *Skory* a modified *Ognevoi*. Stalin went so far as to order battlecruisers armed with 12in guns; he was unique in retaining the naval concepts of the prewar period. However, he also found some of the technological fruits of the Soviet conquest of East Germany well worth developing. For example, he considered stand-off missiles important enough to assign the son of his secret police chief, Beria, to head the program for their development. Stalin also ordered a large submarine program, which can be equated to prewar Soviet submarine programs; he thought of it as a very effective means of

Above all, ASW requires large numbers of fast ships. The Royal Navy tried to produce, in its *Blackwood* class, a 'minimum' ship for mass production: HMS *Dundas* is shown here in 1977, little changed in a quarter-century of service. She never had much in the way of a gun battery, because the new fast submarines were unlikely to fight on the surface. Instead, she had two 'Limbos' aft, and would have had fixed torpedo tubes had they proven successful. Of her ASW sensors, the only visible one is HF/DF at her foremast. *(C & S Taylor)*

The British, as compared to the US, geographical position makes the air defense of merchant shipping extremely important – hence the inclusion of specialized AAW frigates such as the Type 41 HMS *Lynx* (shown here in 1977) in the postwar building program. When this ship was designed in 1945, it was hoped that a common hull and machinery (diesel) would be suitable for AAW, ASW, and fighter control duties. In effect this would have been a continuation of the wartime 'Loch/Bay' idea. *(C & S Taylor)*

Essentially the same hull and machinery as the Type 41's were used in another class of frigate for aircraft control over convoys (and, later, over the fleet at sea): this is *Llandaff* in 1977. In effect the weight and volume required for her more sophisticated radars (and presumably for a large CIC) were bought at the expense of removing one of the two twins 4.5in gun mounts of the AAW frigate. Reading from forward to aft, she has four search radars: Type 277 (height-finding and surface search), 992 Target Indication (short-range air and surface search), 965 (long-range air search) and 982 (low altitude precision air search). There is also a navigational radar, not clearly visible here, on the foremast, and there is an extensive ECM fit, much of it in the fore topmast. *(C & S Taylor)*

Top There was to have been an ASW version of the basic Type 41 design, armed with two 'Limbo' ASW mortars as well as fixed ASW torpedo tubes. However, the diesel power adopted for the AAW and fighter-direction frigates (for ease of mass production in wartime) gave insufficient speed for operations against fast submarines, and the Royal Navy turned to steam turbines for the equivalent *Whitby* class ASW frigate (HMS *Berwick* is shown). Most ships were never fitted with the torpedo tubes originally envisaged. *Whitby*s were anything but inexpensive; their weapon and sensor systems therefore went into the mass-production *Blackwood*s. *(MoD (N))*
Middle left The *Whitby* design assumed that sonar ranges would always be so short that a 1000yd ASW weapon, 'Limbo', would exploit them fully. However, even as these ships were being built, developments in medium-frequency sonar (Asdic 177) made it possible to detect and track submarines at far greater ranges. The Royal Navy introduced a helicopter to deliver homing torpedoes at great ranges; in effect the British MATCH system was a manned equivalent of the US DASH, and provided performance roughly equivalent to that of the US ASROC. 'Limbo' was retained for use against bottomed targets and in bad weather. These developments, plus a requirement for AAW and ASW capability in a single hull, produced the *Leander*, a modified version of the *Whitby*: HMS *Danae* is shown here (June 1977). The davit right aft may be associated with a towed torpedo counter-measures system; forward are visible the 'Limbo' in its well and the helicopter and hangar; and atop the hangar can be seen a quadruple Seacat launcher and its director, with two Corvus chaff launchers. The only visible ASW sensor is HF/DF at the foremast, but under the hull there is an elaborate system including a bottom-object classification sonar (162), a depth-finding sonar (170), a scanning search sonar (184), and an underwater telephone (185). *(C & S Taylor)*
Middle right Many *Leander*s are being refitted with an all-weather stand-off weapon, the Australian Ikara. This is HMS *Euryalus*, photographed in June 1977. Her sensor suit includes a Type 199 variable-depth sonar aft; the big air search radar on the mainmast has been replaced by a simpler IFF antenna; and Ikara guidance radars surmount the bridge. Ikara frigates have a new headlight-like ESM antenna at their foretops – this may be intended to provide directional data for targeting the Ikara missile, for example against submarine periscope attack radar emissions. Ikara itself nestles in its protective 'zareba' in 'A' position. *(C & S Taylor)*
Bottom The role of British surface warships has changed with the demise of British carrier aviation; ships designed for AAW/ASW must now be able to engage other surface ships. Some *Leander*s, such as HMS *Phoebe* (shown here in June 1977) have been refitted with Exocet SSMs forward; their remaining ASW potential lies entirely with their helicopters, and, at least for the present, their AAW capability is limited to self-defense with Seacat and with 40mm Bofors guns. The new ESM array at the foretop is probably intended to assist in targeting; the four broad-band log-periodic 'arrows' probably function as a direction-finder, whereas the cone at the top of the mast is omni-directional and probably functions only as a warning device. Like Soviet SSM ships, and some other Western Exocet ships, *Phoebe* carries no reloads. *(C & S Taylor)*

coast defense, and coastal security was one naval concept the Soviets understood very well. The projection forces which the Allies had developed so successfully in World War II are noticeably absent from Soviet naval thinking. The Soviets had carried out numerous minor amphibious operations on the flanks of German armies, but these were extemporized and involved no large forces; it may, however, be significant that many of them were carried out in the Black Sea by a young Admiral, Sergei Gorshkov, who became Chief of the Soviet Navy in 1956.

In 1953 Stalin died, leaving behind a very expensive naval building program which his heirs considered a pointless extravagance. Khruschev expounded the theory that in the future only 'nuclear-missile' forces would be effective in war. His immediate predecessors had already cancelled much of Stalin's large ship program in 1953, and he suspended most Soviet attack submarine construction, noting that submarines which launched torpedoes were of little interest; he cared only for those firing missiles either at surface ships (which he dismissed as floating coffins) or at shore targets. In line with the 'revolution in military affairs' thus declared, the Soviet naval leadership shifted its interest towards strategic attack on Western shore targets, using ballistic and then air-breathing missiles fired by submarines. They came close to abandoning surface ships entirely.

Then, in 1959, the Soviets perfected their own land-based intercontinental missile to the point where it was no longer necessary for attacks against Western targets to be mounted by submarines. The land-based Strategic Rocket Force was formed, and the Navy, which had fired the world's first submarine-launched ballistic missile in 1955, had to suspend its missile submarine program, at least in so far as it was designed for attack against land targets. The land-based force had been formed from Army missile artillery units, and was infinitely more powerful politically; the Navy had hoped to turn its monopoly on strategic attack into political power such as it had not previously enjoyed, but it had failed. Now it had to look elsewhere to justify its large costs. It found the menace of the Western carrier task forces, and re-oriented its cruise missile technology, mating it with new guidance systems to form a blue-water anti-carrier capability. This combined with a naval air arm already oriented towards anti-carrier attack, to form the navy which first seemed so menacing to the West in the mid-1960s. Since that time the Soviet Navy has once more acquired some strategic attack role, and has become more and more interested in anti-submarine warfare – but in a form quite different from that of Western ASW forces. However, all these roles are essentially reactive, and as such cannot be particularly satisfying to Soviet officers, especially as the latter have lived through several violent doctrinal upheavals in the past three decades. Much of Admiral Gorshkov's recent writing can be read as an espousal of the projection role which has shaped Western navies at least since 1945.

THE PROBLEM OF THE SUBMARINE

If projection and counter-projection have been a major theme of postwar naval development East and West, to them must be added the older theme of undersea warfare. Probably the least pleasant surprise of the late war years, from a naval point of view, was the German Type 21 submarine, which promised to make obsolete most of the huge Allied ASW fleet. The Type 21 was fast enough, submerged, to outrun most of the smaller convoy escorts; it was quiet enough to evade detection by the relatively inefficient sonars of the day; and the new German torpedoes made matters far worse.

In 1945 it seemed obvious to British and American observers that the Soviets, who had captured many incomplete units and much of the German production plant, and who had a long history of interest in submarine warfare, would soon be turning them out in large numbers. Moreover, it was said that although Soviet submarines had not been particularly successful in World War II, the German submarine officers captured in 1945 would soon improve their standards.

Thus a major theme of British and American naval development in the first five years after the end of the war was a crash effort to produce weapons and tactics to counter the Type 21, as well as the more impressive Walter submarine (Type 26) which had been in the prototype stage in 1945. Both navies recognized that any future Battle of the Atlantic would require very large numbers of ASW units, which would be expensive not merely to build but also to maintain in peacetime. Moreoever, each navy already possessed relatively speculative assertions about the future development of the Soviet Navy. At the same time, each navy appreciated that in peacetime its role would be far better served by the maintenance of carrier task forces capable both of showing the flag and of projecting power into localized trouble spots, than by building up large forces of individually rather unimpressive sub-killers.

Various solutions were proposed. For example, at one time the US Navy planned to refit all of its *Fletcher* class destroyers as escorts, maintaining them in reserve against the outbreak of war. Tactics were to be developed by small experimental destroyer units. Work also proceeded on new escorts specifically designed for mass production in wartime – the *Dealey* and *Claude Jones* classes. Unfortunately such mobilization designs tended to be relatively uninspiring ships, and they were soon succeeded by much larger destroyer escorts quite unsuitable for mass production, such as the *Knox* class. All the British postwar frigates were designed for mass production, but only the very austere *Blackwoods* were inexpensive enough to build in very large numbers, and they were severely criticized because they were not particularly useful in peacetime. Had a war been fought just after their completion it might well have been different, but the great feature of the 'Cold War' was that every Western Navy had to be able to go to war at short notice, without adopting those austere measures which look unimpressive (compared with their cost) in peacetime.

Top Like the Royal Navy, the US Navy found that its sonars far exceeded the reach of its weapons. It reacted with two new weapons: DASH, a torpedo-carrying drone helicopter, and the ASROC stand-off rocket, tipped with either a torpedo or a nuclear depth charge. *Dealeys* such as *John Willis* (shown on 3 February 1971) received both a new long-range low-frequency sonar (SQS-23) and DASH; the effect of the latter shows in the enlarged superstructure and clear 'helipad' aft, with the after twin 3in mount landed. Some ships received a twin 40mm gun aft to provide minimal coverage in that sector. DASH was controlled by radio command issued from two dipole antennas, here visible at her foretop and on a dark-colored stub mast (white dipole on top) on the hangar roof; the drone was tracked by either the SPS-5 surface search or the SPS-6C air search set on the foremast.

Middle Even the single-screw steam-turbine *Dealeys* seemed too complex for mass production; the US Navy tried to go one step further with four diesel-powered *Claud Jones* class escorts (*Charles Berry* is shown, on 24 August 1962). They were comfortable but useless against fast submarines, both because of their very low speed and because they were limited to a pair of Hedgehogs forward and to depth charge tracks aft.

Bottom The CNO, reacting to the fiasco of the *Claud Jones* class, called for an updated *Dealey* with the new SQS-26 bow sonar and ASROC. He got the *Bronstein* class, the first of the modern US ocean escorts. By the end of the 1950s it was clear that replacements would be needed for the mass of US World War II destroyers, and a 5in battery was specified for the next class of escorts. That and the new pressure-fired boiler produced the *Garcia*, shown here in August 1972, with the arc of her after 5in gun limited by the enlarged hangar required for the manned LAMPS helicopter which replaced DASH. These ships are capable of exceeding 30kts and have been used in place of destroyers in carrier screens; their chief defect is probably the fact that they have but a single screw.

Below The *Dealeys* were the US answer to the postwar fast submarine; here USS *Hartley*, little changed since her completion, leaves San Juan harbor in January 1962. Her primary ASW weapon was the big Mk 108 automatic rocket launcher (Weapon Alfa), which could fire 12 rockets per minute out of 22 held in ready service. In theory it was equivalent to 'Limbo', substituting rapid fire for the simultaneous firing of three or, better, six barrels. However, the automatic reloading mechanism caused great trouble, and Alfa has died whereas 'Limbo' and similar weapons survive. The *Dealeys* originally had depth charges as well, but these were replaced by the standard US lightweight homing torpedoes (Mk 32 tubes abeam the funnel).

The Soviets did produce submarines in great numbers, although in retrospect their goal, stated in 1948 to be 1200, seems rather questionable. However, it does not appear that Stalin contemplated a new Battle of the Atlantic, even if he did purchase the means to fight one. One irony of the early postwar era was that Western intelligence was so ineffective that it was not until about 1950 that a US study remarked that the Soviets had not as yet begun the expected submarine build-up. Clearly the Soviets could build new submarines whenever they chose to begin a program; in fact, just as the US study appeared, the first of the new Soviet mass-production boats, the prototype 'Whiskey', neared completion at Gorkiy. However, at the time all other Soviet submarines were inferior even to most wartime German boats. It seemed far wiser, then, to spend current (and very limited) funds on research against a future worse threat than against the submarine of 1945. The *Fletcher* program was curtailed in favor of an interim destroyer modification project, in which active destroyers and many active destroyer escorts were fitted with two fixed Hedgehogs and an improved (scanning) sonar. The large funds saved went into the generation of weapons and the associated sensors which entered service in the late 1950s. By that time all of the 'Whiskeys' had already entered Soviet service, but it could be argued that their operators were not as yet so proficient as to present a high-seas threat at all comparable to that which the U-boat arm could have mounted, given the same equipment. Once more it was a case of weapons developed by one side against the ancestors of those developed by the other.

Not every navy could build new frigates in the immediate postwar years. The Dutch, for example, received ASW ships from the United States, but chose to build their own AAW/ASW destroyers, armed with automatic twin 4.7in guns (Bofors design, as in Swedish destroyers) and the Bofors quadruple 375mm ASW mortar (firing over No 1 gun mount). For a short time in the late 1950s some Dutch destroyers also carried fixed ASW torpedo tubes, presumably similar to those aboard British frigates, but these were soon discarded. This photograph shows *Drenthe*, with her forward turret trained aft. Dutch destroyers were unusually well equipped with radar: *Drenthe* shows, on her foremast, DA-01 target indication radar (S-band) with an LW-02 (L-band) air search set on her mainmast; the small antenna atop the pilot house is a surface search radar. The fore topmast carries ESM gear. (*Naval Historical Department, RNethN*)

EUROPE AND THE FAR EAST

For the US Navy, the themes of fleet strike warfare and mid-ocean ASW continued to dominate naval programs throughout the postwar period. Britain and France seemed set on a similar course in 1945, although both have shown a concern with inshore operations (including specialized types of ASW and mine warfare) quite different from that of the US Navy. Each possessed, in 1945, a large colonial empire requiring a substantial *peacetime* ability to project force. The United States, and to a lesser extent the United Kingdom, possessed such a capability simply by virtue of the fact that they had substantial conventional cruiser and amphibious forces. France, which retained considerable influence in its former empire even after granting independence, lacked a large reserve of heavy-gun cruisers and even of amphibious ships. She made up the gap to some extent by providing many of her ships with auxiliary peacetime projection capabilities. For example, the French 12in ASW mortar can also be used, with a special round, for shore bombardment – and French surface warships are designed to accommodate troops.

The Netherlands also retained a colonial empire after 1945; even though it soon lost the East Indies, it retained part of New Guinea and territory in the New World for some considerable time. Thus, like the British and the French, the Dutch retained an active interest in such old-fashioned arts as shore bombardment. For example, they bought an ex-British light fleet carrier and equipped her partly with fighter-bombers. The Royal Netherlands Navy also completed two cruisers begun before the war, arming them with 6in dual-purpose (DP) guns.

Canada, with many remaining war-built frigates, chose to rebuild some of them to match newer concepts: here is the *Sussexvale*, with a new enclosed bridge and high freeboard aft; there is a well aft in which her Squid is mounted, just as 'Limbo' was mounted on the new Canadian frigates. Note the absence of any air search radar; the HF/DF at the masthead is the US DAU type. The radars are probably a US SU X-band surface search type and the standard Canadian Sperry Mk 2 navigational set (the big paraboloid). *(Official)*

The new Canadian frigates (*Margaree* is shown here, on 19 November 1957) were uniquely well fitted to Arctic operations. Even their anchors were covered over, to avoid ice formation; the same motive explains the curved deck-edge forward. Later the 3in guns were enclosed. The clear deck space aft hides a well in which two 'Limbos' sat; much of this space subsequently went into helicopter facilities.

To some extent the experience of the Korean War must have reinforced the view in many Western navies that projection would in future be a major naval mission: Korean operations required large numbers of 6in, 8in and even 16in shells, but very little in the way of ASW or AAW (antiaircraft warfare) action. However, the thrust of naval development at the same time was in the direction of ASW and, to a lesser extent, AAW. There was a tacit assumption that wars such as that in Korea were special cases, that the Western navies had to prepare rather for 'the big war', the Soviet attack on Western Europe in which the main naval mission would be the protection of the vital sea lanes across the North Atlantic. Naval firepower would be provided by carrier aircraft, not by old-fashioned guns firing offshore. Advocates of the new era of missile warfare observed that missiles with nuclear warheads might well replace heavy guns, since they could achieve with a single shot the destruction normally to be expected of hundreds of shells*.

* This was the justification for eliminating 5in guns from the design of the missile frigate *Leahy*; similarly the cruisers *Long Beach* and *Chicago* were designed without any guns. They were provided with single 5in guns after Terrier failed to shoot down a World War II fighter plane drone in a demonstration before President Kennedy; the President was also concerned that such ships would have no effective defense against PT-boats and similar craft.

Right By the mid-1950s it seemed to the French that they had more naval missions in mind than mere convoy escort; they abandoned the construction of lightly-armed ASW ships (and, indeed, cancelled a new class of austere escorts) and built instead the dual-purpose *avisos-escorteurs* of the *Commandante Riviere* type, of which *Commandant Bordais* is shown here (March 1964). Superficially, these ships resemble the E52s (especially those with the 305mm mortar in place of the sextuple ASW rocket launcher), with 3.9in automatic guns in place of the former twin 57s. However, the move to heavier guns required the sacrifice of one bank of torpedo tubes on each beam *and* of all of the reloads; the mortar fires a special shore-bombardment round, and the ships were designed to exchange No 3 gun and the tubes for a light helicopter, and to carry a commando complement of 80 troops. Four similar units were built for Portugal. *(Official)*

The French were probably the first to place great faith in ASW homing torpedoes; their first postwar escorts, the *Le Corse* class (name ship shown here, on 18 October 1954), had twelve tubes plus reloads (note the magazine door abaft the forward tubes); gun armament was limited to three triple 57mm. The new ship shows a fixed HF/DF array, presumably of French design, on her foretop, with the DRBV-20 air search and DRBV-30 surface search radars below it. An IFF interrogator was later added on the platform below the DRBV-20. *(Official)*

The Frency Navy soon decided that something more than the *Le Corse* class was needed, and has fitted some form of rocket launcher to every subsequent ASW ship. The frigate *(escorteur) Le Breton* belongs to the second (E52A) class of postwar French escorts: the torpedo tubes have been moved to the main deck to improve stability, and an ASW rocket launcher fitted forward for a clear field of fire; in the earlier ships a similar launcher was mounted amidships on the 01 level. Each of the triple tubes has a separate ready-use locker with three spare torpedoes, loaded tail-first through the muzzles of the tubes. *(Official)*

The new Japanese Navy was particularly strongly oriented towards the essentially defensive missions of ASW and limited AAW, since the post-war Japanese Constitution forbade the formation of offensive military forces. The Japanese naval role, therefore, was the protection of the sea lines of communication (SLOC) at their end, and, to some extent, defense against amphibious attack. Moreover, the Japanese assumed that their primary defense against direct assault was their alliance with the United States, and therefore the powerful offensive battery of the US Seventh Fleet.

Very few ships were built for any Western navy between 1945 and 1950, partly because of the economic prostration of Europe after World War II. Rearmament began with the Korean War, and with the release by the United States of large Mutal Defense Assistance Program (MDAP) funds. Within the alliance as a whole, there were numerous cooperative projects, which show up in retrospect in the uniformity of many Western weapons, sensors, and even warship designs. Much can be traced to MDAP, which financed a large part of NATO's early warship construction. One condition of such aid was that the US Navy approve designs it was to finance; this in itself enforced a uniformity of standards and operated to transmit the results of British and American war experience to navies which had had little of their own. More subtly, such MDAP control tended to enforce upon other navies Anglo-American priorities developed in the carrier and ASW campaigns of World War II.

However, the European narrow-sea navies expected that a new war would include Soviet bloc amphibious operations, around the North Cape, in the Baltic, and in the Black Sea, the Adriatic, and the Aegean. Even beyond any particular Soviet threat, these navies always considered it an essential mission to control narrow straits, ie to maintain a credible anti-ship capability, and so all invested heavily in large torpedo boats after World War II. The Swedish Navy went further, and, in common with the Soviets, developed its own anti-ship missile, Rb 08, for some of its destroyers. Moreover, postwar Swedish destroyer design emphasized anti-

The Federal German Navy has always been acutely aware of the need for anti-ship firepower in the Baltic. Its first postwar destroyers, the *Hamburg* class (the name ship is shown), were built with five *fixed* anti-ship torpedo tubes: three in the bows and two in the transom stern, as well as two large-caliber ASW torpedo tubes above deck, just abaft the forefunnel. The air search radars are Dutch, and are similar to those in Dutch destroyers, with the LW-02 primary air search set amidships and the DA-02 target indicator forward; a smaller surface search antenna is visible above the bridge. These ships were unusual in that a radar-equipped director was provided for each gun mount. The guns are the Franco-German automatic 100mm type; the directors are the Dutch M44/45; and the torpedoes and tubes appear to be of German origin. The *Hamburg*s have now been refitted with a more efficient anti-ship weapon: Exocet. *(Official)*

ship (torpedo) rather than anti-submarine warfare; of all the NATO navies, only West Germany shared this view*. Later all the narrow-sea navies enthusiastically adopted anti-ship missiles, even at a cost in AAW or ASW capability. Among other things, they had no carriers to escort and their naval staffs apparently preferred not to rely entirely on the depredations land-based aircraft could exact. Moreoever, all these navies were within striking distance of the large fleet of Soviet missile boats, which ranged, during the 1960s, from converted torpedo boats ('Komars') up through substantial missile corvettes ('Nanuchka'). All consider a ship-launched anti-ship missile the best counter to the missile boat, and their current frigate designs reflect such an assessment.

The blue-water navies were slower to appreciate the value of anti-ship missiles. France became urgently interested in such weapons after it became clear that most of the North African navies would soon possess ex-Soviet missile boats quite capable of interdicting trade routes through the Mediterranean, at least in good weather. Italy reacted similarly. In each case the argument that such craft would be easy prey for air attack seems not to have been convincing. Britain and the United States reacted rather more slowly, perhaps in part because at the time both operated very large naval air forces. However, the British shift towards employing anti-ship missiles aboard large surface warships was probably motivated largely by the impending loss of the British carrier force, which had provided the main British naval anti-ship capability, at a time when more and more minor navies were attaining effective anti-ship missile status. In the US case, it was the perception that in the face of even the most insignificant navy, equipped with anti-ship missile boats, US frigates and destroyers were nearly helpless. For example, development of the US anti-ship missile, Harpoon, was accelerated from 1970 onwards, in combination with measures for self-defense outside the carrier task force. Some emergency measures in the latter direction had already been taken as a reaction to the threat of 'Styx' missiles aboard North Vietnamese boats and in North Vietnamese coast defenses.

---

* The French *Surcouf* (T47) also had anti-ship torpedo tubes, but it was effectively a survivor of pre-NATO concepts. Similarly, Britain completed her *Daring* and 'Weapon' classes postwar with torpedo tubes, and retained conventional tubes in some fast frigate conversions; the latter may reflect wartime experience with surface commerce raiders, and the size of the Soviet cruiser fleet.

OTHER THEATERS

Postwar naval development outside NATO and the Warsaw Pact was heavily influenced by the availability of surplus British and American warships, mainly destroyers and frigates. In fact the mass obsolescence of these ships has led to a dramatic increase in frigate construction by private European and British yards over the past decade. These programs have merged with the replacement of the first generation of NATO/MDAP postwar construction; in some cases alternative configurations of the same commercial/standard ship, such as the British Type 21 frigate, serve both purposes. In others a foreign buyer prefers to accept the higher cost of a ship designed to US or Royal Navy standards, such as a *Perry,* a *Leander* or a Type 42.

India and Australia obtained ex-British light carriers, which they, like the Dutch, operated in a dual strike/ASW role*. Others later went to Argentina and to Brazil. The United States tried to cast the navies of its Latin American allies in the ASW role which most concerned it, but these navies themselves remained vitally interested in classical anti-ship warfare – as exemplified by the light cruisers bought by Argentina, Brazil, Chile and Peru. Latin America is now the largest single naval market outside NATO and the Warsaw Pact, but similar remarks apply to Asian and African navies. In Asia one side or another of the narrow-sea problem afflicts the Korean, Iranian, Indonesian, Malaysian, Philippine, Saudi, Taiwanese, Thai, and, to a lesser extent, Japanese navies. Each finds the missile boat useful, but it is limited in range, seakeeping and self-defense, and it is useless for ASW (submarines can operate quite effectively in narrow, shallow seas). Nor is the missile very useful for shore bombardment, a role important to some Asian navies faced with nearby enemies. Each of these navies, then, would prefer to buy destroyers or frigates or, better, a mix of missile boats and larger units. The Middle Eastern navies, for example, all operate fast missile boats in opposition to each other, but each would like something larger, if only to achieve a greater reach. In each case frigates are attractive *if* they have a substantial anti-ship and anti-missile-boat capability.

The existence of a large naval market for substantial surface ships designed quite as much for anti-ship attack as for AAW or ASW is therefore an important influence on British and European commercial yards. Moreoever, if such a yard can offer lower prices to its own navy as a result of a large number of units sold abroad, then these considerations may tend to spill over into that navy's concepts.

There is a final caveat well worth keeping in mind. Very few military procurement decisions are taken entirely on cool rational grounds. In particular the idea that their ships were to be reduced to defensive missions such as AAW and ASW (and, worse, to the 'sensor platform' role in carrier strike operations) was never popular with surface ship operators, who make up the vast majority of the officer corps in most navies. ASW in particular was, at best, extremely frustrating, whereas attacks on other surface ships presented a good chance of highly visible success in wartime. The advent of anti-ship missiles aboard frigates originally assigned ASW and AAW roles must, therefore, have been extremely popular, even if those weapons would have little appreciable value in any war. The anti-ship capability was of course even more popular in those navies for which the wartime scenario was at best ambiguous.

* The Indian *Vikrant* actually operated in the strike role during the 1971 war with Pakistan.

Below *Knox* class frigates, such as USS *Downes* (shown here in June 1971) were among the most spectacular products of the Design Work Study philosophy. One problem was that not all of the weapons and other equipment originally contemplated were available when the ships were completed: *Downes* lacks both a point defense missile (originally to have been the ill-fated Sea Mauler, later Sea Sparrow) and the variable depth sonar; she was also to have received a pair of fixed torpedo tubes (for Mk 37 or 48 torpedoes) in her transom. A less obvious omission is illustrated by the cluster of ECM radomes on her lattice fore topmast: a major reason for the 'mack', funnel of the *Knox* class was the intent to used fixed 'billboard' ECM antennas in the 'mack' to replace the usual cluster of radomes housing spinning intercept and direction-finding antennas. The only advantage *Downes* had over the original *Knox* design was the presence of the manned LAMPS helicopter, as indicated by the control cab beside her helicopter hangar and also by her topmast, which handles the LAMPS sonobuoy-data link.

Right *Trippe* (shown here on 22 December 1971) is a fully-equipped *Knox*, using an air defense system not contemplated when the class was designed: Sea Sparrow, controlled by the small director atop her hangar. Her transom is cut for an SQS-35 VDS.

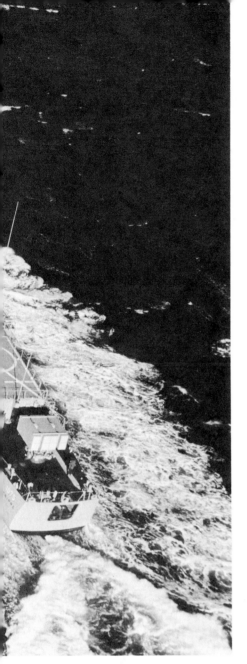

CHAPTER THREE

The Warship as a Weapon System

Every warship begins as a set of naval staff requirements ('Characteristics' in US parlance): to fight some specified range of enemies while moving through seas of known character, maintaining at least some specified speed over a specified distance. In many cases the ship must have the ability to combine tactically with other (specified) naval and air forces, which implies both a level of communications equipment and a level of speed and maneuverability. Often the Characteristics include measures to reduce the chances of enemy detection, such as noise control or a reduction in infra-red emissions. They always end on the same note: everything is to be accomplished at minimum cost, on the minimum displacement. One of the complications of warship design since 1945 has been a series of radical shifts in just what minimum cost implies for a ship.

The Characteristics lay out a series of ship performance requirements, which may be summarized as mobility (speed, endurance, maneuverability and seakeeping), firepower, and survivability. In principle they do not conflict: a larger ship, which has better seakeeping qualities and which is easier to drive at speed, can also accommodate more weapons and will probably be easier to protect against enemy fire. However, the larger the ship and the more sophisticated its weapons, the more it costs. As the US Navy can well attest (to its infinite regret), the more a ship costs, the more difficult it is to persuade a civilian government to procure sufficient numbers, especially in peacetime. Although it must seem to many that this obvious problem has been disregarded, at least in recent US practice, attempts to increase design efficiency and to reduce cost have in fact been the guiding principle in postwar ship evolution.

THE LIFE-CYCLE COST CONCEPT

Two concepts have been particularly important. The first is Life-Cycle Cost: the cost, not merely of the ship and her weapons and other equipment, but also of her crew, over her operating life. The Life-Cycle Cost concept is also often used to justify nuclear over conventional powerplants, especially at times of rapidly rising oil prices. However, its application to ship manning is probably the greatest departure from traditional practice. In the ships of World War II and previous eras the great majority of crewmen were relatively unskilled seamen; their pay was quite low, and in fact most of the cost of running a ship was upkeep, fuel and spare parts. However, as the complexity of the weapons and particularly of their fire control increased, more and more highly-paid technicians were required, to a point where, in the early 1960s, the US Navy initiated special programs to redesign new ships to reduce manning*. The *Knox* class frigate was the first ship to be Design Work Studied. At one point in her design it appeared that, compared to the preceding *Brooke* class, she would benefit from an 8 per cent reduction in personnel, a 300-ton weight reduction, and a reduction in machinery box volume of 12 per cent, which in turn reduced machinery spaces from 5 to 3 and so substantially reduced watch-keeping requirements. The decision to use enclosed twin Mk 32 torpedo tubes rather than the previous triple external type was also made on this basis. It permitted the concentration of all lightweight torpedoes in one magazine, which could serve both the torpedo tubes and the helicopter (at that time the DASH drone). The decision to arm the ship with only a single 5in/54 rapid-fire gun was not, however, made on the basis of Design Work Study, at least not explicitly**.

One drawback of Design Work Study was that it did not take into account problems of reliability: for example, the single 5in/54 was more than equal to two single 5in/38 when it operated, but if it failed the ship was left gunless. The original study included the pressure-fired steam plant of the earlier *Garcia* class, but the Chief of the Bureau of Ships considered this system too risky and cancelled it, so that ultimately the *Knox* reverted to 5 machinery spaces of greater volume, which squeezed the rest of the design.

The effect of manning on Life-Cycle Cost also shows in the widespread adoption of automated gun mounts in Western navies, even when those mounts have considerably lower rates of fire than did their more fully manned predecessors. For example, the US lightweight 5in/54 fires about half as fast as does the rapid-fire version of the same weapon, and has a much lower maximum elevation. However, it can be fired without anyone in the mount proper, and its lower rate of fire buys increased reliability. The most important effect is the need for fewer expensive technicians.

* This effort to reduce manning may have an unfortunate effect in wartime. In World War II, much of the 'excess crew' of a ship was absorbed into damage control parties which actually saved many ships. It is possible that very generous peacetime habitability standards will permit current warships to absorb much larger crews in wartime, as was actually the standard experience in World War II; however, in neither case was that the intention.

** This decision illustrates the perversity of design development. The *Knox* began as a Design Work Study version of the *Brooke* class missile escort, itself a missile version of the two-gun (5in/38 semi-automatic) *Garcia* class. When it became clear that there would be no more *Brooke*s, design work was already well advanced, and efforts shifted to a one-gun ship with a point defense SAM. The Ship Characteristics Board chose to use the economies of Design Work Study to obtain a more powerful ship on about the same displacement, and replaced the previous 5in/38 with a 5in/54 more than equal (in theory) to two of the earlier guns. In a sense the Spanish *Baleares* class missile frigate comes closest to the original *Knox* design concept.

Considerations of Life-Cycle Cost can influence an entire ship design. For example, the contract for the *Spruance* class was awarded on the basis of Life-Cycle Cost, major components of which were the purchase and overhaul costs of the gas turbines, and fuel cost. It was possible to meet the armament and sensor requirements on a waterline length of about 480ft, but Litton's design was considerably longer, which permitted a substantial reduction in shaft horsepower. Gas turbines come in discrete units: Litton managed with three, its competitors with four. In each case fuel consumption favored the General Electric LM 2500, of about 20,000shp, in a gas turbine plus gas turbine boost system. Mixed powerplants were rejected partly because they would complicate spare parts supply (Life-Cycle Cost) and would require additional technicians. Litton alone proposed a complex system, with two turbines on one shaft and an electric drive to distribute power to the remaining one-turbine shaft. That required the waterline length of about 530ft adopted, if the required 30kts was to be achieved on 60,000 rather than 80,000shp. Ironically, the Navy became more and more unhappy with the three-turbine system and ultimately required Litton to go over to the four engines of its original competitors. The result was not entirely displeasing to the Navy, since additional ship space could be used for modifications originally not contemplated. It may be, for example, that modification of the *Spruance* design to the new DDG47 Aegis configuration would have been impossible had the original ship been much smaller.

Design by Life-Cycle Cost is an attempt to control cost growth in warships. It is relatively difficult to apply, particularly in the day-to-day battles over partiular modifications to a design which, although minor in themselves, add up to large increases in cost. Design To Cost is a simpler alternative, introduced in 1970 with the Patrol Frigate (*Perry*, FFG7) project. In this case the CNO, Admiral Zumwalt, stated a series of operational and technical requirements, and the Naval Ship Engineering Center made up a series of feasibility studies, showing the effects on ship size and cost of such choices as single vs twin screw and ASW helicopter stowage vs ASROC. Ultimately it seemed that the desired ship could be built on about 3700 tons at a cost of about $50 million (follow-on ships). In June, 1971, the CNO ordered the Patrol Frigate designed to a cost of no more than $45 million, a displacement of no more than 3400 tons, and, slightly later, a complement of no more than 185, about 30 per cent fewer men per ton than previously. All three limits reflected Admiral Zumwalt's view of the pressures for growth that he had to fight, particularly since he knew he would no longer be in control of the Patrol Frigate program by the time mass production had begun. For example, by 1971 he suspected that the US Navy would soon have to operate without the military draft to induce men to enter its ranks, and that military pay raises would make large crews prohibitively expensive. The manning limit was then in effect a concession to life-cycle costing*. It was, however, far easier to enforce. The tonnage limit was not nearly so closely equivalent to a cost limit as similar limits had been in a time of weight-critical ships, but it (and the associated decision to eliminate the usual weight margin for growth) had the effect of making the usual (costly) additions during design impossible, even were the original cost limit to be removed. Taken together, these three limits did reverse the US trend towards ever-larger frigates: a 1976 study of the *Perry*

---

* A manning limit also limited the extent to which additional equipment could be accommodated.

design estimated that, had they not been applied, the ship would have been designed at about 5000 tons. The displacement limit in particular produces a ship far closer to the weight-critical designs of the past than were its immediate predecessors.

Constrained cost was worthwhile because it permitted construction of enough *Perry*s to replace, at least to a considerable extent, the large numbers of World War II destroyers which left US service in the early 1970s. However, there was a cost, and critics were quick to grasp it: the *Perry* design has little flexibility for future growth. That can be read either as an attempt to make it impossible for internal forces within the Navy to boost individual ship costs by adding without limit, or it can be read as a gross disregard for the necessary modifications to a ship during what is hoped will be a long service life. The two other major 'design to cost' projects of the Zumwalt era, the austere Aegis destroyer (DG) and the Sea Control Ship, were never built, so that the impact of Design To Cost on the designs is far less clear than it is in the case of the *Perry*.

THE WEAPON SYSTEM CONCEPT

The second important modern concept is the weapon system: the word 'system' emphasizes the contribution of non-weapon parts to the success of the system as a whole, but also suggests the range of trade-offs possible in designing the system. For example, system performance may often actually improve if better performance of the non-weapon parts is bought at the expense of the explicitly weapon parts. This frequently means that better search radar or sonar and better fire control may buy more than a better missile. For example, the difference between the new Aegis weapon system and that installed aboard current US missile frigates lies in the new SPY-1 radar and its associated fire control system, and to a much lesser degree in a new faster-firing launcher. Within the Standard missile, the principal

The new *Spruance*s represent another now-discarded US Navy ship-buying philosophy, 'Package Procurement', in which a single contractor designs the ship and then builds the class. In theory such procurement achieves economies of scale. This is USS *O'Brien*, in February 1978. Like others of her class, she still lacks a good number of her electronic and weapon systems – for example, she does not show the ECM radomes and intercept antennas usual in US warships.

change is a modified guidance system. Yet the net effect of the new electronics is to take far better advantage of the inherent performance of the
missile: the Aegis system can engage more targets simultaneously – and at
greater effective range.

However, the ship is part of the weapon system, and such ship performance characteristics as high speed are far from inexpensive, although to
some considerable extent they can be traded off against weapon, sensor,
and fire control performance. One example is the range of anti-ship missiles. The simplest is the torpedo, which is unguided. Torpedo-firing
destroyers had to close their targets in order to deliver effective torpedo fire,
since otherwise those targets would have had time to evade. Such tactics in
turn required of the destroyer a considerable speed advantage over her
quarry. The advent of tactical missiles such as the Soviet 'Styx' changed
matters completely: now the destroyer could fire from 20 miles or more, and
her target could not hope to evade. On the other hand, a much greater
burden was placed on the destroyer's fire control system, and indeed on the
means by which she detected her target in the first place. From the target's
point of view, high speed no longer bought any immunity; it became
necessary to buy countermeasures, such as chaff, directed specifically
against the missile. These in turn required a larger ship, and cost platform
characteristics.

It is possible to go further: a fleet can become a unified weapon
system, in which different capabilities are distributed among its units. For
example, from the late 1950s onwards, the Royal Navy considered large
helicopters the most effective means of ASW attack. In a carrier task force,
they had to be accommodated aboard the carrier, on whose flight deck they
competed for space with fleet air defense aircraft and with carrier strike aircraft: a balance had to be struck between offense and defense. The Royal
Navy could not afford to buy larger and larger carriers, but it could make
matters somewhat simpler by removing its ASW helicopters from the strike
carrier. This was the origin of a new class of cruiser, which was to combine
ASW helicopters and surface-to-air missiles: ultimately it became HMS
Invincible. As time passed and role of the Royal Navy changed, it became
clear that a helicopter-carrying ASW ship was valuable in its own right,
which is why the *Invincible* concept survived the demise of the British fleet
carriers.

In most cases the connection between ship and fleet is more subtle.
Fore example, in the US Navy an automated data exchange system, the
Naval Tactical Data System (NTDS), is used to link the ships of a task
force. In effect, the entire task force becomes a multi-hull ship; targets
detected by one ship are automatically presented to others perhaps better
able to fire upon them, and the carrier aircraft associated with the task force
can make use of radar and sonar data obtained by all of the surface ships of
the force. NTDS is thus extremely potent, but it also imposes considerable
costs on the ships of the task force in terms of internal space devoted to the
radio links required by the system, and of course to the computers themselves.

The NTDS computers also keep track of radar, sonar, and other
sensor data aboard each ship; they provide its officers with a complete and
current representation of the tactical situation. Automation reduces plotting time and effort, which in turn helps make up for the higher speeds of
modern aircraft and submarines. Moreover, plotting time is a major contribution to the 'dead time' which elapses between the first detection of an

approaching airplane and the decision to fire: the greater the dead time, given a fixed radar detection range, the more must be expected of the anti-aircraft weapons. The level of automation inherent in NTDS promises more: it may be possible for the NTDS computers to be linked directly to the shipboard fire control system, so that designation to fire control becomes almost automatic, once a target has been identified as hostile. In the usual situation, with many targets present, the NTDS computers can (at least in principle) do even more: they can identify those targets which the ship can engage most profitably, and monitor the engagements to avoid wasting anti-aircraft weapons.

The current Royal Navy equivalent of NTDS is ADAWS, the Action Data Automation Weapon System. It evolved from ADA, in which radar operators manually entered target data into a computer, which could then produce a master plot. ADAWS increases the level of automation and adds the vital link to the weapons. CAAIS, Computer Assisted Action Information System, has a similar role on a smaller scale. Other NATO navies have similar systems, and the links from ship to ship, shore to ship, and aircraft to ship are standardized throughout NATO and its allies to make it possible for different allied navies to operate together. This is a degree of coordination several steps further along than the usual common signal and code book.

NTDS and its counterparts have one great drawback: the radio links between ships can be detected by an enemy at great distances. For example, because the US Navy sometimes spreads its fleet dispositions over the horizon (as a counter to the Soviet nuclear missile threat), it requires an over-the-horizon NTDS radio link – which in turn is detectable at great distances by enemy as well as by friendly receivers. However, this high-frequency link is not inherent in the NTDS concept: for example, it is far more difficult to intercept a narrow ultra-high frequency beam sent upwards to a satellite, which can rebroadcast it. Such a system has its own built-in vulnerability – the satellite can be put out of action – and does impose a time delay on information transmission, as the information is moving over a very long path, including retransmission at the satellite. However, it is increasingly the case that any interceptible transmission can be used by an enemy to pinpoint the transmitter; in the future, therefore, navies may find themselves forced to choose between almost no communications at all and relatively elaborate systems, such as this one, which sharply reduce the probability of interception.

A COMMON HULL?

The need for numbers is another facet of the concept of fleet operations: in the design of the fleet as a weapon system, some trade-off is made between the quality of the individual unit and the cumulative quality of many, especially as numbers insure to some extent against the effects of losses. Several Western navies have experimented with the idea of a common hull which can be fitted out to fulfill a variety of missions, since the single hull can be built in great numbers, at minimum cost. Indeed, if it is kept in production, the schedule of fitting-out can be shifted to reflect changing conditions. Probably the earliest example of this concept was the wartime British 'Loch'/'Bay' class of ASW/AAW frigate. Looking towards a continuing need for both ASW and air defense for shipping around the British Isles, the Admiralty sought a similar (but faster) unified design in 1945. High speed was needed to combat the new German submarines, and normally that would have meant steam turbines. However, war experience showed that steam turbines were a major production bottleneck, and so the limits inherent in diesels were accepted. Three types were planned: a pure ASW frigate (Type 11), a pure AA frigate (Type 41), and – a harbinger of the new era – a frigate designed to control (presumably shore-based) aircraft over a convoy (Type 61). In fact the speed limitation proved unacceptable for ASW in view of the capabilities of the new German (and presumably Soviet) Type 21 and 26 submarines, and a steam type (*Whitby,* Type 12) was built in place of Type 11. At about the same time the French Navy embarked on a new destroyer program, using a common hull for a fleet destroyer (*Surcouf,* T47) and for its radar picket variant (T53R).

The US Navy had similar ideas, but did not convert them into ships largely because it had just completed over three hundred *Fletchers Sumners* and *Gearings*. However, the *Spruance* was designed as a convertible ASW/AAW destroyer; originally there were to have been about one hundred hulls, thirty of them armed with surface-to-air missiles. The balance between ASW and AAW units was to have been variable, depending upon the observed evolution of the Soviet threat. In fact no *Spruance* class missile destroyers were ordered by the US Navy, although six were ordered for Iran, of which four may ultimately fly the US flag. However, at least some *Spruance*s will probably end up as missile ships, and the missile provision is what made the new DDG47 Aegis version so attractive.

The new *Perry* class frigate was also envisaged as a common-hull program: ASW, AAW, and anti-ship warfare. The ASW version was abandoned in view of the large force of specialized ASW escorts the US Navy had already built up, none of which had much AAW capability. The anti-ship version merged with the AAW version: the latter's Mk 13 launcher can take either the Standard SAM (surface-to-air missile) or the Harpoon anti-ship weapon nearly interchangeably. As for ASW, the main sacrifice made in the *Perry* design was the elimination of a long-range active sonar in favor of the SQS-56. The *Perry* has no ASROC, but her helicopter is more effective – if she can detect a submarine in the first place. Happily, while the *Perry* was being built, the Navy found that its new passive towed array was an excellent long-range submarine detector which, moreover, had minimal impact on a ship and could, therefore, go aboard the *Perry* with little effect on her AAW (or helicopter) capability.

The new *Perry* class frigates (the name ship is shown, December 1977) were designed specifically for mass production; they have been criticized both as too expensive (due in part to inflation) and as too austere. *Perry* appears to present an almost totally weapon-free appearance, but that is deceptive. For example, beneath the launcher arm of her Mk 13 forward is a magazine for forty missiles, which may include up to forty Harpoons – a surface-to-surface battery far in excess of anything in the Soviet fleet. The large and apparently useless superstructure houses two LAMPS helicopters, which are her long-range ASW system; although *Perry* has no very long range ASW sensor at present, she and her sisters will be fitted with the towed (passive) array. The dish antenna abaft the large (and as yet nearly empty) mast is a separate tracking and illuminating radar (STIR) which provides a second-target capability for the Standard missiles fired by the Mk 13. The large louvers set into the side of the superstructure aft are characteristics of gas turbine powerplants: they are air intakes. The short stack just abaft the lattice mast is probably the exhaust for *Perry*'s diesel ship service generators.

Examples of the common-hull approach abound in recent commercial practice; most companies now offer their corvettes and frigates in a variety of configurations, depending upon the taste of the customer. The motive is economy through standardization; the cost is generally some inefficiency, perhaps in the form of a hull slightly larger than that required for a more specialized design.

THE SENSOR NET

A less obvious consideration is that the fleet at sea is integrated into a larger net of sensors, including, now, space- as well as land-based types. These adjuncts to sea power are not new but are often neglected, in part because accounts of naval battles generally begin when two fleets come into contact, rather than when their commanders first decide to seek battle. Indeed, even the need for some means of tracking enemy fleets at very long range appears to have gone largely unappreciated for many years. For example, throughout the early development of steam warships admiralties acted as though they could gain quite sufficient intelligence on enemy fleet movements from information available in neutral ports, for example from ships which had coaled enemy warships in neutral waters. Only in World War I did Britain and Germany discover that land-based radio direction-finders were an essential source of this kind of information. In this sense the land-based D/F systems developed by both navies substituted for what could have become very large strategic scouting formations – the fleets could retain their scouts for tactical work, when enemy units were known to be nearby. At least in its anti-carrier role, the Soviet Navy relies heavily on just such a system, to permit it to contact American carrier task forces approaching areas of interest to it. In fact it might not be excessive to say that D/F makes the configuration of Soviet anti-carrier formations a practical one – as long as their targets are cooperative enough to emit the signals upon which they depend for surveillance.

In World War II, D/F was a primary source of intelligence concerning German submarine formations at sea. Individual submarines could not travel very fast for very long, nor could the crew of any one submarine carry out observation over an area very far from their boat. The German U-boat command therefore sought to locate Allied convoys by a combination of U-boat reports, code-breaking, aerial reconnaissance, and its own network of D/F stations, and tried to achieve concentrations of U-boats against particular convoys by controlling all U-boats from a central headquarters at Brest. The U-boat commander in turn required position and status reports from all of his boats at sea; all the two-way traffic was by high-frequency radio, which the allies could intercept both at shore stations and aboard escort ships. The latter, in fact, could run down nearby U-boats which they had detected in this manner; recent evidence suggests that high-frequency direction finding (HF/DF) was as important as sonar and radar as an ASW sensor in the Battle of the Atlantic. This wartime experience led the US Navy and Royal Navy to employ various forms of D/F as ASW sensors post-war: modern ASW ships show D/F antennas targeted not only at submarine communications, but also at the radars commonly mounted by submarines on their attack periscopes.

The use of D/F in ASW is only one example of an attempt to solve the principal ASW problem: the basic sensor, sonar, has a relatively short range. In fact the great value of the convoy strategy is that it forces the submarine to come to the ASW forces in order to achieve its goal; even if the submarine survives by avoiding contact, the tactic will have succeeded in that the free use of the sea lanes will have been protected. However, in an era of more and more expensive surface ships, it is very tempting to look for solutions which, like D/F, can place ASW forces near their quarry for a high percentage of the time.

Thus any form of long-range underwater surveillance permits important economies in the number of ASW ships, and trade-offs between ASW surface ships and other kinds of units. For example, the United States has for many years operated a system of hydrophones off its coasts under the designation SOSUS, the Sound Surveillance System. SOSUS picks up a submarine by the noise of its propellers or its machinery and establishes a rough position by triangulation among its widely separated arrays. The latter is probably not nearly good enough for an immediate attack, but it is good enough to be used by a fast patrol plane as the starting point for a search: the plane can arrive at the initial position before the submarine has gone very far – especially as the existence of SOSUS is itself a deterrent to high-speed (hence noisy) running by the submarine. The same cannot be said of a surface ship, with the important exception of one equipped with a helicopter. Thus the existence of SOSUS makes it more valuable for US and allied ASW ships which operate within its range to be equipped with helicopters, perhaps even at the expense of other systems. It also permits patrol aircraft to perform, perhaps at relatively low expense, a role which otherwise would fall to large numbers of surface ships. The patrolling aircraft can in turn enforce losses upon an enemy submarine force which may permit substantial savings in convoy escorts.

It is important to distinguish between means of *area detection,* which may often give only poor location data; means of *localization,* such as sonobuoys dropped from an airplane; and *fire control* sensors which establish a target position more accurately. Very often initial detection can be assigned to a shore-based system such as SOSUS or some form of D/F; but the same cannot be said of localization and fire control. An effective warship should show a balance between these two functions and its weapons. That is not, unfortunately, always the case; weapons are impressive, but sensors and fire controls are not. Therefore many warships, especially those built for export to relatively unsophisticated navies, emphasize the former over the latter: it is easier to provide a big anti-ship missile than the system to aim that missile at a target over the horizon, let alone to sense the existence of that target in the first place.

THE EVOLUTION OF THE WEAPON SYSTEM

Perhaps the greatest single difference between the weapon system approach to ship design and the earlier approach is that previously ships were designed around specific weapons, such as 12in guns or, in the case of destroyers, torpedoes. The weapon system approach begins instead with the task the ship is to perform, with a guess as to the *threat* its weapons will have to defeat. Given the threat and a menu of weapons and sensors either in existence or in development, a weapon system can be designed to match, and a ship designed to carry that weapon system into battle. This approach is necessary in view of the great variety of possible combinations of weapons and sensors, all of which can counter roughly the same threat, given alternative hulls – but at very different costs.

The weapon system concept was introduced because modern guided weapons and sensors so dominate warship design that mismatches are extremely expensive; moreover, the format nowadays is usually one or two weapon systems per ship, whereas in the past a ship might have many, more or less uncoordinated. For example, a destroyer designed in 1940 might have guns for surface fire, guns for anti-aircraft fire, torpedo tubes and depth charges. Relatively little effort was made to balance off these different weapons, given some unified statement of the destroyer's mission; on the other hand, interference between them was limited to some problems of topside space and weight. By way of contrast, many postwar escorts of destroyer size were dominated by ASW weapon considerations, with AAW weapons added as an afterthought. In such ships even hull form was affected by the stipulated threat and by the requirements of the sensors (sonars). The penalty for failure to design the ship as a unified weapon system is weapon performance, which in practice is far below that possible in theory.

The weapon system approach to ship design entails great risks, associated with the rapid pace of weapon and other naval technology development since World War II. Typically, the Characteristics with which the design process begins outline the character of the weapon system chosen, although some details may change as the ship is designed or even as she is built. The gap between concept (Characteristics) and ship is a long one, and it tends to grow as equipment becomes more complex and as the different elements of ship design are tied together more tightly. For example, the US *Leahy* class missile frigates (now cruisers) were designed in 1956–57 to a set of Characteristics which evolved in 1955; they were not completed until 1962–64. Their design in turn incorporated the only available surface-to-air missile, Terrier, the study for which had been conceived in 1949 as an outgrowth of the 'Bumblebee' project of 1945. Thus to some extent at least the *Leahy* was designed to counter a threat projected in the late 1940s. It entered service about 15 years later, and had to grow to accommodate shifts in the Soviet threat through the 1980s. What is remarkable is that in fact the Terrier and its successor, the Standard Missile (Extended Range), do seem to counter a large fraction of the threats the *Leahy* might reasonably be expected to meet, given the room for growth built into the system and the direction which US naval technology has taken.

AIR DEFENSE

Modern warship design is very much dominated by weapon system choice. The first weapon system to have this effect was the surface-to-air missile (SAM). ASW ships of the late 1940s and early 1950s were much closer to traditional warships in design considerations than were contemporary SAM ships, that is, in a traditional warship the feasibility of the design depends upon the extent to which the design displacement can accommodate the weights of weapons, machinery and armor. Few postwar warships are armored, but the competition for weight between weapons and machinery shows in a lean hull with little superstructure volume. Destroyers continued to be designed in this fashion until the late 1950s, their hull dimensions being determined largely by the requirements of speed and seakeeping (freeboard forward, for example, for dryness). The SAM ship was different: her missiles and their loading facilities took up considerable hull volume and centerline length, and radars and their equipment took up more, so that SAM ships look bloated above the main (weather) deck level. Their design requires a great deal of empty space surrounding missiles and electronics, so that the weight balance becomes far less critical than the balance of volumes and deck areas, or even than length.

Each class of weapon system implies a different class of trade-offs. In a SAM ship, the important characteristics of the threat include the size (radar cross-section) of the target, its speed and altitude, a minimum range at which it must be destroyed, and the number of targets the system must defeat per unit of time. The last is important: any SAM system has a limited 'raid-handling' ability, which can be overcome if enough attackers approach simultaneously (saturation). The desired raid-handling capacity can be bought in several ways, all of which have implications for ship design.

The threat does *not* include a fixed maximum range for missile engagement: that is a matter for the system designer. The original US SAM concept envisaged an attacking bomber releasing a stand-off missile out of gunfire range; hopefully the SAM would destroy the bomber before it could launch its weapon. However, accepting a SAM range inside missile release range is merely to exchange the relatively large target presented by the bomber for a smaller anti-ship missile at shorter range; since the bomber can only drop one or two missiles, acceptance of shorter range does not necessarily increase the saturation problems of the SAM system. Moreover, the bomber pilot may be able to take far more effective evasive action than can the missile he drops.

Minimum range is more important. If the enemy missile carries a nuclear weapon, then a near miss is as good as a hit: the critical near miss range is determined by the size of the weapon and by the resistance of its target. A non-nuclear missile generally has to hit in order to be effective, but it may continue to its target – 'go ballistic' – if the target is close enough, even though a defending missile may have blow off its wings and wiped out its guidance system. Many Japanese Kamikazes did exactly that in 1945.

From the SAM's point of view, maximum range is a matter of missile size as well as of radar and fire control design. The larger the missile (or the more potent its propellant) the longer the range – at a cost in numbers and, often, in rate of fire. Minimum range is determined by the time lag between missile launch and control by the fire control system. For example, early US naval SAMs were all 'beam-riders', guided by a rotating radar beam generated by their fire control radars. They were not, of course, fired directly into this beam, but rather had to be 'captured' by a wider beam which then led them into the narrow guidance beam to give them accuracy. This process took a few seconds, during which the rapidly accelerating missile might travel several thousand yards.

One essential but largely invisible feature of the SAM system is its weapons direction system, or sub-system, which translates an initial search radar detection into missile firing and fire control commands. It imposes a 'dead time' between initial detection and 'designation' to fire control; the fire control radar then locks on to the incoming target, while one or more SAMs are warmed up, checked out, loaded and fired. Part of the dead time is the time required for a human operator to decide that the search radar has in fact detected a valid target: the limited number of SAMs carried imposes a considerable penalty for false alarms. Anyone who, untrained, has tried to 'read' a cluttered radar scope will appreciate that this element of target detection is far from trivial. In fact incoming missiles ignored entirely by search radar operators are a major problem. Recent US (and, presumably, other) air search sets are equipped with automatic target detectors which trigger SAMs *unless* the human operator objects. Such devices induce the SAM system to fire at false targets which may arise out of the random electrical noise always present. On the other hand, if they are set to reject most false targets, they may also ignore some real ones. The radar element of the SAM weapon system is by no means the clear-cut detection device usually advertised.

In a raid carried out by a large number of attackers, the weapon direction system has the vital role of allocating defensive weapons, to avoid exhaustion of the defenses. For example, it must decide just how many SAMs to fire per target, which requires some assessment of the effect of SAM fire on a salvo-by-salvo basis. Ability to carry out such an assessment depends in turn on the suit of search radars the ship carries. How fast it must be done depends upon the missile's characteristics and upon the additional dead time the SAM system and the weapons direction system itself impose once the decision has been made to fire again.

Every decision made by the SAM system designer affects every other and, in turn, affects the design of any ship which is to carry the system. For example, the specified threat includes some guess as to the number of attackers the system must handle simultaneously. A very long range system can afford to handle relatively few targets at the same time, killing a few and then killing others as they close in. Such a system can also afford a relatively low rate of fire, associated with the low target-handling capacity – which in turn may be reflected in the number of guidance radars and in the characteristics of the launcher and the reload mechanism. On the other hand, long range implies both a large SAM and long-range radars to support it, so that there may be no way of achieving a very high rate of fire in any case. In the face of an attack by cruise missiles dropped by bombers, the very long range SAM may nevertheless be able to destroy the bombers before they can launch, so reducing, perhaps, the total number of targets with which the total system must deal. However, in a carrier task force, the very long range SAM will be operating in the same area as the carrier fighters, and there may be serious problems of identification – SAMs ought not to be fired at friendly aircraft. Tactics may thus limit the value of range and thus of the one asset bought by SAM size.

Early SAM systems were so massive that they required specialized ships to carry them; in the face of the air and cruise missile threat of the 1950s, conventional guns remained quite effective for short ranges, and ships which were not expected to operate under the worst threats could be armed with such weapons. Late in the 1950s, however, the Soviets introduced ship-launched cruise missiles, which could be fired even from converted torpedo boats. It became clear, too, that submarines would soon be able to fire their own cruise missiles, ultimately from underwater – a capability realized in the late 1960s by the Soviet 'Charlie' class submarine with its SSN-7 missile. At the same time more and more air forces came to possess supersonic fighter-bombers, against which guided weapons seemed the most appropriate form of defense. A new category of 'point defense' SAMs was created to counter such weapons. The earlier SAMs had been designed for fleet defense: a few SAM ships in a task force would provide SAM coverage for the whole force; this combined with the air defense cover of the task force aircraft, and guns back up both. Point defense systems,

Much of the design of a guided missile ship depends upon the size of the missiles, and upon how they are stowed. In the 'County' class (HMS *Devonshire* shown, 1977) the very large Seaslug missiles are stowed in linear fashion: their magazine, on the main deck, consumes the middle third of the ship. The helicopter pad, which in a smaller ship might be an important determinant of length, is here easy to fit in because of the length mandated by the missile magazine beaneath it. However, the helicopter was clearly not central to the original design: it is stowed in the superstructure far forward, and must be maneuvered down the port side to the helipad – an operation which must be something of an adventure in a rough sea. The new *Sheffield* (shown here in 1977) makes far more economical use of her length, partly because her missile magazine does not extend (in length) much beyond her twin launcher, forward. Air intakes and massive gas turbine uptakes occupy much of the space below and abaft the large funnel (whose four uptakes indicate two cruise and two full-power gas turbines in a COGOG arrangement). The use of two Type 909 dual-purpose gun and missile control radars (in the radomes) provides both dual-target missile capability and a measure of survivability of firepower. *(Both photos: C & S Taylor)*

such as the US Sea Sparrow and the British Seacat and Seawolf, have too short a range to protect much beyond their own ships; they are intended either to supplement long range weapons or else to provide SAM cover for ships whose major weapon system serves some other purpose.

The growing importance of point defense SAMs is an expression of the fact that large SAMs can dominate a ship design. They have two kinds of influence: on below-decks volume, and on centerline space (and hence ship length). Most of the warships built since 1945 have been destroyers or enlarged destroyers, in the sense that they have had only one continuous deck, the main deck (US parlance) or weather deck. Machinery spaces amidships break up the internal (usable) hull volume. Even in prewar destroyer designs, demands for living and magazine spaces consumed most of the remaining volume. For example, for the US Navy to introduce a below-decks computer space in its prewar Mk 37 fire control system was to cramp the internal arrangement of the *Sims, Benson,* and *Fletcher* classes. Thus internal hull space was definitely not available for the massive post-war weapon direction systems or for their technicians, hence the large superstructures of virtually all postwar surface warships, particularly SAM ships. (In the Royal Navy this development is somewhat obscured: before the war British destroyers and frigates had short forecastles, for sea-keeping; postwar developments show the forecastle extended almost all the way aft in place of more conventional superstructure elements.) The introduction of SAMs made matters much worse, since their magazines took up far more space than did conventional shells, and in addition they required massive loading gear.

One reason was the size of the SAMs. Some of the newer point defense types are relatively small, weighing under 200lb, but the early missiles were anything but small: the US Terrier, for example, which was mounted aboard large destroyers (originally rated as frigates, now as cruisers) weighed, with its booster, about 3000lb, more than a 16in shell. It was far larger than the shell, over 26ft long. It had therefore to be stowed horizontally, and even then economy of space demanded that individual missiles be stowed without their fins. The Terrier loading system, then, had to include both stowage space and a space rather longer than the missile itself in which missiles could be warmed up and checked out – and fitted with their fins. They then had to be loaded horizontally on to a launcher, located far enough from the missile doors that the blast of firing would not burn them open. The result was massive: a typical frigate installation weighs about 200 tons, of which only 60 tons is in the missiles themselves. Even so, the earliest one, on the cruiser *Boston,* was credited with the ability to load one salvo every thirty seconds, which attests the saturation-raid threat built into the system.

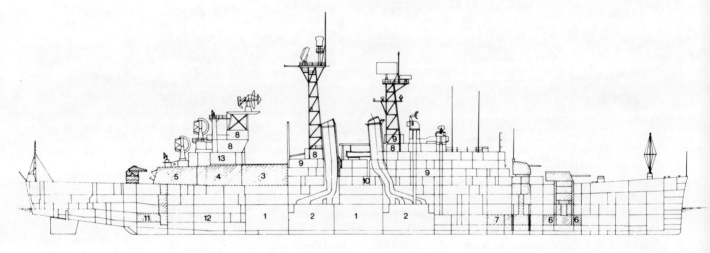

In postwar US CLG conversions – this inboard profile is of *Little Rock* – the entire missile system had to be built out atop the cruiser hulls; this was a consequence of the gross disparity in volume between the old ammunition (shells) and missiles, not to mention missile handling equipment. Forward, flagship facilities replaced No 2 6in turret and two of the three forward 5in/38 twin gunhouses. The six *Cleveland* class conversions (three Talos, three Terrier) all suffered at first from topheaviness.

KEY

1	Engine room	8	Radar room
2	Boiler room	9	Radio room
3	Missile magazine	10	ECM room
4	Missile ready-use	11	Missile warhead
5	Missile wing and fin		magazine
	assembly area	12	Missile computer room
6	6in gun magazines	13	Weapon control station
7	5in gun magazines		

The requirement for which Terrier was designed included the target it was to defend, a carrier task force moving through rough seas at 30kts or more and over considerable distances. Thus the ship platform part of the system had to accommodate a large powerplant, which in turn consumed a large part of the hull length amidships. In a destroyer hull, missile magazines had to be worked in fore and aft of the machinery box: to a considerable extent the combination of Terrier length and machinery box length determined hull length. Cruisers, however, had the inherent stability to accept very massive superstructures; they were also much longer than were the specially designed missile escorts. For example, the Terrier installations in *Cleveland* class hulls incorporated two banks of missiles in tandem (to use the available length), with a hoist between them, and an overhead rail to move the missiles to the finning area and then to the launcher; the forward part of the installation, therefore, was worked in over the machinery spaces. In both cruisers and frigates the Terrier system was an indirect consumer of volume as well, as it required considerable electrical power both for the launching system and for the associated radars; volume was also required for the radar transmitters and for the weapon direction system.

These are demands for hull volume, not length. The two kinds of demand coincide in the case of the missile frigate because the Terrier magazine system is laid out horizontally, and because its length is so great that other Terrier features demanding centerline length can easily be accommodated on top of it. However, the more recent US Standard and Tartar missiles are short enough to be stowed vertically. Their *systems*, however, still demand space along the centerline of their launching ship, and so help to determine ship length.

As in the case of guns, missiles are often mounted on the centerline because such positions provide the maximum training arc. Missile blast makes it unwise to mount SAMs anywhere but at the extreme fore and aft ends of the superstructure; in a very few cases others have been mounted to fire over these end positions and, in still fewer, secondary SAMs have been mounted in broadside positions. Given a SAM launcher at one end of a ship's superstructure, it requires a clear arc not merely of fire but also of blast. The SAM is guided by radars which must have clear arcs approximating to those of the launcher itself; and they in turn are directed by search radars requiring at least similar clear arcs, if not even larger ones. The ship can be maneuvered to bring her SAMs to bear, but her search radars must cover every direction.

Other centerline space is required for uptakes and for the bridge, although to some extent the latter can carry radars on its roof. The US *Leahy* and *Belknap* class missile frigates carry such a combination to its logical conclusion: their funnels ('stacks' in US parlance) are combined with radar masts to form 'macks'. These ships were designed primarily for SAM operations in a fast task force, and although they incorporated substantial ASW capability, the latter had little impact in comparison to considerations of air defense.

ANTI-SUBMARINE WARFARE

In general, ASW had an effect on ship design very different from that of anti-aircraft warfare (AAW), particularly in the early postwar years. The primary sensor, sonar, had so short a range that an attacking ASW ship had to remain close to its quarry. ASW weapons were short-ranged and hence not too large, and the ASW ship required considerable maneuverability and a healthy speed advantage over the submarine. Its speed was determined not by that of the unit(s) it escorted but rather by the speed of the submarine, and it was generally assumed that a speed edge of about 5kts was required. Although the German Type 21 submarine in existence in 1945 had a speed of about 16kts submerged, the usual assumed threat, just after the war, was Type 26, powered by a Walter hydrogen-peroxide engine, and capable of 22kts – hence the 28kts specified for the British *Whitby* class frigates. The US Navy believed that 25kts was a more realistic submarine speed, given a Walter or a nuclear powerplant, and specified 30kts for new ocean ASW units such as the cruiser *Norfolk*. Matters later changed considerably with the perfection of longer-range sonars and the associated longer-range weapons.

There are two alternative ASW strategies: screening (convoy) and hunter-killer. The former is an attempt not so much to destroy the submarine as to prevent it from attaining its objective, by concentrating ASW units around the targets. It requires ASW escorts in proportion to the number of targets, *not* the number of submarines: in effect, the convoy system permits the operator of the submarines to put great pressure upon those defending the convoy. This is the significance of Admiral Gorshkov's observation that the German U-boat arm was able to force the Allies to field 25 ASW craft for every submarine sunk in World War II and 100 men for every submarine. Convoy, however, is the only viable strategy as long as there is no very long range ASW sensor which might permit a rapid and efficient search of wide ocean areas – a point often expressed by the phrase 'as long as the ocean cannot be turned to glass'.

The hunter-killer strategy approaches the ASW problem from the opposite point of view: it involves attacking the submarines directly, using whatever location data can be obtained and then searching the area to find a submarine. For example, a hunter-killer force (HUK) might begin with the 'flaming datum' of a ship sinking after a submarine attack. By the time the hunter-killer force appeared at that point, the submarine might be anywhere within an area whose size depended upon its speed and upon the time delay before the arrival of the force, which would then have to search that 'area of uncertainty'. Thus the supreme value of HUK group is speed: the greater that speed, the fewer HUK groups needed to cover a given area. HUK tactics are particularly suited to a Navy possessing large fixed submarine-detection systems such as the US SOSUS, which can turn the ocean into a murky sort of glass.

In practice most Navies adopt a mixed strategy. For example, NATO possesses SOSUS and SOSUS-like arrays covering the North Atlantic. In addition, it knows that Soviet submarines attempting to attack the NATO sea line of communication across the North Atlantic must break out from their base at Murmansk via the Greenland-Iceland-UK (GIUK) Gap: HUK forces stationed in the Gap can operate profitably. Other HUK forces, mainly long-range patrol aircraft, can follow up SOSUS contacts. However, neither the Gap barrier nor the SOSUS system is so efficient that it can destroy enough Soviet submarines to render the North Atlantic safe for NATO shipping. It is, therefore, necessary to place considerable reliance on convoy operations. In theory the HUK operations impose losses upon the Soviet submarine force, which then finds it more difficult to overcome the convoy escorts. The latter, which have to be numerous in order to cover all the convoys, generally cannot be as sophisticated as those units assigned to HUK duty in the important GIUK Gap.

The advent of Soviet ballistic-missile submarines in the late 1950s somewhat complicated these considerations, and in fact inspired far-reaching improvements in SOSUS. Perhaps largely because of the efficacy of SOSUS, current Soviet doctrine envisages holding ballistic missile submarines in sanctuary areas protected by Soviet naval forces (which ensure their 'combat stability'); the submarines can either fire from these areas (in the case of 'Delta' class submarines) or may be released to close with their targets only relatively late in a war. This doctrine assumes in turn that NATO attack submarines and even surface and air ASW forces would be sent into the sanctuaries in wartime, to hunt Soviet ballistic-missile submarines. The Norwegian and White Seas are a principal sanctuary; the Soviets, therefore, regard the GIUK Gap as the gateway for NATO submarine-hunters, and probably consider a barrier north of it essential for the preservation of their ballistic missile boats. For example, the *Kiev* was probably designed primarily to operate in the GIUK Gap. On the other hand, it seems likely that Soviet naval forces in the Mediterranean are designed in large part to hunt Western ballistic missile submarines which operate there.

Strategic considerations have direct consequences for ASW ship design. For example, the need for numbers of escorts was particularly keenly felt in Britain and in the United States following World War II. It was clear that large numbers could not be built in peacetime, especially as both navies retained hundreds of war-built ASW ships. The latter, however, could not cope with fast submarines, which it was assumed would constitute the new Soviet submarine fleet. Therefore, any ASW convoy escort had to be designed for mass production under war conditions. For the Royal Navy war conditions included the bombing of shipyards and so an important design consideration was that the new escort be adapted for prefabrication, so that she would spend the minimum time on the slip. She had to be fast enough to counter the new submarines, even in a considerable seaway, which in itself required a long, yet maneuverable hull; she had to use the minimum specialized industrial capacity; and she had to carry the most effective sonar and the new 'Limbo' ASW mortar, which in the late 1940s was the best ASW weapon in prospect. Effective sonar implied not merely a space and weight reservation, but also an optimum dome location under the ship, and special efforts at noise control – which in turn imposed time and money costs upon construction, no matter how cheap the new ship was to be. World War II experience had shown, moreover, that a major bottleneck in escort production was the manufacture of steam turbines, so that a mass production escort should have, at best, a single screw. The single screw would, in fact, permit good maneuverability, but it also presented problems of reliability. The latter could be neglected in a ship intended to fight in very large numbers; in any case she would probably be sunk long before her single engine or screw failed.

The Admiralty designed the *Blackwood* class frigate to these requirements: a long, narrow hull driven at speed by a single large propeller, and carrying the absolute minimum battery: the two 'Limbo's of far more expensive ASW frigates, provison for the ASW homing torpedoes then projected, the sonar suit of the larger ASW frigates – but a gun battery of only three 40mm. Size was dictated by ASW tactics, and was acceptable because ship steel was relatively inexpensive compared to steam turbines or guns or air defense radars; however, the *Blackwood*s emerged as apparently under-armed failures.

Similar considerations in the US Navy led to the construction of the *Dealey* class destroyer escorts, which evinced somewhat similar reactions. In fact the *Dealey*s were considered insufficiently simple, and an even more austere 'mobilization' design, the *Claude Jones,* was evolved, with diesel propulsion. It was considered such a failure that only four were built. The irony of the story is that when the Chief of Naval Operations recommended a return to the *Dealey,* he asked that it be modified slightly to incorporate new ASW technology – the SQS-26 sonar and matching weapons, ASROC and, later, DASH. The result was the cycle of US frigates which culminated in the destroyer-size *Knox* – which was austere only in its single-screw propulsion plant. The latter was certainly acceptable under war conditions, in which the test of a propulsion plant is whether it can bring home a damaged ship. The then Bureau of Ships justified the *Dealey* plant on the basis of a war damage study which appeared to show that hits which knocked out one shaft of a two-shaft ship generally immobilized her. However, in peacetime reliability was far more important, and the single shaft might well fail where a twin-screw ship would remain in operation.

The high speed required of both *Blackwood* and *Dealey* is an example of the general trade-off between different aspects of a weapon system. In the case of the SAM ship, speed, other than that required to keep up with the force to be escorted, is almost immaterial, because the ship has negligible speed compared to her target. The only exception would be the speed edge required to maneuver relative to the force to be escorted. On the other hand sustained speed is vital: this requirement for *strategic* speed is imposed by the mission of the force to be escorted. In the ASW of the 1940s and early 1950s, on the other hand, sensor performance was relatively poor, so that platform performance had to be substituted. Matters changed significantly with the advent of long-range sonars, which permitted the development of long-range ASW weapons such as ASROC and Ikara. Thus in the late 1950s US ASW ship Characteristics teamed the 10,000yd ASROC with the new 10,000yd SQS-23 sonar. However, with the development of the SQS-26, which could make convergence-zone contacts at 60,000yds, something of the earlier situation returned. Now platform performance had to make up for weapon performance, given superior sensor performance. In the early 1960s, for example, the US Navy came close to building a 40kt destroyer, Seahawk. Its high *tactical* speed was intended to permit it to close convergence-zone (and other long-range) contacts to bring them within ASROC range. One problem of convergence-zone ASW is that the contact is not sufficiently precise for instant attack: Seahawk would detect a submarine, rush out to its approximate position, re-contact to achieve sufficient precision, and then attack. Seahawk was never built, but the development of shipboard ASW helicopters which carry their own sensors, such as the US LAMPS, has had something of the same tactical result.

One ASW engagement is a lengthy single-target battle: submarine contacts are fleeting, and a ship or ships may chase a submarine for some hours before they can achieve a kill – or before the submarine can escape. By way of contrast, the AAW battle is short but involves many targets appearing almost simultaneously. Ultimately the amount of data involved in both engagements is very much the same. In ASW it is necessary to maintain files of a target's course, speed and signature, so that each time contact is lost some target position can be estimated as a starting point for re-contact, and the signature of the new contact compared with the old for identification. Moreoever, in the murky world of sonar, the longer the contact can be maintained the more the data-processing system can refine its picture of the contact. The ships and the submarine move relatively slowly, so that such time delays do not make the ASW tactics useless. In air defense, on the other hand, the typical engagement lasts a few minutes. Vast amounts of data are collected in the form of course and speed files on each target, but all that data becomes obsolete very quicky, and is discarded as soon as the raid ends.

Weapon system requirements reflect these contrasts. Two of the most important considerations in AAW are 'single shot kill probability' (SSPK) and the number of targets the AAW weapon system can handle simultaneously; the latter is a combination of rate of fire and fire control capacity. A high SSPK is required if the high rate of fire is to be translated into a high rate of target engagement. For its part the ASW ship encounters only one or two submarines at one time, and in addition it experiences a relatively long interval between attacks. For example, in the wake of a failed attack the time to re-detect the target is likely to be far greater than any reasonable reload time for the ASW weapons. However, ASW sensors are such that any realistic ASW weapon system designer would have to expect a high proportion of failed attacks, even given a good SSPK; he must provide, then, considerable weapon stowage – but not a high rate of fire. This is little more than a restatement of the classic ASW tactic: detect, attack, re-detect, re-attack.

The dominant trend in ASW weapons – and sensors – has been the search for greater and greater range; each extension in range involves larger weapons and sensors and hence a greater (or at least more visible) influence on ship design. In 1939 the standard ASW weapon was the depth charge, dropped directly over the estimated location of the submarine. Destroyer sonars produced beams which angled downwards, so that a submarine contact would vanish as a destroyer approached: indeed, it used to be said that submarine depth could be estimated as one-third of the range at which contact was lost. This loss of contact, however, gave the submarine time to evade attack – as, of course, did the time it took the depth charges to sink. The deeper the submarine, the longer the sinking time and hence the better the chance of evasion. Moreover, a submarine could tell that a destroyer was approaching because the 'ping' of that ship's sonar would cease to be heard as contact was lost.

The great advantage of stand-off weapons, then, was that an attack could be mounted while the submarine remained in sonar contact. The first such weapon, Hedgehog, was designed to explode only on contact with the submarine: the sonar provided no depth information, so that the Hedgehog charges had, in effect, to sweep all possible target depths. By the middle of the war, separate depth-finding sonars, such as the British Type 147, had been developed, and it was possible to produce stand-off weapons fuzed to burst at the submarine's precise position. Like depth charges, such weapons did not have to strike the submarine: their concussions could be effective at several yards' range. The earliest such weapon was the British Squid; later ones were 'Limbo', the Bofors 375mm mortar, and the US Weapon Alfa.

All these weapons still suffered from the problem of 'dead time': no matter how quickly their charges might sink into the water, the deep-diving submarine could still evade while they sank; she would, moreover, be warned by the sound of firing, which the water would probably transmit. Homing torpedoes were an attempt to get around this problem; nuclear depth charges, which have a large margin for error, were another. The latter, of course, had to be detonated at some considerable distance from the attacking ship, as in the US ASROC system.

As weapon ranges increased, the 'dead time' problem expanded to include time of flight: for example, a subsonic ASROC requires a minute or more to fly out to the point at which it drops its torpedo or atomic depth charge into the water. Some long-range systems, therefore, permit the ASW ship to exercise control of the weapon in flight. The ultimate form of control, of course, is the use of a manned helicopter which may deploy its own sensors, such as a dipping sonar or sonobuoys.

Each weapon or sensor development has a considerable impact on the ship designed to accommodate it. In the early postwar period, the main weapon was a mortar such as 'Limbo': it required little more than a clear firing arc and a magazine; its fire control system required a computer and connections to a search sonar and a depth-finding sonar. The latter required keel space far enough from the bow to avoid the bubbles it entrained, and far enough from the propellers to avoid their noise. Hull design was strongly affected by the need to avoid bringing the sonar domes out of the water as a relatively small ASW ship pitched in rough seas.

As sonars became larger, some navies began to mount them in the bows: there a sonar would be least affected by ship-generated noise, although pitching motion was actually worse. Long-range bow sonars were often associated with variable-depth sonar aft, which in turn required

Modern large helicopters are voracious consumers of shipboard space. The Royal Canadian Navy was among the first users of independent helicopters with large dipping sonars, such as this Sea King, aboard HMCS *Huron* (June 1977). There are actually two separate hangars, so that one helicopter is always available. *(Paul Beaver)*

The impact of a large helicopter is even more pronounced in ships not originally designed for one; this is one of the original postwar Canadian frigates, *Saguenay,* as rebuilt in 1965 to carry a single Sea King. Her uptakes had to be split to allow sufficient hangar room; presumably the location of the helipad was determined by the desire to retain at least one of the original pair of 'Limbos'. *(Official)*

Given the brutal effects on ship arrangement of even small helicopters, it is no surprise that many ingenious schemes for space-saving systems have been tried. The French *La Galissonnière*, for example, has a collapsible hangar aft, which folds down to provide an apron around the helicopter pad proper. *(Official)*

If a ship is large enough, her helicopter facility may consume very little space, especially if it is for a small machine. Japan is the only remaining operator of the DASH drone helicopter; the effects on the destroyer *Nagatsuki* (shown here in July 1976) are almost invisible. Her forthcoming conversion to take the much larger LAMPS will undoubtedly demand far more room. *(USN Official by courtesy of Norman Polmar)*

specialized hoists and spaces at the stern. Both were generally associated with new long-range ASW weapons, which required larger launchers and more capacious magazines, even though the number of weapons carried generally fell considerably. This was not a reduction in the number of *attacks*, however: most short-range weapons fire many projectiles per attack, whereas the long-range types fired only one or two, relying on high SSPKs to achieve their objectives.

Helicopters have probably had the greatest effect on ASW ship configuration. Ideally, a helicopter pad should be forward of the after quarter-length of a ship, where ship motion is least pronounced; it should be far from any high superstructure elements, which will produce strong winds making helicopter control difficult on landing or take-off; it must be clear from abaft, as that is the way a helicopter pilot will approach his ship; and there should be room forward of the pad for a hangar. The latter should accommodate at least one spare helicopter, to keep one available at all times. Helicopter operation also requires that the mother ship be fitted with some type of homing beacon (generally TACAN in Western ships) and probably with an air search radar.

Even if all of these requirements are not fulfilled, the partial fulfillment turns a modern ASW ship into a length-critical ship; matters are, of course, even worse for any ship designed to carry out a combined AAW and ASW mission, as many are. The helicopter and hangar consume a great deal of length abaft amidships. Other length goes into bridgework, radar masts and funnels. Generally there is at least one other major weapon present: a heavy SAM system (in an AAW/ASW ship); a missile-borne ASW weapon (for example, for weather in which the helicopter cannot operate); a gun for shore bombardment or for ship-killing; or even a small SAM for self-defense. Each competes with the helicopter for ship length; the provision of each stretches the ship, and thus has consequences for her seakeeping performance. That in turn interacts with the choice of bumps on her underwater hull housing her sonars; and what kind of sonar suit she needs depends in turn on what kinds of ASW weapons she is to carry. Both depend, too, on the areas in which she is to operate.

ANTI-SURFACE SHIP CAPABILITIES

Modern warships have one other major mission, which as yet has not had the design impact of either AAW or ASW: anti-surface ship warfare, sometimes abbreviated ASUW. This problem was largely neglected in the West until the emergence of a Soviet blue-water fleet in the early 1960s, armed with ASUW missiles of its own. Until that time it appears to have been assumed that Western carrier aircraft could handle any Soviet surface warships which might venture to sea; moreover, many of the SAM systems then under development had alternative anti-ship modes of operation. Interest in ASUW grew considerably after Soviet-built missile boats of the Egyptian Navy successfully attacked the Israeli destroyer *Eilat* in 1967; Western navies looked (i) for means of neutralizing 'Styx' and other Soviet ship-launched weapons, (ii) for a means of killing missile boats, and (iii) for a 'Styx' equivalent of their own, especially as the high cost of carriers was driving many Western navies out of the carrier business entirely. All of these approaches had to be carried out in the face of existing, indeed mounting, AAW and ASW threats, and limited budgets: no Western navy could afford, as the Soviets could, to devote major surface ships almost entirely to the ASUW role.

For ships designed primarily for AAW, the advent of 'Styx' meant that a higher standard of AAW protection was required: 'Styx' was a relatively short-range missile, which would give relatively little warning. For ASW ships, 'Styx' required some form of close-in defense; work on such weapons had actually begun some years before the *Eilat* incident, but that incident certainly accelerated Western point defense programs. Finally, a Western anti-ship missile was attractive because it could destroy 'Styx' before it could be launched. It had, however, to exact the minimum penalty in ship design, since ships had still be to be designed for optimum fleet AAW or ASW performance. All major Western anti-ship missiles, therefore, are designed for minimum 'ship impact': they are mounted in cannisters, or else can be fired from standard AAW missile launchers (as in the case of the US Mk 13 aboard the *Perry* class frigates). An alternative was a refinement of the anti-surface capability of existing anti-aircraft weapons, such as the British Sea Dart. Finally, the helicopters originally embarked for ASW can fire anti-ship missiles, and have the advantage of rising above the ship's horizon – but such operations eliminate them from the ASW role.

Probably the single most difficult question in ASUW is how a ship can fire her limited stock of ASUW weapons at targets over her horizon, preferably without some investment in sensors which will crowd out those devices more important for her primary roles. Western navies can take little comfort from the fact that the Soviets have had to develop a rather elaborate structure of reconnaissance assets to achieve just such a capability themselves – in ships far more dedicated to ASUW than are any Western escorts.

CHAPTER FOUR

Speed, Power and Seakeeping

Modern surface warships are direct descendants of the fast warships of the past, principally destroyers. The great problem in their design was that a small ship always needs more horsepower per ton than a larger one to achieve a given speed; even after cutting numerous corners (largely to do with reliability) only so much horsepower can be crammed into a given small hull. Destroyers did not become practical at all until great advances had been made in light machinery design, late in the nineteenth century, and from that time to this the chief road to more payload in a small, fast ship has always been via lighter machinery. Until after 1945, ships were, as we have seen, weight-critical; now that they are much more often volume- or even length-critical, the key improvement is not in horsepower per ton so much as in horsepower per cubic foot or in length of engineering space. The need for long endurance only complicates matters: an engine optimized for high power tends to be relatively inefficient at low cruising power, and so demands large fuel tanks (which eat up hull volume nearly as well as do large engine rooms) if a ship is to attain both high speed and long range. World War II experience suggested a need for both; moreover, the Western naval missions and strategies of the postwar period required escorts to be able to maintain relatively high speeds in very rough water. The latter in turn implies increased freeboard and heavier hull construction, both of which increase hull weight and so require more power, even within a fixed hull length – and a fixed volume available for engines.

THE LESSONS OF WORLD WAR II

Postwar US strategy emphasized fast carrier operations in rough areas such as the Norwegian Sea and the North Pacific; high task force speed was vital as a means of self-protection, for example against submarines. Indeed,

Perhaps the virtue most often sought in modern warship hull design is good seakeeping performance, such as dryness forward. Unfortunately it is not always attained: the *Knox* class is notoriously wet, in part due to low freeboard forward – and in part due to the effect of a very large bow sonar dome. The photograph shows USS *Stein*, 14 December 1971.

given Soviet concentration tactics, high task force speed might well have made it difficult for the Soviets to assemble an appropriate strike while the carrier force remained within range of any one target. Existing US destroyers were inadequate: as early as 1945 the US Navy considered these ships too slow to escort carriers which would not have to reduce speed in high seas. It wanted, too, a ship which would have a significant speed advantage over the carriers so that it could maneuver relative to them. At one point the combination of new AAW and ASW weapons and very high rough-water, fully-loaded speed (36kts) appeared to point to a 5000-ton, 100,000shp destroyer. Even the compromise solution represented by the *Mitscher* class was not much smaller, and could not be built in the requisite numbers. The demands of ASW against fast submarines were only somewhat less onerous, but still impressive, and far beyond the powers of pre-war destroyers. The latter might have made 36kts or better in a glassy sea, but perhaps only 12 to 15kts in the face of a moderate storm, which would hardly discourage a submarine.

Wartime ASW operations were carried out very largely in the rough conditions of the North Atlantic, and many postwar escorts, particularly those of the British and Canadian Navies, reflect lessons of the Murmansk run. For example, the lack of a covered passageway between crew quarters forward and stations (such as engineering spaces) aft was found to be a serious defect in wartime British destroyers, and in many frigates as well, and subsequent British frigates were provided with exactly such a covered passageway. Icing was a very dangerous problem: postwar Canadian frigates were designed with carefully faired deck edges and even covered anchor recesses, to reduce icing and so preserve stability under winter conditions in the North. On a subtler level, the US decision to switch from mild steel to Special Treatment Steel as a major shipbuilding material was based in large part on the latter's superior resistance to cracking under extreme cold.

All of these design requirements, as well as the frequent need to accommodate large new sonars, radars and weapons, had to be met at minimum cost: the great virtue of the frigate or destroyer is numbers. Cost was often translated into a requirement that a ship be suitable for mass production in an emergency, which in turn affected machinery selection – and machinery, as remarked earlier, was the greatest single bottleneck in ship production during World War II*. The need to provide for mass production also affected the extent to which sophisticated constructional methods, necessary for weight-saving, could be employed; but any increase in weight, given a fixed requirement for speed and endurance, demanded

The French Navy designs its ships to operate in relatively calm seas; for example, it provides relatively little freeboard forward. The ASW frigate *Tourville* is shown, here with her No 1 100mm gun mount entirely hidden. *(French Navy)*

greater power, and that in turn would require a bigger ship. For example, the first postwar US destroyer design was the 3750-ton *Mitscher,* which was held to that tonnage only by careful construction and by the extensive use of light alloys. Gibbs & Cox was asked to design a mobilization version: it came to no less than 5000 tons, a prospect so forbidding that the US Navy gave up much of the sophistication (at least in weapons and radars) that it wanted and settled for the much simpler 2850-ton *Forrest Sherman* – which was still far more complex than such true mass-production escorts as the *Dealey* and the *Claude Jones.*

Perhaps the single greatest irony of the period was that speed requirements declined just as a truly compact powerplant, the gas turbine, appeared. It made very high speed relatively easy to attain, as the characteristics of a variety of recent commercial frigates show. However, in most Western navies fleet formation speed stabilized below 30kts, one reason being that sonar is not every effective much above 20 or 25kts. In ASW, long-range weapons have tended to discount the value of high tactical speed. On the other hand, to maintain 30kts in Sea State 4 (which was the *Spruance* design requirement) is far more difficult to achieve than the pre-war 36kts in smooth water: although modern destroyers and frigates appear (on paper) rather slow in comparison to their forebears, their effective speeds are rather better. This speed, however, is often bought largely by better (and larger) hull forms, rather than by more power per ton or per cubic foot. What more compact plants do buy is a limit on the growth of the ship due to the proliferation of weapons and sensors: the latter can encroach on volume which in the past would have been required for propulsion.

THE INFLUENCE OF SONAR ON HULL DESIGN

In many cases hull forms are shaped by sonar requirements as much as by those of speed and sea-keeping. Sonar dome dimensions are determined by sonar frequency; they represent a compromise between the high theoretical performance of large low-frequency sets and the losses such sets experience due to the character of the hulls they inhabit. A shipborne sonar loses sensitivity due to a combination of ship noise, ship motion, and the effects of its location on the hull.

* The case of the diesel destroyer escorts is well known, but not unique. The British 'River' class frigates were designed for geared turbine power, but nearly all of them had reciprocating engines instead. Machinery supply problems also appear to have plagued the British minesweeper program.

Ship noise in turn is a combination of propeller noise, machinery noise, and flow noise due to water moving past the sonar dome. For example, sonars are generally placed as far forward as possible to isolate them from the propellers; however, beyond about a quarter-length aft of the bow, the sonar suffers from the noise of bubbles entrained by the bow, and is also subject to pitching motions which draw it clear of the water (quenching) – and it may be damaged as the ship slams back into the water. Machinery noise is not limited to the main propulsion plant. For example, it was calculated that the operation of the refrigeration pumps in the *Mitscher* increased self-generated noise about fivefold and so reduced her search sonar performance by 40 per cent. Current practice is generally to shield the sonar itself from hull-borne noise as much as possible, and also to try to overcome propeller noise by a combination of bubble screens which contain the sound (Prairie/Masker) and by baffles at the rear of the dome. Neither measure has any effect on sonar performance. Unfortunately, rapid motion is one sign of considerable stability (metacentric height), which in turn is insurance against quick loss due to relatively minor flooding. In many recent designs this conflict is resolved by the use of active or passive stabilizers, such as flume tanks and fins. Stabilization has other beneficial effects as well, such as extending the percentage of the time during which a helicopter can be operated, and improving crew performance – as readers of accounts of wartime corvette operations in the North Atlantic will doubtless appreciate. Generally, the larger the ship the less the motion problem, given some particular sea state. For example, US missile cruisers converted from heavy cruisers were effective sonar-platforms even in Sea State 6. Ships limited in size by the requirement for mass production could not do nearly so well – in 1958 a US Bureau of Ships study estimated that a destroyer would lose about half her sonar range due to ship motion in Sea State 4 and that a destroyer escort under similar conditions would lose about three-quarters. In Sea State 6, even a frigate (small missile cruiser) would be helpless.

It was not only that the ship motion affected sonar performance. For a small ship, merely to mount a large sonar anywhere on her keel would grossly reduce her ship performance. For example, the same Bureau of Ships study suggested that a destroyer escort would lose about 35 per cent of her endurance with a big SQS-26 sonar, roughly the size of a 40ft utility boat, mounted in a conventional keel position. There would also be a 1.5kt speed loss. On the other hand, a bow location would reduce both losses: the DE would lose only about 10 per cent in endurance, and about a third of a knot. It appeared that in larger ships, such as missile frigates, careful design might even achieve some speed gains at high speed.

A bow sonar does not solve all problems. It is particularly subject to slamming motions at high speed in rough water, and fear of damage to the sonar dome may cause a captain to reduce speed. Even if he does not, the slamming will reduce effective sonar performance. The Royal Navy argues that frigates are much too small for big bow-mounted sonars, especially if they are to operate in rough water: it prefers a more conventional installation, using a higher-frequency system.

Moreover, the bow sonar introduces hull design problems, especially in anchor location – it would be most unfortunate for a ship to rip up her sonar dome with her own anchor. Ships with bow sonars are distinguishable by their unusual anchor layouts: in the US Navy the typical solution is an extreme clipper bow with an anchor set into the stem itself; the Soviets appear to prefer a clipper bow with the conventional pair of anchors much further forward than is usual.

There is also an internal space problem. A sonar consists not only of its transducer, which is in the dome, but also of a signal transmitting and processing unit. Every foot of cable between transducer and signal processor is itself a source of noise, and so of lost performance. However, there is not nearly enough volume just above the bulbous dome of a bow-mounted sonar for much in the way of signal processing electronics, so some cable leads are inevitable. For a smaller sonar such as the SQS-56 of the *Perry* class, losses due to long cables might well be prohibitive: the bow location is just not worthwhile.

Sonar considerations can have more subtle effects. For example, the first big US ASW ship, the *Norfolk,* had unusually large, slow-turning propellers, which were expected to be relatively quiet. They were also relatively inefficient: she traded speed, given her power, for sonar effectiveness. Her hull form was designed to reduce flow noise, and a single rudder was adopted largely to avoid the noise associated with two rudders in the propeller slipstreams. Even transom immersion (which would have made for better speed performance) was minimized to eliminate burbling at the stern at 20kts. The single rudder reduced maneuverability, even though the ASW weapons with which *Norfolk* was to be armed required considerable maneuverability for their effective use; lesser US ASW craft of the same period were designed specifically for high maneuverability, with unusually large rudders.

HULL DESIGN AND SPEED REQUIREMENTS

Speed performance in smooth water is determined by the size and shape of the underwater hull, principally, at the speeds of frigates and destroyers, by waterline length. Hull form is usually described by a series of coefficients, ratios of actual hull areas and volumes to areas and volumes of the block formed by the underwater dimensions of the hull. If L denotes waterline length, B waterline beam, and T mean draught (not counting sonar domes), $L \times B \times T$ is the volume of a block encompassing the underwater hull; the *block coefficient* (CB) is that fraction of the block actually occupied by the hull. The block has a cross-sectional area $B \times T$, and the fraction filled by the (underwater) midships cross-section of the hull is denoted CM, the *midships coefficient.* Similarly, the block has a *waterline coefficient,* CS. Alternatively the hull can be compared to a prism whose cross-section is the hull's midships cross-section: the fraction occupied is the *prismatic coefficient,* CP, which is given by CB divided by CM. CB and CP measure, to some extent, the fineness of the ends of a ship. CM measures the amount of increased draught caused by any addition of weight: the larger the CM, the less the ship sinks into the water for any addition of weight to her hull. On the other hand, CM also measures the extent to which the ship is affected by the interface between air and water. That is where she makes the waves which dissipate so much of her propulsive power, but it is also where she is most affected by sea wave motion.

The sea resists the passage of a ship by a combination of friction and wavemaking (residual) resistance; the latter is very largely a function of the speed-length ratio, the ratio of speed to the square root of L. Very crudely, a ship is considered fast if her speed-length ratio (speed in knots, L in feet) much exceeds one. Since it takes a length of 900ft to balance off a speed of 30kts, and a length of 625 even at 25, all modern frigates and destroyers can be classed either as fast or as extremely fast. Again very crudely, power required per ton is very nearly a function only of the speed-length ratio, since frictional influences follow much the same trend as residual ones. In effect, then, a 400ft destroyer at 30kts is equivalent to a 600ft cruiser at 36. If the 10,000-ton cruiser requires 140,000shp at that speed (14shp per ton), the destroyer, at 3000 tons, should require about 42,000 – which is about right.

A curve of power per ton plotted against speed-length ratio shows a series of bumps and hollows along its general rise with higher speed. These are due to the interaction of the trains of waves generated at bow and stern. It follows that, for a given maximum speed, a destroyer designer can save considerable power by choosing his ship length carefully. In general he is impelled in that direction because even the minimum powerplant for a fast or very fast ship is so massive as to crowd her hull: that is not nearly the case for large, fast ships which can operate at much lower relative speeds (ie at lower speed-length ratios). Length is not the only factor; wavemaking depends, to a lesser degree, on CP, on the ratio of beam to draught (a deeper hull is better), and on CM. Balancing these factors is difficult. For example, modern naval weapons require positions relatively high in the hull, as do radars and, because of internal space limitations, many internal command and control spaces. Each raises the ship's centre of gravity, which must be balanced by greater beam. The need for stability is only exacerbated by the increased sail area of the ship's superstructure, due to a high superstructure topped by massive masts to support large radars; moreover, sail area has more serious consequences as ships are required to operate in rougher and rougher weather. As if to make matters even worse, the modern trend towards lighter and more compact machinery reduces the one heavy weight in the hull which in earlier times brought down the centre of gravity.

British hull design practice after World War II emphasized seakeeping in rough northern waters, which explains the characteristic hull form of a large number of British frigates: the bow is half a deck higher than most of the weather deck. Even that is not enough in very rough weather, but it raises the threshold at which water comes aboard. This is HMS *Andromeda*, photographed in 1971. *(MoD(N))*

For a modern escort with important gear packed all the way along the hull, seakeeping requirements include dryness aft. This is the US *Dealey* class escort *John Willis* in a rough sea off the Argentine coast, on 19 October 1965, with a very large variable depth sonar installation on deck right aft. Her forward 3in/50 mount is protected in a fiberglass weather shield, with the Mk 108 Weapon Alfa ASW rocket projector just abaft it. The VDS 'fish' cannot be streamed in such rough weather.

Given a constant block coefficient, any increase in beam would have to be balanced by a decrease in draught. However, in destroyers, seakeeping and sonar performance (not to mention speed performance) favor increased draught in relation to beam. On the other hand, a decrease in CP to balance off increased beam without increasing displacement is counterproductive: at destroyer speeds, higher rather than lower CPs are desirable. Any decreases in length to keep draught constant is even worse from this point of view. There remains the possiblity of a decrease in CM, which means a 'slacker' midsection – and a ship which rolls more easily. It also reduces hull space low in the ship. Machinery has to be mounted higher in the hull, and the center of gravity rises once more.

The answer to this particular riddle, as to many others of warship design, is that it is always much easier to design a large ship than a small one, given a constant set of requirements. The weights of equipment which must go into the ship have proportionately less impact on a larger hull, which, among other virtues, is easier to propel at high speed and likely to be more seaworthy. The one important advantage the larger hull *cannot* have is that it cannot generally be less expensive, although if the increase in length is enough to force down required power, the decreased cost of machinery may well balance off the increased cost of ship steel, as in the original *Spruance* design. However, every vacant area on deck or volume within the larger hull is a magnet for those additions which make the larger ship far more expensive than the smaller, more cramped one, and which confirm the old saw that the larger the ship the costlier.

Under these circumstances any technical trick which can reduce wavemaking resistance is very welcome. The most widespread is the transom stern, a stern cut off flat or very nearly flat down to well below the waterline. The flow pattern created by the rest of the hull keeps going past the flat transom, which may actually be dry at high speed – in effect, the hull gains length, at no cost in hull weight. Resistance actually increases at some lower speeds; one German writer suggests that a transom is not worthwhile below a speed-length ratio of about 1.34, which for a 400ft destroyer is about 27kts. However, the transom has value beyond its improvement in speed performance. It increases working area aft (eg for helicopter operation), increases buoyancy and waterplane area aft (eg against battle damage), increases the space available for twin rudders (for better maneuverability in a twin-screw ship), and provides some increase in propulsive efficiency – which goes back to reducing engine power.

The justification for painful measures to reduce the power required for full (trial) speed is that such measures reduce the weight and volume of machinery spaces in a weight- or volume-critical ship. However, the impact of its propulsion on a ship design includes also the impact of fuel oil, which may be a considerable fraction of the full-load displacement of a destroyer or frigate. The amount of fuel oil is generally determined by a specified steaming endurance at cruising, not trial, speed. However, the weight of oil has a big influence on power requirements at trial speed, because most modern warships run their trials fully loaded or with a large fraction (eg two-thirds) of their fuel aboard. Some navies, such as the US Navy, require their warships to have particularly long ranges; it follows that reductions in power requirement at crusing speed can be as important as any power economies realized at full speed. The US Navy tries to achieve good power economy at its cruising speed of 20kts by aiming for minimal waterplane area. Crudely, it is at the waterplane that waves form; any reduction in waterplane area should reduce wave formation and hence residual resistance. However, such a long, slender hull has less inherent stability than has a fuller hull, which many European navies (as well as the Soviet Navy) appear to prefer. Greater inherent stability (in particular, a higher metacenter) may buy survivability not merely through permitting more flooding after damage, but also through allowing for steel rather than aluminum superstructures, perhaps with some armor as well. In the US case the relatively low inherent stability of the small-waterplane hull is compensated for to some extent by the large fuel load carried low in the ship, but this load in turn must be maintained by filling tanks with sea water as fuel oil is burned. The large-waterplane ship may be able to operate with her tanks nearly empty. On the other hand, with tanks full, she may be very stiff: her period of roll may be so short as to make her uncomfortable. In that case a full underwater form (or stabilizers or anti-roll tanks) may be extremely helpful.

PROBLEMS OF SEAKEEPING

Most ships spend a good part of their time in rough seas, in which maximum speed is determined largely by deck wetness (power is spent throwing water over the bow) and by slamming (a captain tends to reduce speed to avoid damage to ship and crew). Slamming occurs when a ship's bow rises, often exposing forefoot and some keel, and then plunges back down, causing the entire ship to shudder. Although the detailed form of the underwater hull determines pitch, heave and roll motions in a seaway, some general comments can be made.

First, any given ocean area presents a wide range of sea states, with waves of greatly varying height and length. In general, the larger the wave the less common it is, beyond a size related to sea state. Ship behavior depends upon the size of the waves in relation to the size of the ship, so that on average a larger ship is far less affected by seakeeping problems. Thus accounts of wartime corvette operations are filled with examples of ships effectively out of action due to mountainous seas, but such things rarely occur in accounts of the larger frigates, which operated in much the same areas. However, given waves of a particular size, their effect on a ship depends very much on her design. It appears that for relatively small waves, slamming is closely related to the form of the waterplane and to the distribution of buoyancy (which amounts to underwater volume) along the length of a ship. Putting it crudely, the bow rises because a wave supports

Soviet hull design emphasizes freeboard forward, bought by sharp sheer, as in this 'Riga' class vessel photographed in the North Sea in 1970. The 'Rigas' were designed around 1950 and so were among the first Soviet warships to show what has since become standard Soviet practice. *(CPL)*

The hull of the British frigate *Aurora* exemplifies modern Western practice, with its considerable flare intended to keep waves clear of the weather deck; in some of the other photographs in this chapter, waves rise above deck level but do not come aboard. Anchors are recessed to avoid spray formation. The problem of spray is not limited to crew discomfort; in northern waters spray on deck freezes into ice – excessive topweight caused by icing became a major problem in the convoys to Russia during World War II. *(CPL)*

Until the 1960s, warships were almost invariably steam-propelled. Exhaust gases had to be kept clear of sensitive electronic gear, but they were limited in volume and relatively small uptakes were permissible. At the same time, the taller the uptake, the greater the air draught and so the more efficient the boilers. The 'mack' installation aboard the Italian helicopter cruiser *Vittorio Veneto* exhibits both characteristics, as well the transom stern typical of modern surface warships. Note, too, the eleborate arrangements made to control flight deck operations, with three separate glassed-in levels facing aft. *(Italcantieri)*

the midships part of the ship while the part abaft amidships is relatively unsupported. If buoyancy is concentrated amidships, then a wave hollow much abaft amidships greatly reduces support aft, even if the stern is riding the crest of the next wave. However, a full hull aft increases support there and reduces the effect of a wave hollow between amidships and stern. In effect it increases the critical wave size required to lift the bow far enough to cause slamming. Even in the absense of a full underwater form aft, a full waterplane and above-water hull aft will reduce slamming to some considerable extent because they will not sink very far into a wave crest aft, and so will damp out the bow-and-stern rocking associated with slamming.

In effect, then, for a ship with a full waterplane area, there may be seas in which she experiences no slamming and perhaps no deck wetness, while a ship with a smaller waterplane area experiences some considerable difficulty. This may well have been the case in the incident which inspired recent US Navy studies of US vs Soviet seakeeping: 'In 1967 the commander of a US Navy destroyer squadron in the Mediterranean reported observing a noticeable difference in the conditions on a Soviet 'Kotlin' class destroyer operating in close proximity to his carrier task group during a period of heavy weather as compared to those on his own ships . . . while steaming into head seas his DD445, DD692 and DD710 class destroyers were taking green water over the bow and very heavy spray on the bridge . . . the 'Kotlin' appeared to be taking no water over the bow and only occasionally raised spray above the fo'csle deck edge . . .'*

The computer analysis which followed looked at ship performance over the average year, given North Atlantic wave conditions, and so may have washed out advantages enjoyed by a full-waterplane (or full-underbody) hull ship in seas with relatively short, high waves, such as the Mediterranean or the Baltic. The study concluded that, on average, slamming behavior was a function only of length, given a ship with a relatively small sonar, such as the SQS-23 or smaller. Ships with the very large SQS-26 bow sonar appeared to be about 2–3kts slower, although at speed-length ratios above 1.3 they would actually enjoy an advantage. Later analysis suggested that the difference in speed was exaggerated by an overly pessimistic set of assumptions built into the computer program, and that the

* Captin J W Kehoe Jr (USN), 'Destroyer Seakeeping: Ours and Theirs', *Proceedings* of the US Naval Institute, November 1973. Captain Kehoe is responsible for a long-term study comparing US and Soviet naval design practices under the aegis of the US Naval Ship Engineering Center. The seakeeping study was one of the earliest applications of a NAVSEC destroyer seakeeping computer program, YF-17.

large-sonar ship would suffer a speed disadvantage of no more than a knot or so. In the study, the criterion for slam-limited speed was one slam per minute in an average North Atlantic sea.

Deck wetness appears to be very largely a matter of freeboard forward and the flare of the bow*. The Soviet 'Kotlin' was dry partly because of her pronounced sheer forward; the *Gearing* (DD710) was wet partly because she had been designed in the first place with little sheer (partly in order to permit No 1 gun mount to fire forward at low elevation) and partly because she had consistently lost freeboard throughout her operating life due to overloading. In fact the *Gearing*s were notoriously wet, and had to have their No 1 gun shields strengthened to resist sea damage. They were designed at a time when seakeeping considerations were not particularly important to US destroyer designers and when, moreover, the US fleet expected to operate mainly in relatively calm waters in the Pacific. Their wetness in turn inspired the designers of the postwar *Forrest Shermans* to provide a high bow. By that time it was assumed that the fast carrier task forces and their escorts would have to maintain high speed in very rough weather; all the US frigates (now cruisers) show very considerable improvements over their World War II predecessors, although it is interesting to note that only the *Adams* class missile destroyers actually exceed current Navy standards in this regard. However, seakeeping features such as the prominent knuckle in the bows of the *Leahy, Belknap,* and *Bainbridge* are noteworthy. In each case, the motive was the avoidance of water damage to the large missile launcher forward. Many Soviet ships, as well as some European-built ones, appear to carry a similar knuckle much further aft.

This knuckle may be a survivability feature. It increases waterplane area as a ship settles into the water after flooding, and so may actually increase her stability, at least balancing off the effects of the free surfaces in flooded spaces. However, the knuckle also has the effect of increasing internal ship volume, which is important in the usual volume-critical surface warship, and it does make for more deck area, given a relatively small waterplane.

STEAM TURBINES

It is useful to distinguish between the power actually applied to the water (effective horsepower, ehp) and that applied by the engine to the propeller shafts (shaft horsepower, shp). Hull design determines the former; but it is the latter which is reflected in machinery weight, volume and fuel consumption. Hence a great deal depends upon propulsive efficiency, the ratio of the two. Unfortunately the requirements of ASW militate against high propulsive efficiency. For example, quiet propellers contribute not merely to the efficiency of hull sonar but also to security against detection by a hostile submarine. Typical silencing measures include a screen of bubbles generated around the hull forward of the propellers, and bubbles emitted from the propellers themselves; neither measure leads to particularly sterling propulsive efficiency. There are also special quiet propellers: large-

---

* Current understanding of the role of flare is somewhat deficient because it is difficult to incorporate it into computer models of hull forms used in seakeeping analyses; typically, ships with very radically flared bows are credited with a few extra feet of freeboard forward. It is possible that this analytic difficulty accounts for a US unwillingness to use much flare in the new destroyers and frigates, given the high shipyard costs associated with complex flared hull forms.

diameter, slow-turning, and inefficient. For a time in the mid-1950s the US Navy experimented with pump-jets, which were supposed to be even quieter. Ultimately, however, sonar development made such radical measures unnecessary, although less radical forms of silencing continue to be extremely important.

The engine that produces that shaft horsepower must satisfy other criteria: it must occupy minimum space and weight in a ship with, at best, minimum available internal space; it must minimize fuel consumption, particularly at the cruising speed at which a ship spends most of her time; and it must place minimum demands upon engine room personnel. ASW operations emphasize the value of a quiet engine, both for good sonar performance and for avoiding detection by submarines. Questions of reliability, maintenance and the need for very skilled engineers sometimes eliminate powerplants quite attractive on all other grounds. Until the early 1960s for example, the US Navy concentrated on improving its steam plants, principally by going to higher and higher pressures and temperatures. Meanwhile the quality of engine room personnel began to fall. In the mid-1960s the new 1200psi (pounds per square inch) boilers acquired a reputation for reliability and even for danger to their operators. A series of accidents inspired the Secretary of the Navy to order a reversion to the well-tested 600psi of World War II plants in 1967. This in itself wiped out much of the competitive edge enjoyed by steam plants as compared with gas turbines, and practically insured the adoption of the latter for the *Spruance*s.

In 1945 the only practical powerplant for a fast frigate or destroyer was the steam turbine. The road to higher power per unit weight, and indeed to better fuel efficiency, appeared to be via higher steam pressures and temperatures, and also via lightweight alloys for turbine construction. The US Navy had been extremely successful in its wartime use of what, for the time, had been the extreme conditions of 600psi and 850°F. Such plants would not produce the power required to drive postwar destroyers at speeds high enough for carrier task force operations; the *Mitscher*s had an experimental plant which was the prototype for the standard destroyer and frigate 1200psi, 950°F system. Even this was insufficient: early design studies for the *Mitcher*s showed that 100,000 rather than the 80,000 or 85,000shp actually installed in frigates (now rated as cruisers) was needed to provide a sufficient speed edge over the carriers. However, the experimental plant fitted to the destroyer *Timmermann* (100,000shp on the weight wartime ships required for 60,000) proved a failure, and effectively ended the advance to higher steam conditions.

Pressure firing was an alternative, an attempt to improve the combustion efficiency of a boiler without changing steam conditions, ie without affecting the operation of the turbine itself. In a pressure-fired plant, exhaust gas from the boiler drives a gas turbine which in turn drives a compressor; the compressed air is fed into the boiler, where it burns more efficiently in a smaller space. Claimed advantages included a 50 per cent reduction in weight and space due to better heat transfer within the boiler, using denser gas; increased ruggedness, shock resistance and decreased maintenance costs due to the elimination of brickwork and fire side corrosion within the boiler; and simplified operation due to the elimination of fuel oil heaters, forced draught blowers, and burner cut-in and cut-out. Costs included the use of more expensive distillate fuel (to run the gas turbine) and a 30 per cent higher initial cost (for the 1961 program destroyer escorts – it was expected to decrease as the pressure-fired system was employed in volume).

The concept apparently dates from before World War II; it was revived postwar initially as a powerplant for a fast (surface speed) radar picket submarine, which would need a great deal of power but which would have little internal volume. A 7500hp pressure-fired boiler for such a submarine was tested in 1952 at the Naval Boiler Test Laboratory at the Philadelphia Navy Yard, but the submarine was not built. In 1956 the Laboratory began work on a 17,500hp boiler for a destroyer, and this time the system progressed to the point at which the *Brooke* and *Garcia* class destroyer escorts were fitted with it; they enjoyed a 70 per cent increase on power over their predecessors, which permitted them to keep up with carriers, at least on a marginal basis. In the late 1950s it appeared that the weight and space economies realized by pressure-firing would ensure its adoption on a large scale, but in fact the Chief of the Bureau of Ships became unhappy about the complexity of the system and refused to authorize it for the *Knox* (DE1052) class (successors to the *Garcia*s), even though there had been no unfavorable service experience – in fact no service experience at all. Indeed, the *Garcia* and *Brooke* plants appear to have performed well, but pressure-firing has been abandoned in US service. Nor does it appear to have been adopted in West European navies. However, the Soviets, who need high power for high speed in ships of relatively modest dimensions, appear to have adopted pressure-firing as their standard steam plant, probably beginning with the 'Kynda' class missile cruisers.

Steam has several drawbacks. It is fundamentally inefficient in its use of shipboard space in that it requires separate systems to burn fuel and then to use the heat the burning fuel releases. This is not necessarily an inefficiency in the use of the fuel itself, since the boiler can be designed for efficient operation, even when it is not producing its maximum output of steam. On the other hand, an internal combustion engine should be fundamentally more compact. Moreover, it takes time to turn large volumes of water into enough steam to turn over a large steam turbine. A long start-up time is inescapable. At sea, there is always the choice between operating efficiently, with most boiler capacity shut down (and slow to start up), and operating at a high level of readiness, with all boilers lit and much of their output wasted – in which case the high steam conditions do not buy nearly the radius of action claimed for the plant. For example, most US steam-propelled warships have two complete engineering plants, split in space to ensure against the effects of a single hit. Even so, such a plant is most efficient at low speeds if a single boiler is cross-connected to the turbines of both plants. Prewar US steaming endurance was calculated on this basis. However, in wartime each plant would be operated separately ('split-plant operation') – and much less efficiently. Split-plant endurance was adopted as the standard of destroyer endurance during World War II, and much of the increase in fuel oil provison for the *Gearing* class can be traced to the discrepancy between prewar requirements, which had been derived from strategic doctrine, and the extent to which ships steaming under split-plant conditions could not fulfill them.

DIESEL PROPULSION

Even with cross-connection, steam is limited in the endurance it can provide on a given weight of fuel. For example, the German Navy adopted diesels very early on for cruising operation, to give relatively small ships a long range. The ultimate development was an all-diesel destroyer, designed during World War II but not built. It would have achieved an endurance of 16,000nm at 19kts, on only 630 tons of fuel oil. However, diesels take up considerable internal volume. They are difficult to build in really large powers: the German destroyer project required eight, four per shaft, to achieve 76,000hp. One problem is that, unlike steam plants, diesels have an optimum power output and perform very badly at other outputs, so that it is easier to cut in additional engines for more power rather than design a single engine for a wide power range. At low output the engine is inefficient: it tends to build up a residue in its cylinders.

The trade-off in volume between diesels and turbines is a trade-off between the base cost of a boiler plus a volume-efficient turbine against the relative inefficiency of a piston (diesel) engine, which loses some power each time its pistons stop and start in their cycles. The way to lighter weight is smaller cylinders with shorter strokes and hence greater losses – not to mention more vibration. In fact vibration seems to be an inescapable by-product of diesel operation, so much so that the US Navy, at least, considers diesels too noisy for ASW. These problems become more tractable at lower powers, where it is a great advantage for the diesel that it requires no boiler and can be started up instantly; moreoever, its fuel, unlike that of a gasoline engine, is not dangerous to handle. This explains the widespread use of diesel emergency generators in warships of the World War II period.

A third drawback of steam is that steam turbines, and particularly their gearing, are relatively difficult to produce in volume: many US destroyer escorts, designed for steam turbines, had to be powered instead by diesels of about half the output, and ships which did receive steam plants generally paid a considerable price in hull length because reduction gears were in short supply. They had to make do with much bulkier turbo-electric installations instead. In Britain, similar experience led the Admiralty to specify high-speed diesels (and the relatively low speed of 23kts) for postwar AAW frigates. In the United States the postwar *Dealey*s were limited to a single shaft on the theory that it would be easier to supply one set of turbines per ship, rather than two. However, most of those concerned with mobilization production suspected that it would be better to abandon turbines entirely in favor of diesels.

The design history of the resulting *Claude Jones* class is almost a litany of the defects of the diesel. Speed had to be reduced to 22kts from the 27 of the earlier ships, but there were other problems as well. Since the ships were designed to cruise at 12kts, some way round the low-power fouling problem had to be found; the solution was to couple four engines to the single shaft, at a considerable cost in internal volume. In fact this plant was very much larger than an equivalent steam turbine plant, which would at the same time have been simpler. Even so, there remained the problem of the *minimum* speed inherent in any diesel plant. For example, the World War II FMR type had a minimum speed of 10.5kts (maximum, 21.5).

Ironically, the *Claude Jones* installation enjoyed none of the great advantages usually claimed for a diesel. It was not compact. Endurance was better than for a steam plant, but not remarkably so: at 13.5kts *Claude Jones* roughly matched the endurance of *Dealey* at 12. However, the deci-

Modern warship propulsion systems. Gas turbines are efficient only over a relatively small range of powers, but on the other hand they offer high power in a very limited volume – hence the use of a variety of mixed powerplants, with a 'base plant' sized to achieve good economy at cruising speed. The most important choice is whether to operate 'base' and 'boost' plants together at high speed; this is a question of gearing very disparate plants in conjunction with each other. Volume considerations may determine the choice of a 'base' plant: gas turbines require large volumes (for large masses of air) for their intakes and exhausts, whereas diesels do not. Steam provides good economy over a wide range of speeds and is, moreover, quieter than a pounding diesel – an important consideration in ASW. However, steam plants require a larger investment in men and in volume than do diesels.

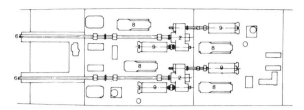

HIGH SPEED DIESEL INSTALLATION (*DESCUBIERTA* CLASS)

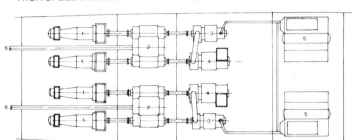

COSAG MACHINERY ARRANGEMENT ('COUNTY' CLASS)

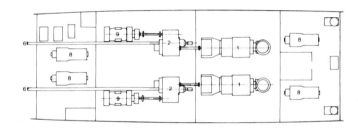

CODOG MACHINERY ARRANGEMENT (VOSPER MK 5 FRIGATE)

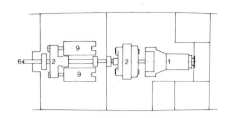

CODAG MACHINERY ARRANGEMENT
(*COMMADANT RIVIERE* CLASS)

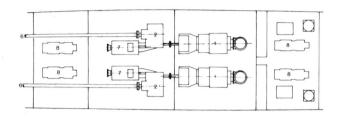

COGOG MACHINERY ARRANGEMENT (TYPE 21 FRIGATE)

KEY
1 Gas turbine
2 Gearbox
3 High pressure steam
   turbine
4 Low pressure steam turbine
5 Steam boiler
6 Propeller shaft
7 Gas turbine (cruising)
8 Auxiliary generator
9 Diesel engine

sion to adopt diesel power in a small hull did limit maximum speed to a level below that which operations against fast submarines seemed to demand. As for production, although in the power range required there was more diesel than steam manufacturing capacity, in the vital bottleneck of reduction gearing the bull gear of the new ship was above the gear diameter 'cross-over' point for mass production, so that, according to a Bureau of Ships critique, 'this controlling item places the same limitation on the mass-produceability of the *Claude Jones* as applies to the *Dealey* class'. The US Navy went back to its steam program.

ENTER THE GAS TURBINE

By that time there was another new powerplant in prospect, the gas turbine. The latter combines, in effect, the virtues of the steam turbine (mechanical efficiency due to smooth rotation without the starting and stopping of pistons) and diesel (space-saving since combustion occurs in the engine, not in a separate boiler). In a gas turbine, air is compressed and heated by fuel burned with it; the hot gas (mostly air) leaving the burner turns one turbine which drives the compressor and another geared to the propellers. Such an engine can be very light in weight, but it demands a

The Soviets were the first to introduce an all-gas-turbine warship, which the Western navies designated 'Kashin'. The gas turbine powerplant is indicated by uptakes of large cross-section, which do not have to be very high, and by the extensive air intakes. The example shown has been considerably modified, with 23mm Gatling close-range guns abreast the after missile guidance radar, 'Styx' box launchers (facing aft), a helicopter pad, and a housing for a variable depth sonar right aft.

large volume. Since it operates largely on air, and since its efficiency depends upon the extent to which its compressor can squeeze down that air, the gas turbine generally requires a very large flow of air into the compressor, which in turn must be reflected in large air intakes above deck, and in large trunks leading down to the engine itself. Similarly, a gas turbine produces a large volume of very hot exhaust gas, which can damage electronic equipment topside. The hot exhaust may also create aerodynamic instabilities in just the area near which a helicopter landing on board must operate. Finally, although the gas turbine, like a steam turbine, is relatively quiet (and hence attractive from an ASW point of view), the hot gases it produces provide a good signature on which infra-red missiles may home. However, it appears that the light weight and quick-start features of the gas turbine are so attractive that these hot gas problems will be attacked, generally, by improvements in uptake design rather than by an alternative choice of powerplant.

Above all, gas turbines are very inefficient in their use of fuel, at least they were initially. Like the aircraft jet engines from which they were derived, they had relatively short lives between installation and replacement, which must have been no great surprise given the very corrosive environment in which they operate. These two considerations together made the naval gas turbine attractive, at first, mainly as a boost plant. Ships operate most of the time at cruising speed, using perhaps half or less of their power. In many situations, however, they must be able to accelerate to full power very rapidly, even though they may not have to maintain full power for very long. A gas turbine could provide the extra power to go from cruise to full speed at a very low cost in plant weight per horsepower; as long as it did not have to operate for very periods, that economy would not be balanced off by the requirement to carry a great deal of fuel for it, nor by the need to keep replacing it.

Gas turbines have two other important characteristics. One is that, optimized for full power operation, they are extremely inefficient at any lesser power setting. Attempts to get around this drawback are sufficiently onerous that designers have been willing to go to the length of connecting one engine to two shafts for cruise, rather than try to operate two engines at half-power. The other important point is that it appears to be very difficult to develop a family of gas turbines to cover any wide range of powers. At any one time, the naval architect can choose from what amounts to a menu of gas turbine powerplants; the spectrum may leave empty just the range of powers he needs, so that he may be forced to choose between installing several engines (at a considerable space and weight penalty) and going back to steam or to a diesel. For example, the US Navy was able to choose a gas turbine plant for its abortive DG/Aegis destroyer project only because of the availability of the new FT9 gas turbine, which had good fuel efficiency and sufficient power.

Finally, like other turbines, a gas turbine has a built-in preferred direction of rotation. In a steam turbine, the problem of reversing is generally solved by providing an auxiliary reverse turbine, into which steam can be channelled for reverse operation. That is impractical for a gas turbine; the solution common in Western navies is a controllable-reversible pitch (CRP) propeller. However, CRP propeller development (at present) limits the level of power which can be transmitted per shaft, and so makes gas turbines less than attractive for very large ships.

The Royal Navy was the first enthusiastic user of naval gas turbines, having installed its first in a fast gunboat, *MGB2009,* in 1946. For larger ships it preferred the combined steam and gas turbine plant, COSAG, which it installed in 'Tribal' class frigates, 'County' class missile destroyers, and most recently in the missile destroyer *Bristol.* When the first two installations were designed, very powerful gas turbines were not available; the steam plant provided more than half the total power, since it could be run economically over a wide range of outputs. For example, the 'Tribal' class plant consisted of a 12,500shp turbine and a 7500hp gas turbine, both coupled to a single shaft. On steam alone the 'Tribal' could make about 20kts, and with both plants connected perhaps about 25. One great advantage of the gas turbine was its ability to move the ship from a standing start in harbor. Another, probably not appreciated at the time, was that a COSAG plant mingles hot gas turbine exhaust with the cooler gases from a conventional boiler, thus reducing overall exhaust temperature and reducing, for example, vulnerability to heat-seeking missiles*.

* The lightweight (per shp) gas turbine boost engine made it possible to design the hull for economy at cruising (base) speed, achieving maximum speed by, in effect, brute force: with gas turbines it is no longer nearly so important to keep down resistance, since these plants radically reduce the impact of engines on a ship design.

These two Soviet cruisers show some of the differences between gas turbine and steam turbine power. The older 'Kresta I' (hull number 542) is steam powered, probably by a pressure-fired plant; her uptakes are small enough to fit within what amounts to a 'mack' and presumably are cool enough not to damage the air search radar fitted on it. The newer 'Kara' (539) has a gas turbine plant, indicated by her broad, flat-topped uptake whose top is just high enough for the hot exhaust gases to clear the after missile-control radar. The difference in hull numbers, incidentally, is of no great consequence, as it appears that the Soviets assign these numbers in almost random sequence.

The alternative base plant was a diesel, which might operate only for cruise (CODOG, diesel or gas) or else at all times (CODAG, diesel and gas). CODOG became practical with the advent of very powerful gas turbines which were, however, inefficient. For example, it was adapted in the US Coast Guard cutter *Hamilton*: diesels sufficed for normal operation up to 20kts, but power was switched to two 18,500shp gas turbines for the range between 20 and 29kts. A CODAG plant would have been somewhat more complex, in that it would have required gearing to run a single shaft simultaneously from gas turbine and diesel, with the attendant synchronisation problems.

More recent gas turbines are competitive with steam turbines in fuel consumption – at full power. It is, therefore, attractive to employ several turbines, cutting in most only when more power is required: COGOG or COGAG, depending upon whether the cruise turbines are employed at full power as well. The *Spruance* and *Perry*, for example, are COGAG ships, and appear to suffer no great loss of range compared to steam ships of similar dimensions. Recent British practice appears to favor COGOG: for example, the Type 42 missile destroyer employs two 27,200shp Olympus for high speed, and two 4100shp Tynes for cruising.

Left As warships require more and more electronic equipment, auxiliary power assumes greater importance. In steam warships auxiliary turbo-generators could always be fitted, but gas turbine warships require separate engines driving their generators, and often there is not sufficient space for the intakes and uptakes that separate gas turbines would require – and the power expended for electricity may be comparable to that of a cruise engine. The *Sheffield* class destroyer *Newcastle* (August 1978) shows a 'mack' abaft her funnel specifically for her four diesel exhausts; it also carries her Type 992Q surface search radar, the usual British tactical radio antennas ('candlesticks') and a variety of radomes probably intended for electronic counter-measures. The 'sword' extending outward to starboard just at exhaust level is an intercept antenna which has been in extensive use in the US and Royal Navies since before the end of World War II. Note also the HF/DF 'cage' visible on the foremast, with the 965 air search antenna visible beyond. *(Author)*

Below No review of modern propulsion could exclude the effects of nuclear power, exemplified by this April 1977 view of the refitted frigate *Bainbridge*. Nuclear power does eliminate uptakes, but it does not eliminate all constraints in topside design, as it is still necessary to provide clearance for access to the reactor during servicing and refueling.

Most Western naval gas turbines are derived from aircraft engines, and hence are relatively lightweight, rather delicate, and are somewhat limited in their choice of fuels. However, there also exist much heavier powerplant gas turbines which can use a much wider variety of fuels, and which are far more rugged. The US Navy tried to obtain 'navalized' versions of such engines in the 1950s but could not buy enough engines to obtain good prices. The Royal Navy actually used navalized 'land' turbines in its initial COSAG ships, and so did the Soviets. In fact it was the Soviets who produced the first all-gas-turbine warship in the world, the 'Kashin' class missile destroyer employing four 23,500shp turbines in a COGAG configuration. Her speed performance was sparkling, but most probably her endurance was not.

Naturally very little can be said of current Soviet practice. The new 'Krivaks' have the short stacks and large air intakes commonly associated with gas turbines, but details of their plants have not become public. With the development of more powerful gas turbines they may well have adopted COGOG which permits the use of cruise turbines of optimum rating, at a cost in compactness and in commonality – which the Soviets might find acceptable, given their preference for shore maintenance.

Gas turbines and, indeed, diesels do introduce one complication as compared to traditional steam plants. Special ship service generators are required, where in earlier installations boiler steam was always available to run turbo-generators, diesel generators being reserved for emergencies. In a gas turbine ship additional generator engines, either small gas turbines or diesels, are required; presumably the same considerations which lead the US Navy to reject CODOG on noise grounds also apply to the large diesel generators required to support the large power loads of modern sensors. The choice of gas turbine vs diesel ship service generators depends in part on how much topside space is available for gas turbine air intakes. In a short ship these intakes, whether for main or for auxiliary plant, present such problems of topside arrangement that they may partly explain the popularity of CODAG propulsion systems. Similarly, it may be noted that although the large *Spruance* has gas turbine generators, the smaller *Perry* does not. This problem may be resolved by the continuing trend towards a reduction of air mass flow requirements for gas turbines.

Finally, there is one other major propulsion development of the post-war era – nuclear power. Security restrictions prevent any useful discussion, but one might remark that in the *Bainbridge* and subsequent nuclear frigates US designers managed to provide weapons and sensors roughly equivalent to those in non-nuclear ships about a thousand tons smaller. That does not mean that the reactor, turbines, and shielding weighed a thousand tons more than a conventional steam plant and fuel of similar power, since such weight additions tend to have a 'multiplier' effect within a ship design. Moreover, the reactor weight is probably concentrated in one place, whereas fuel weights are spread through the ship. Probably less than half the net weight growth can be attributed to the reactor. In the absence of some conventional equivalent to the newer *California* class, no similar judgement can be made concerning what is probably a more advanced reactor design.

CHAPTER FIVE

Sensors and Tactics

World War II at sea was, for the Allied navies, a radar and sonar war; these two devices and their passive relatives have been prime movers in the transformation of warships ever since. The proof, for radar, is to compare the forest of electronic antennas evident even in 1945 with the clean masting of prewar ships. Although primitive sonars existed even before the war, they have only grown to the point of major elements of hull design since 1946. They have even invaded the above-water part of many warship hulls, in the form of hoisting gear and openings for variable-depth sonar.

THE PRINCIPLES OF DETECTION AND RANGING

Radar and sonar are to a large extent analogous. Both send out pulses of energy, and detect objects by their reflection. The time for a round trip measures distance, and the narrowness (definition) of the beam of pulses permits a determination of direction. Generally it is far easier to measure even small time intervals than to form very narrow beams, so that most radars and sonars are much more effective at determining range than bearing, and many are very limited in their ability to distinguish between (resolve) two objects at much the same distance but on slightly different bearings. In both cases there is often a requirement to measure target direction in both elevation (or for sonar, depth) and bearing, which again is a matter of beam focussing.

Both systems can be characterized by the speed at which their signals travel (186,000 miles per second for radar, about 5000ft per second for sonar) and by frequency and wavelength: wavelength is given by velocity divided by frequency. The higher the frequency, the shorter the wavelength. For example, early radars operated at a frequency of 200 megacycles, or 200 million cycles per second, corresponding to a wavelength of 1.5 meters. Later, operating frequencies as great as 3000 or even 10,000 megacycles (9 or 3 centimeters) became common. For sonar, early equipment operated at about 25 kilocycles, 25,000 cycles per second, for a wavelength of about a fifth of a foot. Recently 5 or even fewer kilocycles have been used, for wavelengths of a foot or more.

Wavelength is important because beam dimensions, in angle, depend upon the size of the antenna (transducer in sonar) in wavelengths: the larger the antenna, the narrower the beam. Since antenna or transducer size is very much a matter of ship size, there are distinct advantages inherent in shorter wavelength, higher frequency equipment, both in radar and in sonar. On the other hand, signals of a given wavelength cannot reflect off targets much smaller than half a wavelength. In the case of radar this means that longer-wave radar does not scatter in rain, whereas shorter-wave signals do. It also means that the shorter the wavelength, the more likely it is to reflect from the details of the shape of a target. To some extent such an effect is helpful, as, for example, corners form relatively good reflectors. However, a streamlined target has few corners: short-wave signals do not reflect well, whereas longer-wave ones do not notice the difference.

The behavior of signals depends very much on their frequency. In the case of radars it is a matter of reflections off the sea surface, which break up a radar beam and create zones of greater and lesser signal strength, depending upon the height (in wavelengths) of the antenna. High frequency signals are also subject to absorption in the air to a greater degree than are lower frequency ones; and it is more difficult to generate high-frequency signals of a given power. In sonar the key consideration is signal absorption in sea water, combined with the extent to which background noise obscures returning echoes. It is also easier to generate really powerful signals at lower frequencies – hence the modern progression from low-powered systems in the 25kc range to very powerful ones of 5kc and below.

Given these considerations, sonars and radars generally produce one of two basic beam shapes: the fan beam and the pencil. The fan beam is narrow in one direction, broad in the other; it searches through bearings using the narrow dimension to measure direction. Broadness in the other dimension ensures against missing targets through poor elevation or depth information. Air search radars use fan beams to search through all altitudes simultaneously while they obtain bearing and range. A combination of two

A modern warship's silhouette is dominated by her sensors, not her weapons; *California*, a recent US missile frigate, well illustrates this trend. Fore to aft, her major radars are: SPG-60 (gunfire control and SAM illumination), two SPG-51Ds (SAM illumination), SPS-48 (three-dimensional search, with frequency scan in elevation), SPS-10 (surface search), SPS-40 (air search, two-dimensional), two more SPG-51Ds and, in a radome, the SPQ-9 surface search/fire control radar overlooking them. However, much of the ship's effectiveness is derived from associated sensors. The radio antenna forward of her bow SAM launcher is reportedly associated with her NTDS data link; similarly, the antenna at her foretop is reportedly a LAMPS data link. The TACAN beacon essential for coordination with aircraft tops her mainmast. Beneath the SPQ-9 radome a television camera, for use in heavy jamming situations, can be discerned. Note that the forest of whip antennas for radio communication, characteristic of many postwar ships, has been reduced very greatly by the use of more compact broad-band systems. *(C & S Taylor)*

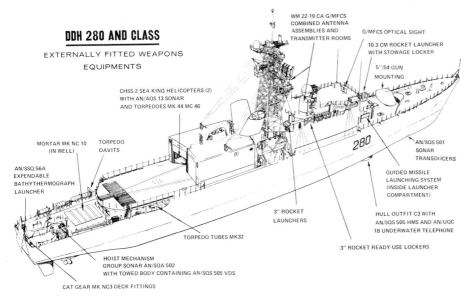

DDH 280 AND CLASS

EXTERNALLY FITTED WEAPONS
EQUIPMENTS

WM 22-19 CA G/MFCS COMBINED ANTENNA ASSEMBLIES AND TRANSMITTER ROOMS

G/MFCS OPTICAL SIGHT

10.3 CM ROCKET LAUNCHER WITH STOWAGE LOCKER

5"/54 GUN MOUNTING

CHSS 2 SEA KING HELICOPTERS (2) WITH AN/AQS 13 SONAR AND TORPEDOES MK 44 MC 46

AN/SQS 501 SONAR TRANSDUCERS

MORTAR MK NC 10 (IN WELL)

TORPEDO DAVITS

AN/SSQ 56A EXPENDABLE BATHYTHERMOGRAPH LAUNCHER

GUIDED MISSILE LAUNCHING SYSTEM (INSIDE LAUNCHER COMPARTMENT)

3" ROCKET LAUNCHERS

HULL OUTFIT C3 WITH AN/SQS 505 HMS AND AN/UQC 1B UNDERWATER TELEPHONE

TORPEDO TUBES MK32

3" ROCKET READY-USE LOCKERS

HOIST MECHANISM GROUP SONAR AN/SQA 502 WITH TOWED BODY CONTAINING AN/SQS 505 VDS

CAT GEAR MK NC3 DECK FITTINGS

An official drawing of the Canadian frigate *Iroquois* provides some indication of the complexity of a modern sensor suit; the air and surface search radars are not even labeled. SQS-501 is a high-frequency sonar intended to classify 'bottomed' objects and thus corresponds to the British Type 162; SQS-505 is a medium-frequency search sonar carried both in hull-mounted and in variable depth form. Effective sonar operation requires data on the variation of water temperature with depth, measurements being made by the AN/SSQ-56A expendable bathythermograph, launched from the fantail. Mortar NC10 is the British 'Limbo'. Further forward, the 3in rocket launcher corresponds to the British Corvus chaff launcher; the WM22-19 CA fire control system is related to the US Mk 92 aboard the *Perry* class frigate and the Patrol Hydrofoil, Missile (PHM). The Canadian SAM system is a modified Sea Sparrow employing an enclosed launcher, presumably in large part to avoid damage to the launcher in very cold Northern waters. Particularly noticeable in this drawing is the short stack enclosing diesel exhausts abaft the pair of main gas turbine uptakes. *(Official)*

fan beams set at an angle gives both elevation and bearing information, as in the US dual-antenna SX radar of 1945, in which one beam scanned in elevation. In fact two fan beams set at any angle other than right angles can give elevation information at a relatively low cost in technology, as the Soviets have undoubtedly realized in the design of their 'Headnet Charlie' air search and height-finding radar.

Similar considerations apply to sonar design. For example, when the Royal Navy introduced the Squid anti-submarine mortar in 1944, it became necessary to supplement the usual search sonar with a depth-determining set, Type 147B. This had a beam extending to 30° or 40° on either side of the bow, but only about 2° to 3° wide in the vertical plane. It combined with the conventional bearing-only sonar to give depth. One reason for the great width of the beam in bearing was that it was fixed relative to the ship's hull and so could not be turned to face in the approximate direction of the target. Frequency was set quite high, at about 50kc, in order to achieve so narrow (vertically) a beam within very limited dimensions: after all, 147B had to be accommodated in addition to the sonar already incorporated in British escort ships.

The pencil beam is an alternative approach to precise target location. It is generally produced, in a radar, by a dish antenna, and it must be pointed fairly precisely in the first place, since otherwise it will miss its target entirely. The usual technique is to scan the pencil beam over the area in which a target is suspected, locking it on when pulses begin to return from the target. In fact even a beam 2° or 3° wide does not give very precise target data at any great distance. However, it is possible to switch the radar among alternate beams pointed in slightly different directions; the radar is pointed correctly when all give the same return. A closely related technique, conical scanning, is sometimes used to keep a radar locked onto a moving target. The pencil beam is spun ('nutated') about an axis, and variations in the returned signal are used to measure the extent to which the axis is off target; for a moving target, these error signals give target motion information which can be used for tracking. Such conical scanning is very simple in principle and in application, but is subject to counter-measures which generate false error signals. Conical scanning is also ill-suited to the fixed arrays of sonar.

LOBE SWITCHING

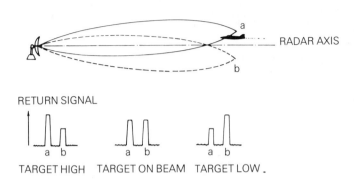

RADAR AXIS

RETURN SIGNAL

a b TARGET HIGH   a b TARGET ON BEAM   a b TARGET LOW

CONICAL SCANNING

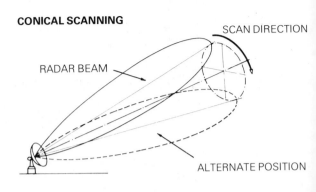

SCAN DIRECTION

RADAR BEAM

ALTERNATE POSITION

Monopulse is an alternative approach to accurate pointing and tracking: the antenna does not scan, but returning signals are broken down into alternate channels corresponding to alternative antenna positions. For example, the US SQS-23 and -26 sonars use a form of monopulse to refine the broad beam of their search mode for attack. In the latter mode, the difference between returns on either side of the target direction is used to achieve more accurate direction data.

Pencil beams are used in some height-finders (most notably the US wartime SP and the current SPS-30), but they are most common in fire control systems, in which precise direction is very important and which can take approximate direction information from search radars. A similar situation obtains in sonar systems, in which the pencil beam is generally used for attack, ie for refining target position after target detection by the search set. One problem in a hull-mounted sonar is that the attack set in itself blocks off part of the search beam. A monopulse arrangement such as that used in the large US sonars eliminates this problem. SQS-4 even has a monopulse depth-finding arrangement, a signal processor called SQR-8. Presumably SQR-8 uses not merely differences in signal arrival from different elements of the array, but also the fact that target signals reflected off the surface of the water will arrive at a time different from those arriving via a more direct path.

Both radar and sonar can be designed to detect moving targets; indeed, such detection is one way of sorting out real targets from the clutter normally present. A moving target shows 'doppler': the frequency of returned signals shifts in proportion to target speed along the line between radar or sonar and target. The shift in frequency is given by the ratio of target speed to the speed of light (radar) or sound (sonar); in the case of a 10kt submarine, for example, a 10-kilocycle sonar would show a shift of about 34 cycles per second. A doppler radar deal with a different class of velocities; a 600mph airplane produces a shift of about 0.00009 per cent in radar frequency, or about 0.02 megacycles in a 200-megacycle air search radar. In both cases detection of target motion depends upon the ability to measure frequency – and shifts in frequency – accurately. In fact the shorter the pulse, the less precise the frequency of the signal, so that a very accurate radar cannot employ doppler-shift moving-target indicators (MTI). Sonars do better because of their relatively long pulses, and doppler is commonly used by sonar operators to classify targets. Doppler is so useful in sonar that 'bottomed' or stationary targets present a real problem, and can be classified only by short-range very high frequency sonars which can present

MONOPULSE

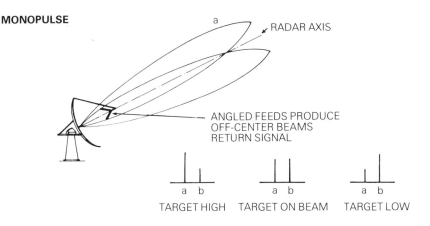

RADAR AXIS

a

ANGLED FEEDS PRODUCE
OFF-CENTER BEAMS
RETURN SIGNAL

| a b | a b | a b |
| TARGET HIGH | TARGET ON BEAM | TARGET LOW |

Radar scanning. In lobe switching, there are two alternate beam positions, (a) and (b). The radar operator compares the return from each; only one beam is present at any one time, but by flipping back and forth very rapidly the radars can show both. In conical scanning, the radar switches beam positions located at various angles to its axis; the way in which the returned signal varies can be used to generate correction signals. The monopulse system, however, involves the production of several beams simultaneously (usually four, although for clarity only two are shown). Returns from each are compared.

some indication of target shape. Among radars, doppler measurement requires very long pulses which can consist of signals very close in frequency; there is a trade-off between the ability to distinguish between neighboring targets and doppler measurement.

However, there is an alternative possible for radars. The radar observes the same scene so often that by subtracting the returns of one scan from those of the next it can distinguish moving objects. This system is useful, for example, to distinguish rapidly-moving aircraft from slowly drifting clouds of aluminum foil (chaff). However, all MTIs of this type are subject to 'blind speeds' related to the pulse rate and the rate of scanning.

A great deal depends upon the power the radar or sonar can put out and on the length and repetition rate of the pulses. Power generally means the peak power of a pulse. For example, SPS-6, a typical air search radar of the 1950s, produced a stream of 500 kilowatt pulses, each 4 microseconds long, with a repitition rate of 150 pulses per second. Average power, then, was 450 watts, since the radar was operating only 0.06 per cent of the time. Pulse length and repetition rate correspond to distances: a radar pulse travels 328yds per microsecond (millionth of a second). The radar receiving a pulse cannot distinguish between one reflected at its beginning or its end, and thus cannot determine distances to within less than about 1300yds. Moreover, it cannot unambiguously determine distances greater than about 510 nautical miles; in 1/150 of a second the pulses travel about 1020nm, but there must be time for one pulse to travel up and back before the next is sent. Any pulse from further than 510nm will appear as a 'second-time-around' (STA) pulse, apparently at relatively short range. STA pulses generally do not present a problem because they are very weak compared to returns from close targets. SPS-6 was designed to use long pulses to detect distant targets; it had an alternative short-pulse mode (1 microsecond, 600 pulses per second) for shorter range and better resolution. The average power produced, ie the drain on the ship's power supply, was the same in both cases.

Average power is one factor in determining effective radar range in the presence of noise, against some particular radar target. A target is detected because several pulses echo from it and because there is a statistical chance that enough are received to come to the attention of the radar operator or of some automatic target detector. The entire process is statistical. Average power is significant because it translates either as the return of a great many pulses, many of which are lost in the noise (because they are weak), or as the return of a relatively few, which are, however, so energetic that they stand out better. It follows that in radar design it pays to increase both peak power and the pulse rate, but the latter reduces maximum range and the former invites electrical breakdown of the sort which plagued many of the more powerful air search radars, at least in the US Navy, in the 1950s. One way out was to pack more power into a pulse by lengthening it, accepting, as the price of long range, poor range resolution; pulse compression is a newer and subtler solution.

All these numbers, but none of these concepts, change radically for sonar. For signals moving about 5000ft per second, reasonable pulse lengths are measured in milliseconds (thousandths of a second). For example, the US SQS-23 operates at pulse lengths of 2 (later increased to 5), 30 and 120 milliseconds, corresponding to distances of about 10 (25), 150, and 600ft. Low sound velocity must also correspond to a low pulse repetition rate: for example, a repetition rate of only 10 pulses per second corresponds to an unambiguous range of only 250ft, and the echo from a submarine at 10nm requires about 24 seconds for the round trip. SQS-23 is calibrated to employ range scales of 1000, 2500, 5000, 10,000, 20,000 and 40,000yds, which should correspond to pulse rates of no more than 0.8, 0.3, 0.16, 0.08, 0.04 and 0.02 pulses per second. With such long pulses and with kilowatt power, a big sonar requires a great deal of power. For example, SQS-4, the sonar which preceded SQS-23, had a normal peak power of 30kW and at a pulse length of 30 milliseconds, corresponding to an average power output of 900w, considerably beyond the requirement of the SPS-6 air search radar the same ship might carry.

Both radar and sonar performance are strongly affected by the environment in which these sensors operate. Naval radars are affected by reflection from the sea surface; there are always two paths from radar to target, one direct, the other via reflection off the sea. The second may be more or less important depending upon how smooth the sea is; a rough sea so scatters radar pulses that it has little effect. However, a smooth sea is a good reflector, and much depends upon the altitude of the target. At some angles of elevation reflected and direct paths merge, the radar reflection is more intense than it would have been had the sea not intervened and effective radar range increases considerably. At others, the opposite occurs and a target simply vanishes ('fades'). This effect makes for fading at zero elevation; the other fade angles depend upon the height of the radar in wavelengths, so that a short (centimeter-) wave radar shows considerable fading but also can detect targets quite close to the sea surface, whereas a longer-wave radar is ineffective at low angles but shows only a few angles at which fading occurs, and many at which range is considerably enhanced. A great deal of course depends upon beam shape, since a pencil-beam radar or a carefully designed fan-beam radar may avoid much reflection off the sea surface in the first place. Moreover, beam shaping is easiest at relatively short wavelengths.

The reflection phenomenon is also useful in airborne early warning radar, such as the set used in the Grumman E-2C Hawkeye. There are two paths to the target, one of which, the longer one, is via the sea surface. If the radar is far enough above the surface, the signals from the two no longer simply merge; they can be distinguished and the time difference measured – and used to measure target height. A similar technique can be used in sonar. Both the sea surface and, often, the sea bottom can act as sonar reflectors, so that sonar 'pings' may travel both by direct paths and via a variety of reflected paths; time differences give depth, if the sonar is designed to measure them and to distinguish the appropriate series of echoes.

Top left The current standard British long-range air search radar, Type 965 (AKE2 antenna), is shown aboard a 'County' class missile destroyer, with a height-finding Type 278 below and abaft it. In each case the larger dimensions of the antenna correspond to the narrower dimensions of the radar beam: the metric-wave 965 produces a beam narrow in bearing but relatively broad in elevation, to provide good two-dimensional data; it corresponds roughly to the US SPS-29/-37/-43 family. The height-finder produces a similar beam turned on its side, using shorter waves to gain similar beam dimensions (angular) with a smaller antenna. Its short wavelength is also indicated by the heavier construction of its antenna. The 'sword' visible in the foreground is an ECM intercept receiving antenna. *(C & S Taylor)*

Middle The Royal Navy introduced 'cheese' antennas, which produce a very well defined beam (in bearing but not in elevation) either for short-range air search ('target indication') or for surface search. HMS *Hermione* (1976) shows both applications, with Type 993 above and Type 975 (navigation) below. The 'cage' at the masthead is an HF/DF, a direct descendant of World War II types, with a variety of unidentified (but apparently standard) ECM radomes below and the usual British tactical radio antennas on the yards to port and starboard. *(C & S Taylor)*
Right Gunnery radars are generally dishes designed to produce pencil beams: this is a Type 912 aboard HMS *Antelope*. The television camera peering through the antenna permits operation in heavy jamming, and can also operate to avoid

alerting an enemy to radar emissions. Such 'optical sensors' are increasingly common; they permit fire control operation without exposing personnel to radiation or gas. *(C & S Taylor)*
Bottom Many early-generation missile guidance radars resemble large searchlights; they employ microwave 'lenses' to form beams along which missiles can fly towards their targets. This Type 901 aboard HMS *Fife* (1973) is intended for Seaslug missile guidance. Note what appear to be cameras beneath it. *(C & S Taylor)*

RADAR SYSTEMS

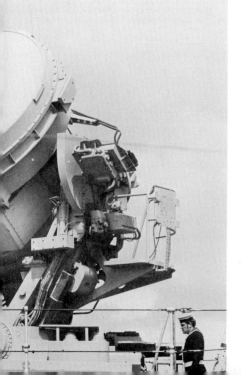

Fading explains much of the variety of shipboard radars. Most operate in a series of well-defined frequency ranges ('bands') which were assigned code letters during World War II. The earliest sets were designed to operate at what was then the upper range of radio frequencies, the P-band or metric band. For example, for many years the standard US air search radar was a 1.5 meter type, such as the SC and SK, and the current SPS-37 and -43. Wartime efforts concentrated on higher and higher frequencies, which promised more compact sets with better defined beams (airborne intercept radar with metric wavelengths was both cumbersome and often ineffective, as the Germans found). However, at sea very short wavelengths were the keys to surface search radar and to tracking fire control radar. The great wartime radar achievement was the British magnetron, which could generate waves first at 9, and then at 3 centimeters (S- and X-bands). More recently many sets have been built to operate at the intermediate C-band (6 centimeters). In 1945 it seemed that even shorter wavelenghts would permit even better performance, but then radar was unduly affected by rain, and at some wavelengths the signals were absorbed by water vapor in the air. However, the development of shorter-wave radars did make it possible for effective radars to be built into guided missiles. These generally operate at about 1 centimeter, in a band originally called K.

Since World War II many naval air search radars have been built to operate at wavelengths intermediate between P and S, to gain good definition without excessive fading. Examples include the US SPS-6 and -12, and many Dutch and French systems, all at about 25 centimeters. The United States was unique in returning to P-band in the late 1950s, as it required greater and greater range against fast jets. The Royal Navy never did go to the intermediate L-band, although in its huge 984 it did produce an S-band long-range search set. Its 965 corresponds to the current generation of US P-band sets.

The old band designations may seem less than logical. No one has ever published their derivation, but P probably comes from the same source as the P in the US SPS radar designator, the word 'pulsed': in the beginning P was the radar band. S probably meant short (wave) and X, whose development came next, was both exciting and experimental at first. The late-war and postwar L-band was long in comparison to S. C was the third in a series of sub-bands, the other two of which, A and B, were associated with early IFF (Identification Friend or Foe) systems. In recent years, as if merely to increase confusion, a new set of band designations has appeared. It originated not with radar developers, for whom P, L, S, X and K meant different kinds of equipment, but rather with the electronic intelligence community, for which signals had to be categorized in some systematic way. Thus the new system began with A at the longest wavelength and progressed through the alphabet – J is now the designation used for the popular missile homing band. In this language I/J is the old X-band, E/F the old S, and B is the old P – which the US Navy likes to call ultra high frequency, UHF.

Radar frequencies and beam shapes can often be read from the shapes of radar antennas. Nearly all antennas consist of sources of radiation and the reflectors which focus their emissions into beams; in this sense they are equivalent to the filaments and reflectors of car headlights. For long-wave radars the usual emitter is a dipole, a wire half as long as the radar wavelength. A typical P-band radar, such as the British 965 or the US SPS-37, uses several dipoles backed by a flat reflector to form a 'mattress' or 'bedspring'. The beam is formed by a combination of the effects of delays in emission between dipoles, and the effect of the reflector. At shorter wavelengths it is generally simpler to use a single source of radiation, a microwave 'horn', shining on a curved reflector. This practice began with S- and X-band surface search radars of World War II, such as the US SG and the British Type 293; it continued postwar with sets of longer and longer wavelengths. Current examples include the L-band SPS-40 and the new SPS-49.

To some considerable extent a navy's choice of radars and of their operating frequencies betrays its tactics. For example, the earliest British radars operated at very long wavelengths, typically 3 meters in the Type 281 introduced in 1941. The corresponding frequency was a symptom of the relatively undeveloped British radio industry and of the higher priorities assigned to land equipment. However, it meant that 281 could have only an ill-defined beam, about 35° wide: its reflector was the most primitive possible, a single dipole behind each transmitting dipole. By way of contrast, the principal US large-ship air search radar of World War II, SK, employed 1.5 meter waves and had a beam 20° wide, a performance matched by the principal small-ship set, SC-2. The Royal Navy considered accurate air search less important and provided its destroyers with the 1.5 meter Type 291, which produced a 40° beam. At first the British sets were

In some cases electronic gear is the main battery of a ship. For example, in the early 1950s the US Navy converted many destroyer escorts to serve as radar pickets supporting the North American Air Defense Command; in effect they were floating radar stations with the capability to control land-based fighters. USS *Lansing*, shown here off Hawaii (16 November 1963) was an example. Her most important equipment was her large air search radar forward (SPS-28) and her SPS-8 height-finder (largely hidden by the tripod mainmast) aft; the TACAN beacon would have been essential for operational fighter control, as it would have given fighters a point of reference.

designated 'air warning' rather than 'air search' because their angle information was so poor; ultimately accuracy was improved, but only when the radar was pointed at a target, so that it could not search for others.

Thus, early in the war, British air search radar was generally a means of alerting lookouts. British fire control radar was effective for measuring range but not direction, again because it was impossible to achieve short wavelengths. However, once the magnetron had been devised, the Royal Navy produced a back-up short range air search set which it called a Target Indication Radar, an S-band 'cheese' designated Type 293. This acted as a link between long-range air search and fire control. Its short range was acceptable because it was still well beyond gunnery range; in fact many postwar British warships dispensed with the air search set entirely, in favor of 293.

The US Navy approached matters somewhat differently. Even in the pre-magnetron era, its shorter-wave search radars and 40 centimeter fire control sets together required no specialized target indicator. Moreover, the function of fleet air search radar shifted quite early on to fighter control. This required effective long range detection coupled with good bearing data – and altitude data. Thus the US Navy made intensive efforts to develop height-finding sets for ships intended to control fighters within a task force, both carriers and many other surface combatants.

The closest Britain came to a height-finder was a dish radar called 277, which produced a pencil beam and which could be elevated. It could, then, scan in elevation to some extent, although it appears to have been more important as a surface search set: in that role its great virtue was that its beam could avoid contact with the sea surface, at least at ranges much less than that of the horizon.

For ships intended for fleet AAW operations, the ability to control aircraft is quite as important as the ability to control SAMs. The French fleet missile ship *(frégate) Suffren*, shown here in 1974, was fitted with a very large three-dimensional radar (radome-enclosed) far more powerful than her Masurca missile battery required; her missile control radars are barely visible aft. The location of her anchor so near the bow suggests that she has a large bow-mounted sonar; a variable depth sonar is mounted at the stern. Large radomes such as the one depicted here may serve for weather protection; they also protect large flat antennas from wind loading as they rotate. One feature particularly prominent in this photograph is a row of encapsulated life rafts, the successors to the old World War II floats which used to be so common in Western warships. *(J A Jedrlinic)*

Postwar surface warships, therefore, show suits of radars which vary according to the extent to which they were designed to control aircraft – including pilotless ones, since anti-aircraft missiles, like manned interceptors, required accurate elevation and bearing data. To some extent modern 'three-dimensional' radars, which use pencil beams to scan in elevation and in bearing, moving the beam very rapidly by electronic means, are reminiscent of the British target indicator. They trade away very long range in favor of high precision, and act as a link between conventional air search radars and missile fire control sets. In effect, the increased range of the missile has greatly tightened the pointing requirement for its fire control radar, so that even the relatively high precision of most modern air search sets is insufficient to permit designation to the missile control systems. For example, a typical US guided missile destroyer has an SPS-40 long-range air search antenna which provides very long-range warning; actual target designation is by means of a pencil-beam SPS-39 or -52. The use of the rapidly scanning pencil-beam in itself considerably reduces the probability that such a radar will pick up a small target at very long range – hence the SPS-40. In this sense the US missile frigates of the *Brooke* class correspond to British ships equipped only with Target Indication Radar; they have only an SPS-39 or -52, and no two-dimensional air search set.

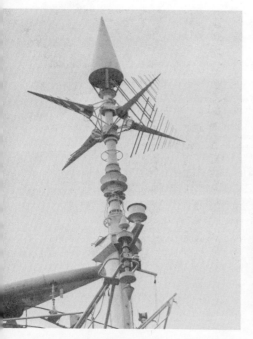

British ECM gear on the topmast of an Exocet-equipped *Leander* class frigate (August 1978, at Portsmouth). The broad arrows are actually broad-band intercept antennas consisting of an array of dipoles; they indicate both the presence of a signal and its direction. The dimensions of the domes below indicate the wavelengths on which they operate. *(Author)*

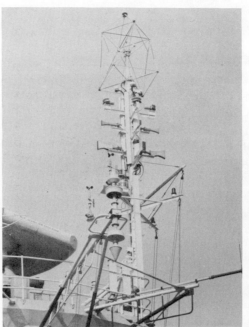

Typical British ECM/ESM gear on a frigate topmast (photographed in August 1978). The cage at the top is HF/DF; below is are two sets of microwave horns which provide direction-finding as well as interception of incoming signals. The four objects at the very top resemble the standard US ULQ-6 counter-measures gear introduced in the 1960s as an anti-missile ('Styx') measure. Horn dimensions indicate the wavelengths at which they operate. *(Author)*

Despite very great electronic sophistication, one of the best radar counter-measures remain chaff, strips of aluminum foil fired to produce a simulated target. This is the standard Royal Navy type, Corvus, aboard the frigate *Ariadne*. *(C & S Taylor)*

SONAR

If radar performance is affected by the boundary presented by the sea surface, then sonar is even more strongly affected by a far greater number of boundaries and semi-boundaries. The most obvious is once again the sea surface, which acts as a reflector for sound as well as for radar signals. The sea bottom can also serve as a sonar mirror: one important means of increasing sonar range, introduced in the very powerful sonars of the late 1950s, was 'bottom-bounce' propagation, in which sonar 'pings' (pulses) were deliberately directed downwards to bounce off the sea bottom in very deep water. However, the sea bed is not the only important reflector of sonar pulses; sound waves bend in the complex structure of the sea, their paths determined mainly by variations in the velocity of sound. Most are concerned with temperature: the higher the temperature, the higher the velocity. Pressure also increases velocity, so that sound waves travel more rapidly at greater depths: the figure of 5000ft per second is no more than an average.

Sound waves bend *towards* regions of lower velocity. Thus, for example, in water of constant temperature but increasing pressure (and hence increasing sound velocity), a sonar beam directed downwards tends to curve upwards towards the surface. Similarly, in water which is warmest towards the surface, a beam pointed up tends to bend down, towards the cooler (slower) region. When there is no change in temperature with depth, therefore, sound bends upwards towards the surface; when there is a temperature difference, it bends away from the warmer water.

Under typical conditions, wind churns the surface of the sea and mixes it with water from considerably greater depths to form a surface layer of nearly constant temperature; layer depth, the depth to the point at which temperature begins to change sharply, varies with geography and with the season. It is proportional to the storm action which produces a layer in the first place – in the Atlantic, for example, the layer may extend downwards as far as 300 to 600ft. Sound produced by a sonar within the layer is very nearly trapped in it; when both sonar and submarine are within the layer, the sonar can obtain long ranges, but submarines diving below the layer are nearly undetectable. Thus a shallow layer makes surface ship sonar particularly ineffective. In tropical waters such as the Red or Arabian Seas, the surface is sometimes cooler than the water just beneath it, partly because wind during the day reduces its temperature. The result is sharply increasing sound velocity with depth, in a shallow surface layer; sound waves are bent sharply upwards, trapped in this layer. In the summer the Mediterranean has both a very shallow surface layer and a sharp decrease in sound velocity with depth, so that, for example, sound rays from a submerged variable depth sonar are pulled sharply downwards.

In fact the Mediterranean is a notoriously bad sea for sonar operations. So is the Baltic, where an unusually high salinity (salt content) affects sound velocity. Shallowness reduces sonar effectiveness through excessive reflection, as well as unusual refractive effects; the same holds for other shallow seas, such as the Sea of Japan and the Yellow Sea. Sea currents, such as the Gulf Stream, present their own problems, mainly due to the sharp variation in temperature at their edges. Off the north-east coast of the USA, for example, the Gulf Stream creates the 'north wall': sound is not transmitted across the edge of the Stream. The same applies to river mouths, where part of the effect is due to the difference in salinity of the river water as compared to sea water.

Sonar domes are usually invisible, which is why they receive less attention than do radar antennas. However, they are often at least as large. This is the newly completed *Spruance*, in drydock, January 1975. Not the least of the problems associated with such large bow domes is drydocking: note the way the SQS-53 dome overhangs the dock.

In many ways, then, the deep ocean is the simplest sonar environment. The very deep part of the ocean has a constant temperature of about 39°F; between it and the (generally) far warmer surface layer is a pair of regions of variation, the thermoclines. The upper or seasonal one varies with surface conditions – for example, it may disappear in very stormy weather in which the upper layer mixes deeply – but the lower or main thermocline is not affected by weather. Towards the top of the thermocline region, as water temperature falls with depth, sound velocity also falls, but there comes a point at which increasing pressure causes the sound velocity to begin to rise once more, at least if the ocean is deep enough.

Classical sonar conditions are best within the surface layer. Typically, the layer is deepest in winter, and deeper at night than in the middle of the day (especially in spring and summer) when the sun has warmed the immediate surface layer to form a shallow thermocline which itself refracts sound waves. Conditions are also better in the morning than in the afternoon, in spring and summer, but there is little change between the two if the wind is strong enough to produce whitecaps, and conditions are better in the afternoon as prevailing winds become stronger.

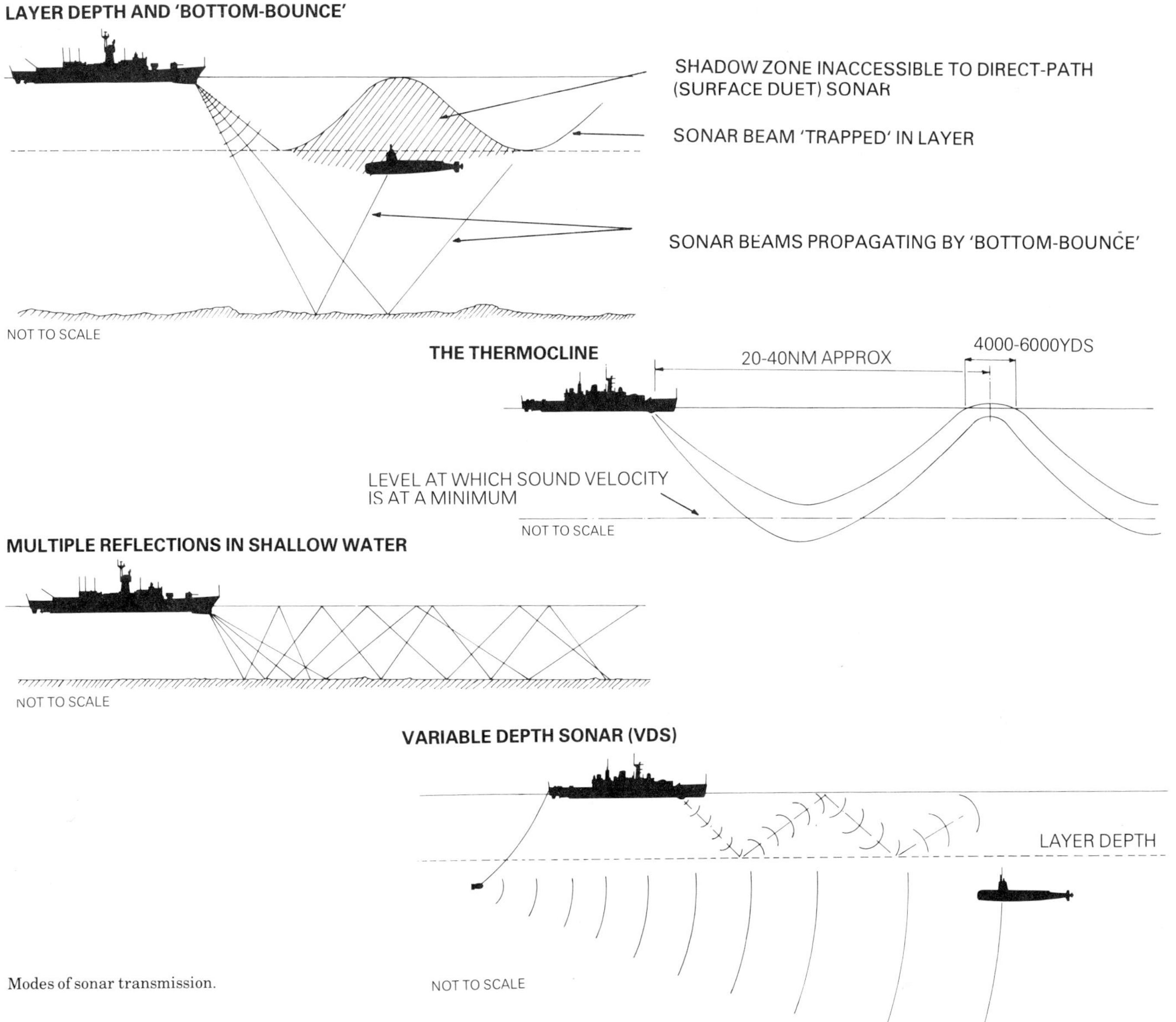

LAYER DEPTH AND 'BOTTOM-BOUNCE'

SHADOW ZONE INACCESSIBLE TO DIRECT-PATH (SURFACE DUET) SONAR

SONAR BEAM 'TRAPPED' IN LAYER

SONAR BEAMS PROPAGATING BY 'BOTTOM-BOUNCE'

NOT TO SCALE

THE THERMOCLINE

20-40NM APPROX

4000-6000YDS

LEVEL AT WHICH SOUND VELOCITY IS AT A MINIMUM

NOT TO SCALE

MULTIPLE REFLECTIONS IN SHALLOW WATER

NOT TO SCALE

VARIABLE DEPTH SONAR (VDS)

LAYER DEPTH

Modes of sonar transmission.

NOT TO SCALE

World War II sonars were ineffective below the layer. In principle they should have been most effective in winter in the North Atlantic, but in fact a small ship pitching violently brings her sonar dome out of the water so often that it becomes inoperative, if not damaged. In the late 1940s, at least in the United States, it appeared that the best solution to this problem was a shallow-depth towed sonar. However, before it could be built as more than an experiment, sonar development had turned towards lower and lower frequencies, at which hull-mounted sonars could penetrate below the surface layer. Thus in the mid-1950s the US Navy went from the 25kc of its wartime equipment to 14 and ultimately to 8kc in its first major postwar set, SQS-4, and to 5kc in SQS-23, introduced in 1958. SQS-26 uses an even lower frequency, and is proportionately larger.

Each decrease in frequency brought a increase in range, simply because sound is not absorbed nearly so easily at lower frequencies. Given lower frequencies and higher power, the layer problem could be tackled. The key was the fact that sound waves approaching the thermocline at a steep downward angle would suffer relatively little refraction and so could generally pass through into the very deep layer. In water deeper than 500

Above The SQS-26 bow sonar dome of a US *Knox* class frigate, at the Long Beach Naval Shipyard, December 1971. At sea the dome is flooded with water which transmits the sound impulse from transducer to dome surface; exactly what type of surface will transmit energy most cleanly to and from the ocean surrounding the dome is a major consideration in sonar dome design.

Right The planar array is one alternative to a big sonar dome: the transducer is replaced by a series of flat plates strung out along the surface of the hull. HMS *Matapan* was modified to support a sonar development which clearly included both a bow sonar and the panels of a planar array. She is shown here in drydock, August 1973. *(C & S Taylor)*

fathoms, a sonar beam directed downwards at between 15° and 45° can be reflected off the bottom, towards the surface. This 'bottom-bounce' mode leaves large blank regions around a ship, in which a submarine is undetectable. However, in theory, such regions are acceptable if it is expected that the submarine cannot reach them without passing through zones of detection further out. The detection zones are rings around a ship; to some extent continuous tracking should be possible if the sonar depression angle can be varied to shrink their size as the submarine approaches.

'Bottom-bounce' range depends, of course, on just how deep the sea is as well as on the angle of depression of the beam. This must be steep enough to avoid trapping in the surface layer. For example, a beam depressed at 15° meets the sea bed (at 1500 fathoms) at 12,000yds, for a possible detection range of 24,000yds; under some circumstances detection after two or three bounces off the bottom is possible, as the beam also bounces off the surface. In shallow water, 'bottom-bounce' is a curse afflicting all sonar operation, leaving blank ('shadows') regions near a ship. For example, the same angle of depression in 150 fathoms of water corresponds to a detection range of 2400yds, and to very poor detection at shorter ranges*.

The other major means of very long range detection available with modern low-frequency sonars is convergence zone operation. In the deep layer, a sound wave directed downwards curves upwards as sound velocity increases due to greater pressure. The beam returns to the surface at a range, in the Atlantic, of about 30nm, in a zone 3–5nm wide, the convergence zone. It is again refracted or reflected at the surface, travels down, and repeats the pattern to form a second zone, about 6nm wide, at a range of about 60nm, and again at about 90nm (9nm wide). In the Mediterranean, the same sharp variation of sound velocity with depth which bends down the beam of the variable depth sonar also shrinks the size of the convergence zone: the first convergence zone is commonly at about 15 rather than 30nm. The focussing effect of the ocean is considerable; one US Navy textbook suggests that a surface or near-surface contact detected in the first convergence zone will have about the same signal strength as a target detected at 30nm, when no zone is formed. Convergence zone searches require a minimum depth of about 1000 fathoms and 2000 is considered normal; both convergence zone and 'bottom-bounce' techniques are limited to deep water. A convergence zone detection is almost necessarily a transient one, since it is only effective within the ring-shaped area of a zone fixed relative to the ship. By way of contrast, the angle of depression – and hence the range – of a 'bottom-bounce' beam can be varied to achieve 'solid' coverage around a ship at long range. However, the value of 'bottom-bounce' sonars is limited by the requirement for particular sea bed (and even surface weather) conditions.

*In general, long range performance requires deep water: for example, in the 'bottom-bounce' mode, multiple-bounce paths develop at less than 1000 fathoms, resulting in a loss of intensity. About 85 per cent of the ocean is deeper than 1000 fathoms, and most of the ocean floor also satisfies the requirement that its slope be 3° or less. 'Bottom-bounce' operation effectively bypasses the layer problem by projecting sound through the layer at so steep an angle that it travels through without refraction; in optics this would be referred to as a critical-angle effect. It has one great drawback, apparently unrecognized when 'bottom-bounce' was developed: in some places the sea bed, while at the right depth and the right slope, also absorbs so much sound that very little is reflected. For example, the sea floor off Italy is spongy volcanic rock, and 'bottom-bounce' sonar is worthless there.

The great advantage of the SQS-26 over all previous equipment was its ability to secure 'bottom-bounce' and convergence-zone detection, ie to achieve ranges of 30 and even 60nm under favorable conditions. Its immediate predecessor, SQS-23, has an electronic tilt feature which in theory should have made such detections practicable, but apparently it has insufficient power. When it was introduced in 1958, it was generally described as a 10,000yd sonar, and its electronic tilt feature is described as a means of maintaining contact with an approaching submarine. Both SQS-23 and its predecessor, SQS-4, could penetrate into the thermocline at short ranges (steep angles), but they could not achieve substantial ranges in its face.

VARIABLE DEPTH AND SCANNING SONARS

Many modern surface warships are equipped with an alternative solution to the layer problem, variable depth sonar (VDS). This is a separate sonar transducer in a towed 'fish': it can be lowered into the thermocline region to supplement the hull-mounted sonar effective only within the layer. VDS has experienced widely varying fortunes from time to time and from navy to navy. It suffers, sometimes, from the effects of training restrictions. For example, to be effective, VDS must be streamed at a considerable depth – where, in an exercise, it might collide with a submarine. In peacetime such collisions are frowned upon; in wartime the ship streaming the VDS might well be able to fire a long-range weapon before the submarine comes within collision range. VDS also imposes some manoeuvering and speed restrictions upon the ship towing it, and these may make it unpopular, when its positive effects are less apparent.

As in the case of radar, sonar suits reflect tactics and operational requirements; they also reflect the areas in which various navies operate. For the Royal Navy, British coastal waters constitute a major operating area in wartime; much of this area is no more than 100 fathoms deep. To some extent such shallow water acts as a waveguide or duct for sound waves of the appropriate frequency, which is one reason the Royal Navy has preferred medium- to low-frequency sonars. Reflections off the shallow bottom produce a strong reverberation effect; the greater the effective range to which the sound waves travel, the worse the reverberation. Navies which operate in shallow water therefore often prefer higher-frequency sonars, which have inherently shorter ranges than the large low-frequency types. Submarines can lie on the sea bed in an effort to avoid detection; the Royal Navy employs a specialized 'bottomed target classification' sonar, Type 162, as does the Canadian Navy. In addition, homing torpedoes are likely to be ineffective against silent bottomed targets – and reflection effects in shallow water may confuse them. This explains to some extent the retention of a depth-charge mortar, 'Limbo', which requires what amounts to a three-dimensional sonar, to obtain accurate target bearing and depth (Asdic 170).

The Royal Navy prefers medium-frequency, hull-mounted sonars partly because its ships operate in such rough water that a very large hull dome would cause problems. On the other hand, the Soviet Navy, which certainly operates in rough water, does employ bow sonar domes (evidenced by bow shapes and the location of anchors), which probably indicates sonars of SQS-23 size or larger.

Navies differ considerably in their interest in VDS. In the Mediterranean, for example, France has adopted such equipment with considerable enthusiasm, but Italy has not, at least for the most part. Canada developed a variable depth sonar, SQS-504 (as well as a towed version of the lower-frequency SQS-505), and Britain employed its own version, which it designated Asdic 199; recently, however, it has been removed from many British frigates on the grounds that it was ineffective in normal British operating areas in the Eastern Atlantic. The United States, concentrating on very deep ocean ASW, developed a series of variable depth sonars, but has shown their low priority by not installing many of those scheduled for ships with the powerful SQS-26, and by not providing for their installation in ships with SQS-23 medium-frequency sonars.

One problem all sonars share is the low velocity of sound, which limits their data rate. World War II sonars typically emitted a 'ping' focussed in one direction; the operator then listened for a returning echo before turning his transmitter to 'ping' again. The angle through which he turned was related to the large beam width of his sonar, in turn a consequence of its small size. The time he waited was proportional to his maximum range. For example, a wait of five seconds gave an unambiguous range of less than 5000yds – actually much less, given the angle of depression of the sonar beam. If the beam were 5° wide, a complete sweep might require 72 'pings', or 6 minutes. Just how circular the pattern would be depended on ship speed. At 10kts, a ship travels about one nautical mile in six minutes; at 15, 1.5, which begins to approach the effective range given by the five-second 'pinging' ('keying') interval. Matters would be much worse for a really long-range sonar, even with a beam so broad that far fewer 'pings' would suffice to make up 360° – or even deleting the sector aft on the ground that a ship's self-generated noise would make searching aft worthless.

The directional sonar is an underwater 'searchlight'. At high speed and long range it is not very useful as a search instrument. However, given a narrow sector in which to search, its focussed energy gives the greatest range for the least total power input. World War II ASW tactics took note of this limitation. Sonars were used for search, but they were far more important as a means of maintaining contact with a submarine which had revealed itself in some other way, for example by firing a torpedo. Wartime refinements were much concerned with maintenance of contact and with improvement of bearing data looking towards attack. For example, the split-beam technique called bearing deviation indication was actually equivalent to lobing in radars of the same period.

These sonars produced a broad beam tilted downwards; contact was generally lost as a submarine approached. Thus one rule of thumb for estimating target depth was that it was one-third of the range at which contact was lost. Late in World War II the US Navy introduced a tilting transducer in its QGB sonar, for Maintenance of Close Contact (MCC); postwar scanning sonars achieve similar performance by an electronic tilt.

Scanning sonar has been a most important and indeed fundamental development. In such equipment the sonar produces a pulse sent in all directions simultaneously; a rapidly rotating receiver – 30 revolutions per second, ie 33 milliseconds per revolution, in the early US QHB – sampled the returns. Such a sonar would pick up any returning echoes, and would not be subject to a loss of search efficiency at high speed, a particularly important consideration in the face of the Type 21 submarine. However, it required far more power than the searchlight sonar to maintain even similar performance – 72 times as much for the case of the 5° searchlight. In effect, the scanning sonar traded effective range for a good search rate, a trade-off

More and more of the interior volume of modern warships is being consumed by their sensors. This is part of the sonar installation of the new British frigate *Broadsword*. *(The Plessey Co)*

not all navies accepted in the face of the relatively poor searchlight ranges of the late 1940s. For example, the Royal Navy employed Type 174 and Type 177 searchlights in frigates built well into the 1950s, although it now prefers the Type 184 scanning type. The US Navy, on the other hand, abandoned searchlight operation at the end of the war, and QHB and its lower-frequency successors in all reconditioned ASW ships and in all new ones. From the early 1950s on, one reason was probably that low frequency, which promised better range performance, required a fixed array well suited to scanning operation.

The pure scanning mode is now generally termed Omni-Directional Transmission (ODT). In the mid-1950s it was found that the big fixed arrays could be wired to concentrate their beams into what amounted to an electronically scanned searchlight, a mode termed Rotationally Directional Transmission (RDT). In many cases the loss in search rate due to the searchlight mode is reduced by adopting tri-beam transmission: three widely-separated beams rotate together, in a cross between scanning and RDT. The low data rate inherent in sonar, in view of the low speed of sound, generally makes it necessary to design large sonars to track targets already detected while searching for new ones; relatively few radars have a similar track-while-scan (TWS) feature. On the other hand, sonars are rarely presented with the density of targets which radars face.

The data rate problem actually applies to both sonar and radar. A radar has a data rate given by its rotation rate, ie the rate at which it renews its examination of a given area. Radar range is generally defined by the probability with which a given target is detected on a scan – the blip/scan ratio – and the more pulses are reflected from a target the better the chance that they will show above the ever-present noise. The slower the rotation of

An early US VDS installation, SQA-8, aboard the destroyer *John W Thomason*, 4 January 1960. The towed 'fish' contained a transducer half the size of the SQS-4 mounted under the destroyer's keel, and operated from the same power supply.

the radar, the more pulses it will send out in any one direction; the radar distinguishes one direction from another according to the width of its beam, so that a radar with a beam 5° apart cannot distinguish two objects 3° apart, unless it employs some exotic technique such as lobing. The wider the radar beam, the more pulses it throws in any one direction per rotation – and the worse its angular definition. The faster the radar rotates, the better it can keep track of fast-moving objects, such as jet aircraft, but the fewer pulses it can throw in any one direction, and hence the lower its chance of detecting anything in the first place. In effect, then, there is a point in accepting a wide beam and low angular accuracy (and resolution) in return for a high data rate. However, in such a case fire control demands a very different kind of radar, one which emphasizes accurate pointing.

In the case of sonar, similar considerations are the basis for the distinction between search and attack variants, although, as in the SQS-23 and -26, it may be possible to employ the same sonar for both purposes (but in very different modes). In sonar as compared to radar, a high search rate is particularly important in view of the inherently low pulse rate of the system.

Both radar and sonar are, of course, useful not merely aboard ships but also aboard their weapons. However, these weapons are quite limited in size, and that limitation imposes restrictions on the radars and sonars which they can carry. For example, even large anti-ship missiles operate in J-band mainly because a wavelength any longer would give insufficient definition. Torpedo sonars undoubtedly operate at very high frequencies and consequently at short ranges for very similar reasons.

PASSIVE DETECTION SYSTEMS

Radar and sonar are active systems. All sensors look for some signature which indicates the presence of a target, and active sensors illuminate the target to impose a signature (radio waves or sound) upon it. However, most targets also produce signatures of their own, which passive sensors can detect. In general a passive sensor measures the direction of a target, whereas the active sensor can obtain both direction and range. However, if the target moves along a steady path, and the sensor keeps track of its path, changes in target bearing can be used to obtain target range – given time. Similarly, two separate ships each equipped with a passive sensor can form the baseline of a triangle and thus locate a target simultaneously. Indeed, one of the important roles of NTDS is to make the passive location of submarines more effective. However, it should also be noted that in many cases characteristics of the signal detected are themselves enough to suggest range. During World War II, for example, many Allied HF/DF operators became so familiar with German U-boat radio transmissions that they could guess how far away a boat was by the intensity of the signals they received; consequently single ships were able to run down HF/DF bearings to attack individual U-boats.

The great advantage of a passive sensor is that it does not give away the presence of the ship using it, as an active sensor does. Thus, for example, a ship loudly 'pinging' is inviting attention from submarines which can hear it far beyond the range at which it can detect them. A ship listening via a passive array gives away nothing. Moreover, sonar data comes in twice as quickly, since the signals do not have to make the full round trip from ship to target to ship. On the other hand, a passively obtained signal may be ambiguous; the active sensor can code its signals to make them stand out against a noisy background when they are reflected back.

The classic passive sensor is electronic intercept gear, such as HF/DF; it is now generally termed ESM (electronic support measures). ESM gear is often confused with ECM, which is counter-measures; ECM systems require ESM components to warn them that counteraction of an enemy radar or radio may be required. However, ESM gear can be used as a simple sensor of enemy presence, as in the case of HF/DF and some radar detectors. At present ESM promises detection of enemy radar-guided anti-ship missiles without the use of an active defensive radar which might in itself be used by enemy anti-radar weapons as an aim point. At close range, moreover, ballistics (of missiles and guns) become quite flat, so that direction is sufficient for aiming; range is almost superfluous.

The other great passive sensor is passive sonar, which for many years was almost the exclusive domain of the submariners. In recent years escort-towed passive arrays have shown remarkable performance, even at high towing speeds. They listen for such sounds as high-speed submarine propellers, and they may be able to reach out to the second convergence zone or beyond. The combination of high speed and great sensitivity has important tactical consequences. For example, a high speed force screened by escorts towing arrays is invulnerable to all but a few submarines in a narrow forward triangular zone, plus others willing to close from the flanks at high speed – a speed which in itself opens them to detection through the noise they make. Of course, the efficacy of the towed array depends in turn on sea conditions and the extent to which its complex signals can be processed.

Finally there is infra-red, and its cousin optical radiation. Infra-red radiation has so short a wavelength that even a very well focussed reflector or lens can be quite small. Yet all high-speed targets are hot, and an infra-red search detector should be able to pick up small fast targets such as anti-ship missiles, never revealing its own existence. This is evidently the rationale for using an infra-red detector as part of the Target Acquisition System which is intended to control US Navy point defense missiles; such a system must search continuously without ever providing a signature upon which enemy missiles can home.

Television is valuable because it can place almost the equivalent of an eyeball in an exposed position (or in one inaccessible to a man); in addition it can be connected to an automatic naval data system far more easily than can a man. Moreover, television (and often infra-red) can be used as an emergency back-up in the face of heavy jamming of more conventional sensors. Like infra-red, the best television can do is define the direction from which some object is coming; but at short range that is quite enough. In some cases it is enough at long range, too, as witness the great variety of television-guided 'smart' bombs.

CHAPTER SIX

Air Defense by Missile

From the point of view of the ship which carries it, the primary attributes of a SAM system are the size and number of the missiles, their propellants (which may require special storage), the rate of fire demanded, and the size and weight of the guidance system(s). All add together as ship impact: a ship which carries a high ship-impact SAM system is first of all a SAM ship and second something else, but almost any ship can carry a low ship-impact SAM. High impact is also high capability; naval SAMs are commonly graded as area vs point defense, ie as protective of several ships vs self-protective only. However, in looking at SAM systems as they affect the ships which carry them, ship impact is the better distinction.

In fact the distinction between area and point defense is not nearly as clear as might be supposed. When SAMs were first conceived, it seemed obvious that they would always impose so great a burden on the ship carrying them as to preclude installations on more than a very few ships in a fleet. The others would rely on their guns, effective at short and medium ranges, to protect themselves against leakage through the SAM screen. Just how far that screen had to extend depended upon task force disposition and SAM ship numbers. For example, it was assumed that only the carriers at task force center, separated by perhaps a few thousand yards, would need SAM protection. Two SAM ships near force center, with SAM ranges of 20,000yds, would suffice to destroy an attacking bomber before the latter could release its weapon. The range necessary for this concept to remain valid increased as stand-off missile ranges increased and as task force formations opened up in response to the threat of nuclear attack. There were two alternatives: a shorter-range SAM disposed in escorts surrounding the task force center, far enough out to catch either the bombers or their missiles; or a rapid-firing SAM ship near task force center, capable of handling all the incoming missiles. In effect the small number of very long range SAMs and the larger number of shorter-range SAMs are both approaches to the problem of handling a large number of targets in a relatively short time.

AREA DEFENSE AND POINT DEFENSE

Long range buys time and so makes up for a limited ability to handle many targets simultaneously. The current US very long range SAM is Talos, which is nearing retirement. It is usually credited with a range of 75–80 miles or more, but suffers from a limited capacity to handle multiple targets simultaneously: each missile requires the continuous attention of a director from booster burn-out through interception. Thus the most powerful Talos ships can engage only four targets simultaneously. The missile flies at about Mach 2.5, better than 30 miles per minute. Thus, against an incoming raid moving at 600mph (10 miles per minute), Talos might have seven opportunities to engage: first at 80, then 60, 45, 34, 23, 15 and 10 miles. In fact the close-range engagements are limited by the rate of fire, one salvo every 46 seconds (corresponding to a range of about 20 miles); and these estimates do not take into account time lost in switching directors from target to target, which might well exceed half a minute.

The total number of targets Talos could actually engage would depend upon the details of the raid and also the location of the ship with respect to the raid target at task force center. For example, Talos has a nuclear warhead, which can destroy several bunched attackers at once. A raid commander might, then, spread out his aircraft; but that would make it easier for the Talos and other SAM ships to engage them one by one. The task force commander might be able to place his Talos cruiser far from task force center in the direction from which a raid might be expected (ie on the 'threat axis', in which case she might engage both as the raiders approached and as they departed en route to their target.

The one air defense problem Talos would not be able to address would be the short-range anti-ship missile, launched either from a submerged submarine ('Charlie') or from the tubes of a 'tattletale' destoyer ('Styx'): flight time for such a weapon would be too short for a Talos engagement.

Talos was the most powerful US area defense weapon, with a range of at least 75nm. Its great size is suggested by a comparison with the light cruiser *Little Rock*, seen here firing a Talos on 4 May 1962. The two large radars pointing in the direction of missile flight are SPG-49 target trackers; they fed data into a computer which determined a flight path, which in turn directed a pair of SPW-2 radars which produced a beam along which Talos rode. One of the latter is barely visible above the upper SPG-49. All these guidance radars were directed by three powerful search sets: forward, an SPS-37A very long range two-dimensional metric-band radar; amidships an SPS-39 frequency-scanning pencil-beam three-dimensional radar for medium- and short-range height-finding; and aft an SPS-2, employing seven separate radar beams stacked in elevation to provide height data at very long range.

The shorter range (about 20nm) Terrier was still rated an area defense weapon. To be effective, it had to be disposed among several ships, in a ring around the task force. Terrier had a better target engagement rate than Talos, largely because it was a smaller and simpler missile, but it shared very similar fire control electronics, and thus did not have so much better an engagement rate that one Terrier ship could absorb a large attack. To some extent its lower cost and, more importantly, the lower ship-impact reflected in its smaller platforms, compensated for its shorter range.

The new Aegis returns to the concept of the SAM ship at or near the force center, absorbing large numbers of attackers. It trades missile range for rate of fire and target-handling capacity; its range is somewhat better than that of Terrier, but nowhere near that of Talos. Yet all three are area defense weapons. There is no question but that any of the three dominates the design of any ship carrying it. In each system the SAM designer was able to work according to the threat, letting the naval architect design a hull to accommodate his system.

Point defense is very nearly the opposite. Most point defense systems were designed to give existing ships, with their relatively small inherent space and weight margins, some measure of air defense. In a few cases, such as the Canadian version of Sea Sparrow, the SAM could be incorporated in a new design, but even then it had to have minimum impact on the primary task of the ship, in this case ASW. Probably the best example is the British Seacat, development of which began in 1957: Short Brothers conceived it as a modern replacement for the classic 40mm Bofors, and sold it for installation aboard many ships of World War II or even earlier vintage.

Inset Talos was stowed without its fins; here crewmen aboard the cruiser *Galveston* 'fin' a Talos prior to firing, 28 May 1958. The missile hangs from an overhead monorail along which it will be rammed on to the twin launcher.
Above Talos formed the main battery of seven US missile cruisers; this is USS *Columbus,* October 1965, firing a Tartar of her secondary battery. Her two SPW-2 radars are clearly visible, with the two big SPG-49s between them. The radar beyond is an SPS-30 pencil-beam height-finder.

Short Brothers' Seacat was the world's first point defense guided missile for warships. The radome at the center of the standard quadruple launcher houses the transmitter for the command guidance system. This one is aboard the Swedish destroyer *Södermanland. (CPL)*

Minimum ship-impact means, first, a minimum missile, which reaches out, therefore, to a minimum range. However, minimum ship-impact involves much more than this. Nearly all point defense systems eschew the automatic reloading systems common in area defense SAMs, thereby also giving up much raid-handling capacity. Instead, they use multiple-shot launchers (eight rounds in Sea Sparrow and Crotale, six in Seawolf, four in Seacat) which are reloaded by hand. Such a launcher need not limit the SAM to a single target. For example, if standard doctrine is to fire a salvo of two weapons per target, an eight-Sparrow box can engage four targets, if it has enough time to engage them one by one: minimum ship-impact generally also means minimum fire control complexity.

Inherent in the area/point defense dinstinction is the concept of a 'layered' fleet defense: carrier-borne interceptors at long range, backed by long- and medium-range SAMs and ultimately by guns and point-defense weapons to stop attackers leaking through the other lines of defense. In such a concept relatively low point defense performance is acceptable; the same is true of single-ship defense because it can be assumed that single ships will generally operate in areas of relatively low air threat, ie one or two 'Styx' fired by a fast patrol boat, rather than the sixty 'Badgers' a carrier task force in the Norwegian Sea might face.

An alternative expression might be that the Soviets must face the US naval air arm anywhere on the world ocean, but the US Navy must face massed Soviet naval air power, at least at present, only within 'Badger' or 'Backfire' range of the Soviet Union, and even then only when it presents a really worthwhile target: Soviet tactics almost guarantee that the elite bomber force will be reserved to counter US carrier task forces. Soviet surface tactics, moreover, require that many units operate independently. It follows that for the Soviet Navy the distinction between area and point defense is less valid than it is in the West. The layered air defense must be executed by each unit facing attack, and there is no long-range carrier-based interceptor force to form the outermost layer. Recent Soviet missile cruisers carry a combination of the long-range SAN-3, (equivalent, perhaps, to Terrier) and the shorter-range, encapsulated SAN-4 (their equivalent of Sea Sparrow). On the other hand, their specialized ASW ship, the 'Krivak', the rough equivalent of a US *Knox* class ASW frigate, makes a minimum

concession to SAM requirements: she mounts SAN-4. Both types are more extensively gun-armed than are Western warships, perhaps partly because both must expect a higher rate of leakage through defenses than would obtain with a layered defense of greater depth.

THE LIMITATIONS OF GUNFIRE

The SAM guidance system determines, to a large extent, its ability to handle simultaneous targets, to counter saturation attacks. Guidance is also what makes a SAM, as compared to an anti-aircraft shell, effective at long range. It eliminates the 'dead time' inherent in shell fire: the airborne target moves unpredictably between the moment of firing and the arrival of the shell at the predicted target position. The longer the range, the longer the dead time and, therefore, the lower the probability that the anti-aircraft fire control system can predict target position accurately. The proximity (variable time, or VT) fuzes introduced in World War II increased the permissible margin of error relating to AA gunfire control in that they (i) reduced dead time by eliminating the need for (time) fuze setting and (ii) made the shell lethal if it passed near the target at any range, and so relaxed the need for accurate rangefinding, especially at short ranges. However, at very long ranges even the VT fuze was far from enough. For example, the high-velocity (2650fs initial velocity) 5in/54 shell requires 15.8 seconds to reach a target at 10,000yds. During the same period a 600mph airplane moves over 4600yds; it takes only a very small error, even one due to a random gust of wind, to throw the shell off by more than its lethal radius, which cannot be more than 10 or 20ft considering its size. Moreover, random variations in the winds between gun and target, and in the condition of gun barrel and powder, reduce accuracy. The error is generally in pointing: at a longer range, a given angle error is equivalent to a longer miss distance. In fact each problem worsens at longer range: the dead time increases, the winds aloft have more time to act, and aiming errors have worse consequences.

Moreover, the gun is inherently limited in range, since its shell loses momentum constantly after leaving the muzzle because of air resistance. Gravity, too, limits gunfire range, given an initial impulse. Gun range can be improved by increasing that initial impulse, but that in turn requires a larger and heavier gun barrel and a larger mount – not to mention a more massive powder charge, which in turn means more massive handling equipment. There is not, after all, a very large market for 8in anti-aircraft guns with 5000fs initial velocities which can be accommodated only aboard 15,000-ton cruisers and which wear out after 55 rounds.

The gun's ammunition is relatively inexpensive and its rate of fire can be high: given enough rounds, a poor SSPK can accumulate into a good chance of killing a target. For example, if one round has so much as a one per cent chance of killing a target, fifty rounds have a cumulative kill probability of almost 40 per cent. It follows that, given a high enough rate of fire *and* enough time, a gun can be quite effective. Beyond about 5000yds, however, the SSPK is so low that even rate of fire is not enough, which is why guns are effectively limited to medium ranges. In many cases, at least before the advent of the Kamikaze and the stand-off bomb, it was acceptable for anti-aircraft fire not to destroy too many aircraft, particularly at long range. Airplanes had to close their targets to deliver the only two accurate anti-ship weapons, dive bombs and torpedoes, and in either case it was enough to make the pilot flinch, or release his weapon at a great enough range to permit a maneuvering ship to evade it. Thus the density of fire tended to throw an attacking pilot off his aim – no matter how brave he might be, he would probably wince. This of course did not apply to the bombardier in an airplane above anti-aircraft range, but prior to the advent of the FX 1400 he had been no great problem because his bombs were inherently inaccurate and because the dead time between bomb release and hitting gave plenty of time for a ship to maneuver.

However, FX 1400, like a SAM, could follow its target's motion and so improve its own SSPK. The Kamikaze pilot, too, was unimpressed by density of fire: he wanted to die, and so was quite happy to fly directly into anti-aircraft fire. Moreover, once he had gone into a dive towards his target, the Kamikaze would remain on course no matter how badly control surfaces and pilot were damaged. Although he often missed (he could become somewhat confused), it was clearly best to design defenses to disentegrate the attacking Kamikaze outside some minimum range. In effect such a requirement changed the definition of killing an airplane, and so reduced again the effective SSPK of shellfire.

GUIDANCE SYSTEMS

SAMs overcome both the dead time/fire control and the range limitation of the gun by a combination of guidance and self-propulsion. Given a fast enough SAM, guidance permits it to fly a course which requires almost no initial prediction of target motion. For example, at any given moment, the SAM can fly along the line pointing from fire control radar to target, a line which curves more and more tightly as it approaches the target – and which therefore requires the SAM to have and to retain a considerable speed advantage over its target, not to mention the ability to remain aloft over a distance considerably greater than the straight line from launcher to ultimate target position. This need not imply self-propulsion, but it does for any considerable range.

This 'line-of-sight' guidance technique is very common, but it is also very inefficient. Even though a SAM is self-propelled, it has a limited supply of propellant, and the method of guidance chosen determines, to a considerable extent, how efficiently that propellant can be used. Most SAMs are rockets. They are given an initial boost to cruise speed, after which a much lower-powered sustainer engine may burn for a time, over-coming drag. After that the missile begins to lose speed. It may still climb and still maneuver, since it flies by means of its wings and its control surfaces, as well as the thrust of its engine. However, like a shell emerging from the muzzle, it is losing energy, and hence its scope for maneuver. For a given missile, ie for a given size (almost a given ship-impact), then, guidance alone has a great part in determining effective range, which is one reason why it is very difficult to associate any given SAM with an unambiguous effective range.

Alternatives to line-of-sight generally involve some element of prediction of target position, which reduces the sharp, energy-inefficient curvature at the end of the SAM flight. It is this curvature which becomes even worse as the target maneuvers violently; such maneuvers can overcome the limits built into the SAM and so cause it to miss, as happened in Vietnam and in the Middle East. In particular, as the missile approaches its target in the line-of-sight system it tends to go into a tail chase, in which it has to follow any target maneuver, perhaps in exaggerated form, as it tries to catch up. Any measure of prediction, which permits the missile to 'lead' its target, improves matters considerably.

There are two standard alternatives. The simplest is *proportional navigation:* given the relative *speeds* (including direction) of missile and target at any one time, the missile can lead the target by an angle proportional to the target's relative speed. The path so defined is slightly better than line-of-sight, and a guidance system utilizing it does not introduce very great complexity. However, from the point of view of energy efficiency, the best fire control system flies the missile along a path determined only by energy efficiency, to place it at the predicted point of impact, just as an AA gun fire system would. The advantage of the SAM would be that, once placed near the target, it can be guided into it, and so make up for all those factors which degrade gun SSPK. Talos exemplifies the latter approach: it flies an 'up-and-over' path, directed towards a predicted target position, and then homes at the far end. Any other alternative would not have made full use of the very great range inherent in its long-burning ramjet engine.

Self-propulsion has an advantage beyond permitting guidance and long range: it allows a relatively large warhead to be flown from a relatively simple launcher. The warhead can have a large lethal radius, which in itself must improve SSPK. However, the missile is quite large and so cannot even nearly match the gun in number of rounds or in rate of fire. It is, therefore, tempting to apply missile technology to shells. For example, the US Navy tried to develop an anti-aircraft guided shell, Zeus, in the late 1940s: it was an 8in shell containing a small rocket which could be ignited in mid-flight to alter its course – once. That was hardly enough mid-course guidance, and Zeus was dropped. However, the new guided shells will probably have a significant anti-aircraft capability, as long as they retain enough velocity to maneuver with their targets. They will still suffer from the range limitations inherent in guns, although these may be relaxed somewhat if they are rocket-assisted. In that case, however, range will have to be bought by reducing warhead weight, and hence lethality: in effect guidance will have to be more effective at just those longer ranges at which it is more difficult.

POINT DEFENSE MISSILES

Comparative profiles of point defense missiles. All these missiles are light enough for hand-reloading in multi-salvo launchers: 143lb for Seacat, 180lb for Seawolf and Crotale, 186lb for Sea Chaparral and about 450lb for Sea Sparrow. Ranges are generally about 4 to 6nm.

SEA CHAPARRAL   SEA SPARROW   CROTALE   SEACAT   SEAWOLF

AREA DEFENSE MISSILES

Comparative profiles of area defense missiles. Note that Masurca is very similar in profile (and in guidance) to the US Tartar/Terrier/Standard, but is rather larger (16.1in in diameter and 4585lb including booster, compared to 13.5in and about 3000lb for Terrier; range is reportedly 31nm, compared to about 20nm for the US weapon). Tartar is very nearly identical to the upper stage of Terrier, with an alternate (dual-thrust) engine; Standard is essentially a developed Tartar. Tartar could be loaded automatically by virtue of its folding fins; Terrier could not, because the fins on its booster were too large to fold. Both Talos and Sea Dart are ramjets; part – by no means all – of their difference in weight (7000lb vs 1200lb) is traceable to vast improvements in ramjet technology since the early 1950s. In fact, Sea Dart somewhat resembles (in size) the abortive US Typhon, albeit with a rather shorter range. Sea Dart is a much 'hotter' missile, with a more powerful ramjet (35,000lb vs 20,000lb thrust) in a lighter airframe (Mach 3 vs Mach 2.5). Standard illustrates the effect of guidance on range: using the same airframe and engines, Standard 2 (MR) has a range officially given as about 70 per cent beyond that of Standard 1 (MR) ('over 10.6nm'); in Standard (ER) the appropriate ratio is about 120 per cent on a base figure of 'over 32.3nm' for a range of about 70nm, comparable to figures previously claimed for the now-defunct Talos. Published figures suggest warhead weights of 200-300lb for area defense weapons (eg 297lb in Seaslug, 265lb in Masurca). By way of contrast, Seacat has only a 221lb warhead.

TALOS   TARTAR   STANDARD ((MR)   STANDARD (ER)   TERRIER   MASURCA   SEASLUG   SEA DART   SAN-1 'GOA   SAN-2 'GUIDELINE'

SHIPBOARD FIRE CONTROL

Guided missile systems can be characterized by the way the guidance decisions are distributed between missile and shipboard fire control system. At one end of the spectrum, the missile homes on its target, using only a seeker it carries. The role of the shipboard fire control system is limited to placing the missile close enough to its target for its own homing devices to function; how close this is depends upon how powerful the missile-carried seeker is. One example of such a self-homing missile was the US Sea Chaparral, essentially four air-to-air heat-seeking Sidewinder missiles carried together on a trainable mount. Once in the air, they were entirely free of the shipborne fire control system, which could then engage another target without waiting for missiles fired at the first to hit or miss.

Sea Chaparral was conceived as a minimum-cost point defense (anti-cruise missile) system; low cost was ensured both by the simplicity of the shipboard fire control and by the low cost of individual Sidewinders. The latter in turn resulted from their short range and also from the short wavelength of the infra-red radiation on which they homed, which in turn permitted the design of a small and self-contained seeker. In theory, Sea Chaparral could engage any target which entered the field of view of the missile seeker, and to which the missile could therefore lock on. In practice, one of the great failings of this (and any other IR-homing) ship-based system was that the chief IR signature presented by a cruise missile is from its tail, whereas the missile would more probably be approaching the ship the system was trying to defend. Infra-red is, however, probably the simplest self-contained missile homing system, and therefore it remains attractive; some IR seekers can now home on the 'glint' on the forward end of an airplane or missile, and probably such a seeker will form the basis for a new generation of very lightweight self-contained missile systems, eg for small combatants.

The self-contained guidance system is not in itself a guarantee of a lightweight missile system, only of a relatively simple shipborne fire control mechanism. Sophistication transferred to the missiles may well make up for the weight and even the space saved, and certainly for the money saved. In theory, for example, it might be possible to build into a single missile a phased array search radar, which in turn would trigger the missile engine and drive the missile towards its prey; the phased array could then switch over to a homing mode. No such missile exists as yet, but small phased array radars do exist, and with the rise of inexpensive integrated circuits a fully autonomous missile is a distinct possibility, for example for the air defense of submarines or of small fast patrol craft. In other applications no radar which could fit on the nose of a small missile could possibly rival a ship-mounted radar in efficiency, but even a wide-field-of-view homing radar on the missile could accomplish a great deal.

For the present, however, it appears to be impracticable to fit a full radar in the nose of an anti-aircraft missile: the constraints on missile weight and volume are too severe. What can be done is to fit a radar *receiver* to the missile nose; a shipborne radar tracking the target also illuminates it like a searchlight, and the missile can home on the reflected radiation. This is *semi-active* homing. One of its disadvantages is that the missile follows a line-of-sight path, which is inefficient. Proportional navigation is better: the missile can compute target speed relative to its own. One particularly neat solution to this problem is to mount antennas on the rear of the climbing missile; they receive the beam from the launch ship, while the nose antenna receives a reflected beam which includes a Doppler shift due to target motion. Comparision between reflected and 'reference' beams provides target motion data. This is still far from the most efficient missile flight path, but it is the best the missile can do without receiving commands from shipboard. It is employed by such weapons as the French Masurca Mod 3 and the US Standard missile, Tartar, and the semi-active version of Terrier.

Although semi-active homing permits a simplified shipboard fire control system, it does require that a shipboard radar be trained on the target throughout missile flight: the number of targets which can be engaged simultaneously is limited to the number of illuminating radars, although it should be noted that there is no limit to the number of missiles which can be fired at the same target, as long as that target remains illuminated.

Command-guided weapons lie at the other end of the scale: the missile flies towards the target, tracked by the fire control system, which also tracks the target itself. The fire control system observes the missile's deviation from an appropriate intercept course, and orders corrections: all the missile needs on board is a radio receiver and the appropriate servos. From the point of view of guidance electronics, it is little more than a sophisticated version of a hobbyist's radio-controlled airplane. Pure command guidance has the great virtue of minimizing the electronic load

The first platform for the US Aegis will be a greatly modified *Spruance* class destroyer, DDG-47, a sketch of which is shown. The 'plates' mounted on her forward deckhouse contain two of the antennas for the SPY-1 electronically scanning radar, which tracks both targets and missiles; illumination of the targets for terminal homing is to be the role of the Mk 62 dishes atop the pilot house. Like other *Spruances*, DDG-47 will have the dome-enclosed Mk 86 Gun Fire Control System; she will also have Phalanx, visible abaft the big radar house. Below it is the new electronically scanning SLQ-32 ECM (active and passive) system. The foremast also carries an SPS-55 surface search radar, and the mainmast an SPS-49 such as that fitted to *Perry* class frigates, in place of the lower-performance SPS-40 of *Spruances*. Note the bulwark forward, intended to restore some of the freeboard lost by the addition of the Aegis system to the basic *Spruance* hull. The first DDG-47 is to be delivered to the US Navy in 1983.

the missile must carry; for that reason it was the earliest surface-to-air missile guidance system. The first US SAM was Little Joe, essentially a radio-controlled combination of an aircraft bomb and several JATO (jet-assisted take-off) booster rockets. It was designed and built in less than three months, an achievement possible at least partly because of its very simple guidance system. A shipboard operator was to observe the missile's flight towards its target, 'flying' it into the target using a simple joystick connected to a radio control. The only computer involved was the one between his ears, yet in principle Little Joe was equivalent to far more complex command-guided weapons.

Command guidance can reduce missile size, and therefore it is attractive for the point defense role. Moreover, at short range the best SAM course is so close to line-of-sight that a single radar (or eyeball) can keep both missile and target continuously in view. For example, command guidance was chosen for the first point defense missile system in the world, the Short Seacat. Seacat exemplifies the flexibility of command guidance: it can function with a wide variety of directors, some of which are little more than pointers. More sophisticated forms of command guidance were chosen for the new Seawolf and for the less powerful French Crotale. In the former, it was important that the director had merely to keep both Seawolf and target continuously in view. That in turn permitted the system's designer to provide a variety of non-radar back-ups against the possibility of jamming: infra-red and television. In fact the only real vulnerability of a pure command guided weapon to jamming is in its guidance link, but that link is picked up by an antenna on the missile pointing back towards the launching ship, away from any target-borne jammer.

The original attraction of command guidance, however, was that it minimized the missile performance penalty paid in consequence of the relatively bulky electronics of the 1940s and early 1950s: for example, of US SAMs, the chief examples of command guidance were the early land-based types, Nike and Bomarc. The Soviets persisted much longer with command guidance, and all Soviet naval SAMs thus far have used this system. Generally, Soviet practice is to provide a single director to control the weapons fired from each twin launcher. It has antennas to track both missiles and target, plus dishes from which guidance signals can issue. As in the short-range systems, these SAMs must fly very nearly a line-of-sight course, since missile and target must remain simultaneously in view of the two coaxially mounted sets of radars. Such command guidance not only limits the missile system to one target per salvo, but it may also limit the number of salvoes which can be in the air at the same time, unless the considerable complication of separate coded beacons for each missile is accepted. A more fundamental problem of command guidance is that it becomes harder and harder for the tracking radars to decide just how far the missile is from its target at increasing range: the beam has a fixed angular width, which amounts to only a small distance at short range but must become unacceptably large at a sufficiently long range. Solutions include using larger and larger tracking antennas (which soon become too large for shipboard installation) and using more and more lethal warheads, eg nuclear ones, which can tolerate longer and longer miss distances. Neither is entirely satisfactory, which is why the United States Navy had to shift to semi-active homing as Terrier range increased with an improved propellant; Tartar was designed for semi-active homing for another reason – simplicity of the shipboard radar installation. The accuracy of semi-active homing *improves* as the missile nears its target, since then the angular size defined by the missile's radar receiver corresponds to shorter and shorter distances.

The US Navy began its SAM development with a modified form of command guidance – beam-riding. Both Terrier and Talos were designed to

Seawolf is the successor to Seacat, a missile designed specifically to defeat anti-ship missiles. Here it is shown mounted aboard the test frigate *Penelope*, October 1976. *(Royal Navy)*

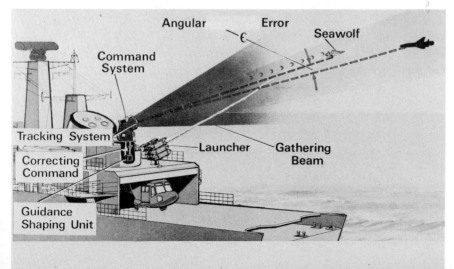

Seawolf guidance. The functions of the fire control radar are (i) to track the target and (ii) to measure the difference between Seawolf course and the direct path to the target; the command system attempts to correct missile path. Note the complete absence of below-decks spaces such as would be common to any larger missile system. *(Royal Navy)*

Loading a Seawolf. The chief defect of this and similar point defense systems is that they have only a very limited ability to deal with saturation attacks. If two Seawolfs must be launched per incoming missile (to achieve a very good kill probability), then the launcher can deal with only three attackers before it requires manual reloading. Matters are actually worse because the guidance radar limits the number of attackers which can be dealt with simultaneously, and Seawolf range is short enough (surely well below 10nm) that it cannot engage several of a group of attackers on their way in. (*Royal Navy*)

ride along a beam generated by a specialized radar. In the Terrier system one radar tracked the target, and the same radar generated the beam along which the missile ascended. The beam spun ('nutated') around the direction the missile was to fly; antennas on the rear fins of the missile permitted it to sense deviations from this path by the level of the signal, and by the way that signal varied. This system was both elegant and difficult to jam: like other command systems it used only antennas on the rear of the missile. However, unlike other command systems, it could accept multiple missiles fired at a single target, since the shipborne part of the fire control system never tracked the SAMs, only the target.

Such simple beam-riding was impractical for Talos, in view of the great range demanded of it. An efficient Talos flight path would never be a direct line towards a target which, at the start of flight, would be near the horizon. However, there was nothing about beam-riding which demanded that the beam be pointed directly at the target; Talos was designed to ride a beam pointed by the ship fire control computer, which flew it into the area of the target. There the missile switched to semi-active homing, using illumination from a second radar which had tracked the target while the SAM had been beam-riding. The net effect was a massive guidance system, which added to the already considerable bulk of the Talos missiles themselves. One advantage of the system was that the guidance beam could also fly Talos into a surface target, achieving maximum range by means of an energy-efficient flight path.

Except for Talos and one version of Terrier, the US Navy abandoned beam-riding in the early 1960s; so did the Royal Navy, in Sea Dart (successor to the beam-riding Seaslug), and the French Navy, in the Mk 3 version of its Masurca*. All adopted semi-active homing instead; the latter is inherently simpler, and hence more reliable. Even though beam-riding is in principle a command-guidance system, it does require the missile to recognize its deviation from the beam axis. The switch to semi-active homing therefore involves a smaller increase in missile complexity than might be the case in a shift from a purer from of command guidance. Semi-active homing is also more effective at long range, at which the accuracy of pointing of the beam-rider radar does not suffice. Moreover, the beam-rider may suffer severely from beam movement as the ship carrying its radar rolls and pitches, no matter how well it is stabilized. The relatively broad beam of a semi-active radar illuminator, however, allows for ship motion without missing the target; similarly, its width can make up for some target maneuvering without requiring detailed guidance radar follow-up.

All these points aside, semi-active homing does have one great drawback compared even to simple beam-riding: it increases vulnerability to counter-measures, in that the missile now receives its information from the direction of the target, where the jammers and other deception devices are. The small radar-receiving antenna in the nose of the SAM has only a limited field of view: once it has been drawn far enough from the target, it will not be able to return, even if the decoying transmitter is soon switched off. To fool a beam-rider, on the other hand, requires that the much more powerful radars on the SAM ship be deceived, since it is virtually impossible for a jammer to intercept the guidance link between missile and guidance radar.

*The US Navy retains the beam-guided nuclear Terrier, BT(N), because the US Government will not deploy any nuclear weapon not under positive control from launch to explosion. There is some possibility that a data link may satisfy this requirement in such semi-active systems as the Standard missile.

Moreover, beam-riding (and any other form of command guidance) has an inherent ability to switch targets, within limits set by missile aerodynamics. Let us imagine two missiles of a salvo, launched a few seconds apart, both proceeding along the same beam towards one of two airplanes. Although each has only a 60 per cent chance of destroying the first airplane, in fact the first scores a direct hit. *If* the SAM radar system can detect this hit in time *and* slew the director around, the second SAM can fly into a new target. This procedure is unlikely to be possible with a pair of semi-active missiles in the same beam.

All the systems so far described have the inherent defect of a limited ability to handle large numbers of targets. However, very accurate guidance is required only towards the end of a missile's flight: until then it is really quite enough to guide the missile into a position from which its own radar can receive target-reflected illumination. This observation is the key to new systems such as the US Aegis, designed specifically to defeat saturation raids. The Standard 2 missile associated with Aegis has an autopilot, which the shipboard fire control system sets when the missile is launched; Aegis also provides a limited degree of mid-course command guidance while the missile is in flight, to maneuver it into position. Then the illuminating radar needs operate for only a very short time. An incidental benefit of the system is that the missile can fly a particularly energy-efficient path, so that in itself the Aegis fire control system almost doubles the effective range of the Standard 2 missile.

These guidance systems operate effectively only after a SAM has entered the field of view of its radar director; however, the director's beam must be a narrow one if it is to operate effectively at any great range. There is, therefore, an essential auxiliary control function during launch: the missile, whose launcher may be some distance from the director, is boosted to high speed (at which its control surfaces become effective) *and* brought into the purview of the director, which generally uses a wide beam to 'gather' or 'capture' it. For example, in the Seawolf system the missile launcher is outside the cone of vision of the radar of the command-guidance system: the latter cannot guide it into an appropriate path. To fill this gap an auxiliary radar, consisting of four microwave horns, is added to the

Missile propulsion has advanced greatly since 1945; the British Sea Dart, shown here aboard HMS *Bristol,* shows how much can now be achieved in a small (14ft 5in, 1210lb) ramjet-powered missile. Reported performance approaches that claimed for early models of the 7000lb Talos, but Sea Dart is actually slightly shorter than the US Tartar. Reported range is 50nm. The missiles are stowed vertically, and rise through a pair of doors alongside the launcher, which is elevated to the vertical to receive them. *(British Aerospace)*

director; it has a very wide cone of vision which the missile does intersect soon after firing. In the French Crotale matters are simplified: the radar is mounted on the missile launcher, and so sees the missile almost as soon as it leaves the tube. Such quick acquisition probably reduces greatly the minimum range of the system, which is certainly an advantage for a point defense weapon.

PROPULSION SYSTEMS

The size of the SAM is determined by the range it is expected to achieve, as reflected in its propulsion. For a supersonic missile there are two choices: ramjet and rocket. The ramjet cannot function at all below a 'threshold' speed, and so requires a booster to accelerate it to that speed. Because it burns air with its fuel, the ramjet can go further than a rocket on a given weight of fuel. Against this, it pays the penalty of a booster; some of the weight saved must go into a more complex missile structure. Ramjets, then, are best at long range. The only major current naval examples are Talos and Sea Dart. However, the abortive Typhon was probably the most striking instance of what ramjet propulsion could buy: it achieved about ten times the Terrier's range on the same size and weight. From the point of view of shipboard operation, a ramjet may impose special fueling requirements, since its liquid fuel may not be storable in the missile bodies.

A rocket is simpler, but pays a weight penalty because it must carry both fuel and oxidizer. Moreover, a solid-fuel rocket cannot be throttled, which limits its ability to trade speed for range. Generally, two separate rocket motors are provided, one for high initial (boost) thrust, the other, longer-burning, to provide just enough thrust to overcome drag at high speed (sustain). Only point defense missiles fly for so short a time that they can manage with only a single motor. However, two separate motors generally mean two stages, and a large and unwieldy weapon. The US Tartar was an alternative solution: a single motor contained two simultaneously-burning components, one fast-burning, the other slow-burning for sustaining thrust. The single-stage configuration saved missile length (ship-impact) as well as weight (one motor and one casing vs two of each; the lighter missile of course required less boost and less sustaining thrust).

Neither rocket nor ramjet is entirely satisfactory, but a third option is a hybrid of the two. Its ramjet sustainer increases range, but the use of a rocket booster integral with the ramjet reduces the weight penalty. To date the only such missile is the Soviet SA-6, but others will probably appear in the West during the next decade. For example, the current US Navy research and development program includes both surface-to-air and surface-to-surface hybrid missiles.

Fire control and missile propulsion together determine the greatest effective rate of fire a SAM system can support. For example, a beam-rider such as Terrier can engage only one target at a time; the number of missiles to be devoted to each target depends upon some estimate of SSPK. If each missile has an SSPK of 60 per cent or better, two missiles have better than an 85 per cent chance of destroying a target, and it is reasonable to expend two SAMs per target. At Mach 3 each covers about 40 miles per minute. Let us suppose, then, that the missiles generally engage targets at a range of about 20 miles. At best each director is tied up for 30 seconds per target, but in fact there is considerable time lost as it slews from one to another, so that each director may have a cycle time of a minute or more. Thus for a two-

director system, as fitted in many US Terrier ships, a salvo fired every 30 seconds exhausts the capacity of the directors. Anything faster is just so much weight or complexity or ship volume wasted. However, to accept a much slower rate of fire is to make the SAM system too easy to saturate. In practice, at least in US systems prior to Aegis, the limiting factor in target engagement rate is usually the number of directors, rather than the rate of fire of the launcher; that in turn is limited by available topweight and, far more importantly, by available ship length – which goes back to the greatest single limit in modern warship design

STOWAGE ARRANGEMENTS

Missile shape, determined by missile propulsion, decides the form of the missile magazine and the missile stowage system. Many SAMs require long boosters and therefore are long compared to the hull depth of the ship carrying them: completely assembled, for example, Terrier is about 26ft in length. It was carried vertically in the two converted heavy cruisers *Boston* and *Canberra,* but horizontally in all other US ships which mounted it. In the latter, standard installation missile and booster bodies, mated, were carried on large cylindrical frameworks ('rings'), which could revolve to align the uppermost missile with a hoist. Cylinder diameter, and hence capacity, was dictated by the space available, given, at first, one cylinder per launcher rail: the US Navy fixed capacity at twenty missiles per ring. The sole exception was the very cramped installation aboard the converted World War II destroyer *Gyatt*, limited to seven missiles per ring. Given a fixed ring capacity and horizontal stowage, the best means of increasing capacity was to provide a second bank of cylinders below the primary bank; in this way the capacity of each Terrier launcher aboard the cruiser *Long Beach* was increased to eighty rounds, albeit at a cost in hull depth.

Terrier is so large that the US ASROC anti-submarine rocket-launched depth charge or torpedo can fit within the space it occupies. In 1960 the Bureau of Ordnance proposed a combined ASROC-Terrier launcher with three rings, the upper two to take ASROCs and Terriers in alternate positions, the lower only Terrier. By installing such a system the designers of the *Belknap* class missile frigate (now cruiser) were able to reduce the length problem by eliminating the separate ASROC launcher;

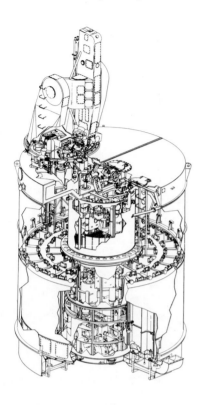

The Mk 13 launcher introduced automated operation and a high rate of fire; forty missiles are set in fixed positions, and the launcher arm assembly moves about the cylinder to select weapons to fire. A major part of the penalty paid is limited flexibility in type of missile fired, but the compactness of Mk 13 and of the even smaller Mk 22 has made possible installations aboard destroyers and even ocean escorts. European warships, such as the Dutch *Tromp*, which employ the Standard missile, also generally employ the Mk 13 launcher. *(FMC Corporation)*

they also gave up one twin Terrier and mounted a 5in/54 gun and a helicopter platform in its place. A similar economy of space permitted the use of a large helicopter deck in conjunction with ASROC and Terrier in the Italian *Vittorio Veneto*.

In order to achieve maximum density stowage, Terriers were carried in the rings without their fins, an arrangement which in itself required special spaces for finning before launch, as well as a crew to fit the fins. Talos was much larger. Its long range made a much lower rate of fire permissible, and vertical space was saved by restricting the rings to a few ready-service rounds. In the standard Talos installations, on the other hand, the missiles were stowed in racks, from which they could be lifted on to an overhead monorail for transfer to, first, a finning/warm-up/check-out station, and then on to the launcher. In the *Cleveland* class conversions, which had relatively little hull depth aft, the racks were all above decks in the large after superstructure, with ready-use missiles nearest the launcher (16 missiles in two banks of eight each, one for each launcher arm, two missiles high) and another magazine further forward. In the larger heavy cruiser conversions, however, hull depth was available whereas length was not; the missiles were stowed in vertical magazines with blast doors separating them from the missile-handling spaces. All were ready-service rounds, assembled, whereas in the *Cleveland* conversion thirty of the missiles were stowed in magazines separate from their boosters. Even this arrangement was logical: any single Talos launcher was unlikely to fire more than about eight salvoes (as noted above) in any one raid. There was no point in providing a very expensive capability for missile stowage which would exceed the limits set by the Talos fire control system.

Although Terrier was suitable for mounting aboard super-destroyers, it was not the mass SAM envisaged by US planners of the 1950s. They wanted a weapon to replace the standard 5in/54 of a fleet destroyer with minimum effect on the design. That requirement alone determined the fact that Tartar would fit within the vertical envelope normally occupied by a gun mount whose magazine lay directly below it. Moreover, to eliminate most of the launch crew, Tartar was designed with long, narrow wings and folding tail fins: it required no assembly space on board ship. Its short length was probably dictated by this vertical-magazine requirement.

Nor could the narrow hull of a destroyer accommodate the pair of missile rings characteristic of Terrier and Talos. Tartar was designed for maximum automation. Its magazine consists of one or two concentric rings of missiles, atop which the launcher sits on a rotating deck pierced by a blastproof scuttle. The magazine itself does not turn, which permits a considerable saving in weight and complexity. The original Mk 11 launcher had two rails, which could adjust to load either from the inner (16-missile) or the outer (24-missile) ring; in the more recent Mk 13, only a single launcher rail is used, and there exists an austere version employing only the inner (9-missile) ring*. However, the use of the single rail requires a very high rate of fire (8 rounds per minute in the Mod 3 version of the *Perry* class), since the Tartar missile system still requires salvoes of (say) two missiles per target no matter what its launcher looks like. The interval between missiles has to be short compared to total engagement time, otherwise the second missile

*The sixteen-missile system, in the *Brooke* class missile frigates, is designated Mk 22. For a time General Dynamics/Pomona tried to convince the Navy to buy a twelve-missile box launcher that could have replaced one twin 5in mount in a FRAM conversion; guidance would have been provided by a modified 5in fire control radar forward.

ties up the director and so delays its switch to a new target. A Tartar needs about 30 seconds to fly from launcher to target, which actually makes the cycle time of 7.5 seconds per missile fairly slow compared to the design requirement for which the Mk 13 was probably built.

Perhaps the chief defect of the Mk 13 is that it has only a very limited capacity for expansion. In the latest US launcher, the Mk 26, missiles are set on a conveyor belt, not very different from that in the early Terrier cruiser conversions *Boston* and *Canberra*: different versions of the launcher employ different lengths of magazine space and conveyor belt to accommodate different numbers of weapons. The use of a twin-arm launcher maximizes firing rate. One important advantage of the conveyor belt is that it allows some leeway for different types of missile; at the least, it can accommodate Harpoon and ASROC as well as Standard/Tartar. For example, Mk 26 can accommodate a missile length of up to 200in (Terrier is still too long) whereas Mk 13 is limited to 176in.

Both horizontal- and vertical-load systems are limited to loading at a fixed angle, like nineteenth century naval guns; they suffer from a dead time between loading and training into synchronisation with a missile director. For example, the Mk 10 (Terrier) requires up to 7 seconds, the M 13 up to 3.

Unlike the US Terrier and Talos, the British Seaslug employed a booster wrapped around the missile proper – in effect it traded length for diameter. Instead of a ring of missile bodies, Seaslug stowage is a string of assembled missiles, each on its own trolley, leading up to the launcher rail. Ship-impact was tremendous: much of the superstructure deck of a 'County' class missile destroyer conceals the Seaslug ready-service stowage, one line of missiles for each side of the launcher. Other missiles, not assembled, are held in a magazine. The newer Sea Dart is far neater; it is stowed vertically under its twin launcher.

Soviet practice also appears to be vertical stowage, since no horizontal structures or missile doors appear on any Soviet warship. Any further comments must be conjectural. However, the vertical stowage of a relatively large-finned weapon such as SAN-1 suggests low density. SAN-3 appears in two alternative installations, one with two and one with four loading hatches. One likely interpretation is that each hatch leads up from the edge of a separate loading ring, so that the four-hatch system has twice the capacity of the two-hatch type. The single published photograph of the SAN-3 missile appears to show a dual-thrust type comparable in concept to Tartar/Standard, but with large wings requiring either assembly (for which it is unlikely that space is available) or else low-density stowage. These observations would appear to be confirmed by published estimates of the low capacity of Soviet SAM magazines.

One of the great complications in missile stowage design is the need to be able to select particular weapons for firing. Both Talos and Terrier, for example, were produced in alternative conventional and nuclear versions, and many ships carried both. Nuclear fire, for example, was called for against formations of aircraft and in some auxiliary anti-ship and shore-bombardment roles. During the 1960s, the *Belknap*s carried four types of missile in one system: nuclear ASROC, torpedo ASROC, nuclear Terrier and conventional Terrier. Generally one of the two upper rings was devoted to a mix of Terrier and nuclear ASROC, the other to Terrier and torpedo ASROC; in this way the appropriate missile was never more than one missile away on a ring. However, in general, as the variety of missile grows,

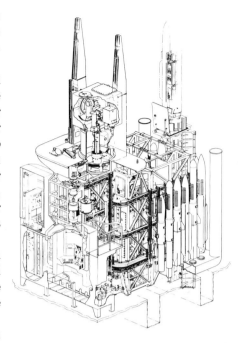

Some new US warships employ a more elaborate but more flexible system, the Mk 26, in which, as in earlier systems, the missiles move into position with their launcher. Note the strikedown hatch at the far end of one of the missile lines. The major defect of Mk 26 is that it cannot accommodate the Standard (Extended Range) missiles; the new Aegis ships, which will have 26 launchers, will not therefore be able to exploit the full potential of their fire control system. *(FMC Corporation)*

it becomes more and more awkward to have to cycle a storage system until the appropriate weapon appears. Moreover, even the fastest systems have an irreducible loading and firing cycle.

An alternative type of launcher has recently been suggested: the vertical-launch box. Missiles are stowed side by side, and each can be fired directly from its stowage position. The only limitations arise from the possibility of interference if two neighboring missiles are fired simultaneously, and from the problem of post-launch capture by the guidance system. The latter can be obviated by an autopilot such as that employed by the Standard 2 missile. Ship-impact may be more serious. For a large missile battery, the vertical box is by far the bulkiest system and the disposal of exhaust gas generated during launch must be a problem as well. On the other hand, because it does away with the heavy fixed weight of a conventional reloading system, the low-capacity vertical box is probably an ideal arrangement for small warships such as fast patrol boats. Horizontal box launchers, which have much the same virtue for small capacity, are already standard in Western point defense systems. The transition to vertical launch increases the capture problem (hence, perhaps, minimum effective SAM range) but does away with launcher training and elevation weights.

The Royal Navy's Seaslug was a rough contemporary of the US Talos and Terrier; it was very unusual in that its four booster rockets were clustered around its nose. This configuration made for a relatively compact missile, which could be stowed in tandem. Seaslug is credited with a range of over 28nm and a capability up to 50,000ft; it carries a 297lb warhead and is 19ft 8in long. By way of comparison, Terrier is 27ft 1in long with its booster and, at least in its early version, has a rather shorter range, often quoted as about 12nm. *(British Aerospace)*

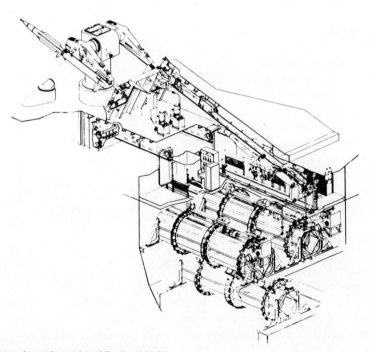

This drawing shows the combined Terrier/ASROC system installed in *Belknap* class missile frigates; up to twenty ASROCs can be carried in alternate positions in the upper two rings, with Terriers in the other positions and in the lower ring. The missile is finned in the space above the rings (one is shown in position for finning) and then rammed up on to the launcher; note the racks of missile fins alongside the finning station. *(FMC Corporation)*

Seaslug is fired from a rather elaborate twin launcher; this one is aboard HMS *Kent* (1978). Much of the complexity presumably arises from the irregular shape of the missile. Note the reload hatches in the magazine on the left. *(C & S Taylor)*

CHAPTER SEVEN

ASW since 1945

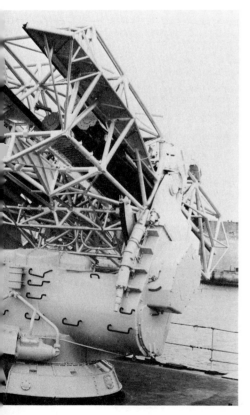

In some important ways the evolution of anti-submarine weapons since World War II has paralleled that of anti-aircraft weapons; both use sensor and guidance technology to progress towards longer ranges and to overcome problems of dead time. Much of the very considerable difference between AAW and ASW weapons can be traced to the contrast between the media in which they operate: air permits easy movement of both target and weapons at very high speed, and in addition does not impede the transmission of radio signals, which travel in very nearly straight lines. Water, however, sharply limits the speeds of submarine, torpedo, and even sinking depth charge. Although it does transmit sound fairly easily over short distances, it is not a reliable medium for long-range acoustic communication. On the other hand, even though the submarine is far larger than any airborne target, it can be damaged, even fatally, by relatively small explosive charges.

ASW differs from AAW in one other basic way. The performance of ASW sensors and weapons depends critically upon the character of the particular ocean area in which they operate. Weapons quite adequate for one Navy may fail another. Shallow water, less than 100 fathoms deep, is particularly difficult for ASW: sonar is almost always inadvertently affected by 'bottom-bounce'. Homing torpedoes may be attracted towards the mirror-images of their targets, reflected off either the surface or the sea bed. Submarines may find it useful to lie bottomed, noiseless and not readily distinguishable (at least from a torpedo's point of view) from the bottom itself. Confronted by such conditions over much of the vital sea area surrounding the British Isles, the Royal Navy chose to retain in service a relatively primitive, non-homing weapon, the AS Mortar Mk 10 ('Limbo'); the same reasoning apparently motivates European and Japanese users of similar mortars and rocket-fired depth charges.

Squid was the progenitor of the present British
'Limbo' (Mk 10) ASW weapon and the inspiration
for the US Weapon Alfa. Here the destroyer
Crossbow fires two out of a standard salvo of three
or six bombs, 28 March 1952. A typical pattern
consisted of three charges equally spaced around a
circle 140ft in diameter, each charge having a
lethal radius of about 21ft against a World War II
submarine. 'Double Squid' generally fired two
patterns, forming a hexagon, with the triangles
abotu 65ft apart vertically; 'Limbo' appears to use
the same 400lb projectile; recent unofficial
estimates are that such charges are lethal against
modern submarines out to about 5yds, and
produce shock damage of varying severity out to
about 50yds. Psychological effects, which would
not be present in the case of an unsuccesful
homing torpedo, may extend to 100yds or more.
(CPL)

Bottom left After 1945 the United States
developed its Weapon Alfa automated rocket
launcher, but retained the wartime Hedgehog,
usually in dual mountings. Here the converted
Fletcher class destroyer *Waller* fires her
Hedgehogs (August 1959).
Bottom right The US Navy also experimented
with extremely large Hedgehog patterns; one
piece of equipment under consideration would
have had 61 bombs arranged on a converted 5in
gun mount. Several destroyer escorts were rebuilt
as mobilization prototypes: USS *Tweedy*, shown
here in December 1958, was one of them. Her
battery of four launchers was probably intended to
permit a sequence of two quick attacks, since
reloading a 24-spigot Hedgehog took some
considerable time. Note that she retains six depth
charge throwers but no depth charge tracks.

The US Navy, on the other hand, expects to fight its ASW war primarily in mid-ocean, where homing weapons and even nuclear depth charges should be effective, and where sophisticated active and passive sensors may achieve reliable 'bottom-bounce' and convergence-zone performance. The US Navy did have an equivalent to 'Limbo' – Weapon Alfa – but it was ultimately replaced entirely by homing torpedoes.

HEDGEHOG, SQUID, 'LIMBO' AND WEAPON ALFA

'Limbo' and Alfa are examples of the gun school of ASW weapons; others are the wartime Hedgehog and Squid, from which they are descended, the postwar French and Italian (Menon) 12in depth charge mortars, and a variety of Bofors rocket launchers. Each has the strengths and the defects of the gun, all of which can be translated from the language of AAW. Each round is relatively inexpensive, and each has a relatively poor SSPK due to the dead or blind time which elapses between firing and arrival near the submarine, both the flight through the air and the relatively slow descent to submarine depths contributing to this. In each case multiple shots are used to generate a pattern of explosions which bracket the area in which the submarine must be, given its initial position, some estimate of its possible speed, and the elapsed dead time. The faster and deeper the submarine, the longer the range and the larger the volume in which it may be when the charges arrive. Additional dead time is contributed by the mechanics of the fire control system.

The central trade-off in such weapons is pattern size (number of projectiles) vs charge size (lethality per projectile), given a projector size limited in weight and in recoil distance by destroyer or frigate dimensions. Ideal pattern size is determined by submarine size, speed and maneuverability, as well as by the characteristics of the sonar used for fire control. For example, the size of the standard Hedgehog pattern of World War II was determined largely by submarine size and by the dead time inherent in the weapon – about 18 seconds at a range of 283yds and a depth of 200ft. During that time a 10kt U-boat could move about 300ft. The Type VII U-boat, against which Hedgehog was designed, was about 200ft long, although its vital area was much shorter. Under these circumstances, the usual Hedgehog pattern (an ellipse allowing a 195ft error in deflection, or 168ft in range, or a circle 267ft in diameter) was appropriate. Charges had to be distributed along the pattern so closely that a submarine would not be likely to pass between two of them; on the other hand, it was necessary to minimize the number of charges so as to achieve sufficient effect with each. Ultimately a 24-charge spread was chosen, which, in the circular pattern, gave a separation between charges of about 34ft; the maximum beam of a Type VII was just over 20ft, not all of which was pressure hull. However, it takes a great deal of explosive to damage a submarine from a distance. The designers of Hedgehog compromised; they used small (30lb) charges fuzed to explode only on contact. Late in the war an influence (magnetic) fuze was developed, but it was of little value, given the small size of the Hedgehog charge.

Squid was an alternative approach and used three or six much larger projectiles (12in as opposed to 7.2in, 400lb as opposed to 60lb), each so big that it could damage a submarine at some distance. The only way to achieve such near-miss explosions was time (depth) fuzing, which in turn

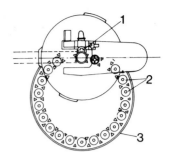

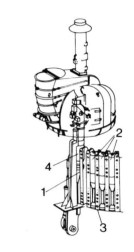

KEY	
1	Hoist lifter
2	12.75in rockets
3	Ready-service ring
4	Tube assembly

'Weapon Alfa' was the US equivalent of 'Limbo' and the ubiquitous Bofors 375mm ASW rocket. Like the postwar heavy AA guns, it was mechanically ambitious and a maintenance disaster. In theory, the entire ready-service magazine (the ring below the mount) of 22 rockets could be emptied at the rate of 12 per minute, the mount automatically forming an appropriate pattern of shots. Rocket exhaust was ducted out of the rear of the enclosed mount. Early sketches of US ASW destroyers show an unshielded triple launcher very similar to the Bofors system, but this sophisticated automatic Mk 108 launcher took some years to perfect. The Weapon Alfa program began in 1945; there was also to have been a Weapon Baker ('B' in the US phonetic alphabet) suitable for smaller craft, but its much lighter explosive charge would not have been effective against fast submarines and it was abandoned in 1946.

required a depth-finding sonar, Type 147B. Not only was Squid more effective than Hedgehog, but the Royal Navy claimed that even when its explosions produced little damage, they had a considerable effect on the morale of the crew being attacked, an effect Hedgehog could not have.

The standard single-Squid pattern was an equilateral triangle of explosions around a 140ft circle. However, the ideal installation consisted of two Squids, which produced a pair of triangles 65ft apart in depth, forming a hexagonal pattern. The heavier Squid projectile sank much faster than that of a Hedgehog, so that Squid was far more effective against really deep-diving submarines such as the Type 21. For example, the projectiles might reach the water 600yds from the firing ship in about 7.5 seconds (10 seconds for Hedgehog to reach 280yds), then sink at 40 or 45fs (compared to an average of about 25fs for Hedgehog). Although the smaller pattern of Squid might appear at first to make it less effective than Hedgehog, the depth-finding Type 147B made it possible to explode the large charges at effective distances from the submarine. Accurate depth-finding probably also improved the accuracy of Squid fire control, in a three-dimensional situation; the best proof of this is that in 1944–45 many US destroyer escorts were fitted with Type 147B sonars even though they retained their Hedgehogs.

The US Operational Evaluation Group estimated that a Hedgehog with the elliptical pattern should have had 28 per cent effectiveness against a Type VII U-boat, and that a single Squid should have had 16 per cent effectiveness, given the 21ft lethal radius of the Squid charge. The double-Squid would have a kill probability (per attack) of 26 per cent, still short of Hedgehog performance – but that performance was being calculated for a relatively shallow, slow submarine, whereas only the fast-sinking Squid could counter a deep, speedy Type 21. In fact, British operational figures suggest that the double-Squid was about 2.5 times as effective as Hedgehog by the end of the war.

The West German frigate *Köln,* built in 1958-61, is armed with two of the standard Bofors quadruple 375mm ASW rocket launchers; many French ships have a sextuple version, while Swedish, Colombian, Dutch, and Japanese ships use this one. Each launcher carries 36 projectiles, reloading automatically from the vertical position. *Köln* also has four ASW torpedo tubes. Her broad funnel proclaims her gas turbine propulsion (actually CODAG – note the air intake louvers abreast her foremast). The rest of her weapons and electronics suit is a mixture of international programs: the Franco-German 100mm gun, the Bofors 40mm AA gun, Dutch search and fire control radars, and what appears to be US Navy ECM gear; in one case the radome has been removed, perhaps for maintenance, and the radar direction-finding antenna is plainly in view (right-hand antenna). The sonar is German. *(CPL)* **Inset** The US Navy has now standardized on a single conventional surface-fired ASW weapon, the lightweight homing torpedo, versions of which are used by nearly every other friendly navy: it is fired from ASROC, dropped from helicopters, projected by Ikara or, as here, fired from a standard lightweight torpedo tube. This particular ship is the old destroyer *Newman K Perry,* photographed in June 1967.

That was certainly the way the Royal Navy saw matters, since its primary ASW weapon of the 1950s was a longer-range Squid using what appears to have been the same projectile, the AS Mortar Mk 10 ('Limbo'). Longer range, reportedly up to 2000yds, was necessary to deal with fast submarines with which an ASW ship might not be able to close. However, longer range brought its own problems. The small Squid pattern subtended a very small angle at 2000yds, only about 1.5°. For a search sonar to maintain that kind of angular accuracy while searching would reduce its search rate just at the time the rate had to increase to handle faster targets – which might well appear while the ship was concentrating on one submarine. The depth-finding broad-fan beam sonar of Squid was, therefore, replaced by a specialized pencil-beam attack sonar, Type 170, to give accurate bearing as well as depth information.

Squid and 'Limbo' had 3- or 6-charge patterns because a 3- or 6-barrelled mortar represented a kind of limit on available deck space and weight. Both were relatively slow-loading weapons, although 'Limbo' does employ a mechanical loading system. However, it is possible to divorce pattern size from launcher size, given a fast-firing launcher. The US Navy tried to achieve this result in its postwar ASW weapon, Weapon Alfa: it fired its 22-round ready-service magazine at the rate of 12 rockets per minute, while the gun-like launcher moved to form the pattern. Range limits were not quite so ambitious as those specified for 'Limbo'; for example, the Mk 2 projectile (12.75in, 500lb total weight including a 250lb charge) had a minimum range of 250yds and a maximum range of 975yds; its charges would reach a 200ft submarine at maximum range in 18.9 seconds, roughly the time it would take a Hedgehog charge to reach a similarly submerged submarine at much closer range. One reason the Navy was willing to accept a medium-range system was that it placed its faith far more on homing torpedoes than on Hedgehog or Alfa. For example, although Alfa was by far the most prominent weapon aboard early US postwar escorts such as the cruiser *Norfolk* and the *Mitschers,* in fact it was considered secondary to much less (visually) prominent fixed torpedo tubes. Its relatively large pattern, which was quite flexible in configuration, required no special attack sonar, only a depth-finder (SQG-1). Time fuzing was adopted in view of the size of the charges, although the US Navy felt that a magnetic influence fuze would be far better, and ultimately developed one.

Alfa was a very expensive system; it was the size of an automatic 5in/54 gun mount and, like many of the very advanced electro-mechanical systems of its time, it was an operational nightmare. Moreover, it was not necessary for combating anything short of a Type 21; the US Navy found it profitable to improve the performance of its Hedgehogs instead, pressing towards some really long-range system meanwhile. Hedgehog could be improved in two ways: its pattern could be enlarged and the density of charges increased, or it could be made trainable so that the burden on ship maneuver, important in combat against a fast submarine, might decrease. Both approaches were tried. Most US destroyers and many destroyer escorts were refitted with dual Hedgehogs, one on either side of the bridge, to give a 48-charge pattern. Some specialist ASW ships were provided with a single trainable Mk 14 or 15 Hedgehog, which produced a circular (279ft) pattern at a range of about 265yds. A few destroyer escorts were rebuilt as prototype ASW ships, with as many as four Hedgehogs mounted together, to give, alternatively, a very heavy pattern or the option of two attacks in very quick succession: the standard Mk 10 or 11 Hedgehog required three minutes to reload, the Mk 15 five minutes. A 61-charge projector (Mk 17) was designed, but never tested.

The NATO navies each adopted a long-range ASW projector, generally multi-barrelled. The earliest was developed by Bofors for the Netherlands Navy from 1948 onwards; it fires a 500lb rocket (375mm) to a range as great as 4000yds in its current version, although the original maximum range was only about 900yds. All versions reload automatically, but that does not necessarily mean that the launcher fires a salvo larger than the number of tubes it has. For example, the 4-barrelled type fires one of its rounds every second. It holds eight rounds on the rocket table below the launcher, but reload time is three minutes for all four rounds. Even France adopted a version of the rocket launcher in place of her earlier 12in mortar, presumably because rockets apply far less stress to the firing ship and so impose far less ship-impact. The earliest example of this home truth was the US decision to develop a rocket, Mousetrap, which could be fitted to small craft, and yet give them the same ahead-throwing capability as the larger Hedgehog mortar – whose recoil force was 40 *tons*.

From a conceptual point of view, these stand-off weapons are not really very different from the original depth charge, except that in the earlier case it was an ASW ship which carried the explosives to the point at which they hit the water, rather than a rocket. The depth-charge pattern was always predicated on possible submarine movement during the 'dead time' from the beginning of the run, a dead time due both to sonar inefficiency at high ship speed and to the usual loss of contact as the ship neared the submarine. Compared to a mortar such as Hedgehog or Squid, a destroyer was much slower but could dash over a greater distance. Of course, her acceleration signalled the submarine to begin evasion. Dead time was so great and the number of depth charges so small that direct hits were grossly unlikely; SSPK was increased to a useful level by the use of very large explosive charges in quick-sinking packages which in turn produced enough noise to make difficult any new contact after the attack – let alone an evaluation of the effect of the first. As in the case of the mortars, the ideal depth-charge fuze was an influence fuze (proximity fuze) which would make full use of the explosive content of the depth charge by detonating it not where the ship sonar estimated the submarine might be, but within lethal range of the submarine. Such an influence fuze would also reduce the noise of an attack – although it would also reduce the moral value of near misses. The US Navy tried to develop both acoustic and magnetic influence fuzes during World War II and actually adopted at least the magnetic type postwar, but apparently neither was successful enough to overcome the low inherent efficiency of the depth charge attack – an inefficiency traceable to the dead time problem.

HOMING TORPEDOES

As in AAW, the alternative to the low-SSPK gun was a high-SSPK guided missile, in this case an underwater missile (torpedo). Like a SAM, the torpedo trades off large numbers of rounds (and an expensive launcher) in favor of lower direct ship-impact and a more sophisticated weapon. Low underwater speeds (which reduce the need for a high data rate) and the relatively large diameter of torpedoes make self-homing far more attractive than full command guidance, although many homing torpedoes enjoy some degree of mid-course command guidance. Even so, the diameter of a

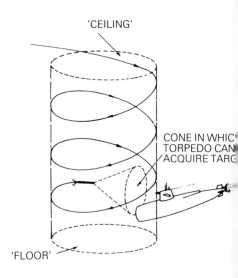

A typical homing torpedo path, showing the 'lethal volume' in which the torpedo can acquire its target. The 'ceiling' represents the depth at which the torpedo search begins; the 'floor' is the present lowest search depth. In some cases, the torpedo begins another spiral when it reaches its 'floor' depth.

ASROC is the current US Navy stand-off weapon; here one is fired by the missile escort *Brooke*, 15 May 1969. Note the modular construction of the launcher, and the boom on the superstructure for replenishment at sea. Later escorts carry reload rounds below the bridge. At about 5nm maximum range, ASROC seems ill-matched to current sonars; projects for Extended Range ASROC have not, however, succeeded.

torpedo limits the size of the sonar, active or passive, which it can carry. In order to achieve sufficient bearing discrimination, it must operate at high frequency, and in any case torpedo dimensions limit onboard sonar power – and range. The torpedo, then, is unlikely to detect (acquire) its target at much more than a few hundred yards. For example, to overcome noise an active torpedo sonar probably must employ a high pulse rate, which limits its maximum range. The size of its effective field of view is likely to be related to the angle through which the torpedo can turn once it detects a target to one side, surely little more than 20° or 30° and probably far less.

Passive sonar was the earliest means of homing torpedo guidance; if the target is noisy, it can be detected by even a primitive listening device at a great range, and bearing information improves as the torpedo closes its target. However, the passive homing torpedo is subject to counter-measures which can lure it away from its target, and in addition it tends to hit the submarine aft, where it may be able to destroy its mobility but is unlikely to destroy it completely. Moreover, if the passive torpedo approaches a submarine from ahead, it may not sense the submarine at all because most propeller noise is radiated aft.

Active homing, on the other hand, has a shorter inherent range because of power and size limitations in the torpedo. However, it is effective from a bow aspect and, perhaps more importantly, it permits the design of a weapon which attacks the submarine broadside-on. The main counter-measure is sound-absorbing material on the outside of a submarine, which may reduce effective sonar range to the point where the active torpedo never acquires its target. Many current homing torpedoes are described as active-passive weapons, combining both forms of guidance, and using passive homing for initial acquisition.

The launch profile of ASROC, the US Navy's stand-off ASW weapon. When a depth charge payload is carried, the parachute is not employed.

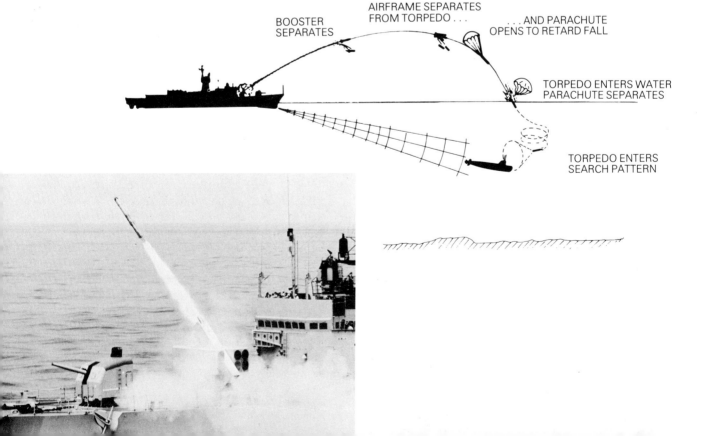

BOOSTER SEPARATES

AIRFRAME SEPARATES FROM TORPEDO . . .

. . . AND PARACHUTE OPENS TO RETARD FALL

TORPEDO ENTERS WATER PARACHUTE SEPARATES

TORPEDO ENTERS SEARCH PATTERN

Both forms of homing are affected by the noise the torpedo itself generates, both 'self-noise' due to its propellers and flow noise around its body. In fact at very shallow depths a torpedo might conceivably begin to home on the 'image' of its own sound reflected off the surface of the water; a similar problem might arise near the bottom in very deep water. Torpedo speed, then, can only be bought at the expense either of homing range or of additional guidance sophistication which may overcome a noisier weapon. Moreover, torpedo noise alerts the target ship, which may then have more time to take evasive action, eg to use decoys. No matter what the speed edge of torpedo over submarine, if the torpedo is detected at a great enough range, the submarine can outrun it; and, given the fixed internal volume of the torpedo, for any particular system of propulsion higher speed must be bought at the expense of range – out to the target area, searching, and pursuing the target.

Most of the water resistance the torpedo encounters is frictional: the greater the surface area of the torpedo, the more shp per pound of its weight it requires to move at a given speed. The larger the torpedo, in general, the less surface area it presents per cubic foot of internal volume – per cubic foot of warhead, electronics or powerplant. In particular, the longer the torpedo in relation to its diameter, the worse the problem, which is why small-diameter lightweight torpedoes are quite short in relation to their calibers.

Typically, a shipborne homing torpedo travels some pre-set 'run-out' distance before it begins its search. For at least part of this distance its homing mechanism is turned off to prevent it from homing on the launch ship. Often there is also a pre-set 'ceiling' as a further safety measure. Once the torpedo has been 'enabled' and has run out to the expected location of its target, it begins to search, generally in a descending spiral pattern, the size of which depends upon its acquisition range, maneuverability and field of view. For example, a typical torpedo might be able to attack any submarine target it encounters within a cone 200yds long and with a cone total angle (field of view) of 20°, ie about 100ft up or down or to either side. Against a 300ft submarine, such a torpedo would describe a spiral about 500ft in diameter, descending at such a rate that successive parallel parts of the spiral were about 200ft apart (vertically). It would dive to some set 'floor', and then, if it still had power left and had not yet encountered its target, rise into a second spiral, or a third. The better the torpedo sonar, the larger the search spiral and the faster the search; for example, the torpedo need complete fewer full circles between ceiling and floor.

Search speed and acquisition range together determine the probability that the searching torpedo will actually find a submarine passing through its search volume. Torpedo endurance (and speed) determines just how many vertical spirals it can search, and the extent to which it can convert acquisition into attack, since after it acquires the target it must still pursue and hit it. As in the case of the SAM, the pursuing torpedo is condemned to a line-of-sight course which requires it to make more radical maneuvers than its target, a course which is useless without a very considerable speed edge or the ability to endure a long stern chase. For example, a 30kt homing torpedo pursuing a 25kt submarine closes only 5nm each hour – only about 170yds per minute. It therefore takes about three minutes (1.5nm) for the torpedo to close 500yds, if it begins the chase in the most favorable possible position – which is unlikely, and which is why most homing torpedoes have much higher speeds. In fact, nearly all torpedo attacks on submarines, even those guided by active sonar, end in tail chases, and even a small speed advantage on the part of the submarine can exhaust the torpedo, which may have only a 10- or 15-minute life *in toto*, including search time.

The homing torpedo behaves much like a depth charge with a lethal volume several hundred yards across and several hundred feet deep, a volume quite comparable with the lethal volume of a nuclear depth charge. In fact, at least in the US ASROC system, there are alternative nuclear depth charge and homing torpedo warheads. The primary advantage of the nuclear weapon is that it is resistant to counter-measures: electronic warfare has no effect on several kilotons going off nearby, and pre-set like a giant 'Limbo' bomb. On the other hand, nuclear weapons tend not to be released in most wars that navies can imagine fighting, and, moreover, they can have unfortunate effects if detonated near one's own ship – indeed, much of the early impetus for US Navy shock protection was resistance to the effects of their own ship- and air-delivered nuclear depth charges. In a more mundane vein, the early US lightweight (short range) homing torpedoes, such as the Mk 32, were conceived very much as replacements for the old-fashioned depth charge, and actually replaced depth charges, weight for weight, aboard many escorts in the 1950s.

Like a depth charge, the homing torpedo must still be brought into the presumed neighborhood of its target before it can become effective; on the other hand its large lethal volume makes it an attractive payload for very long range stand-off weapons with their large inherent dead times. In this sense ASROC is the true successor to a weapon like Alfa, except that the large number of individual depth charges is replaced by a single one of much greater individual efficacy. This is particularly obvious for the version of ASROC carrying a nuclear depth charge.

In fact no matter what its built-in range, the autonomous homing torpedo is inherently a short-range weapon, simply because its run-out (to search area) time, ie its own dead time, is relatively long. The practical torpedo speed limit is well below 60kts. Even at that rate, it takes a torpedo about three minutes to run out to, say, 6000yds – during which a target submarine (at, say, 20kts) can travel 2000yds, almost certainly well beyond the torpedo search pattern. Thus for a 60kt torpedo with a 500yd search spiral attacking a 20kt submarine, effective range may be less than 1500yds, depending upon how fast the torpedo passes through its first spiral to begin its second.

Sonar on the ship launching the torpedo can help solve the dead time problem: command guidance during run-out can make long homing torpedo range worthwhile. The only reliable command system yet devised is wire guidance: the torpedo trails a long thin wire. Its success in surface ship applications has been mixed, since the trailing wire is difficult to deploy from a maneuvering ship. For example, the US Navy planned to fire the big wire-guided Mk 48 torpedo from fixed stern tubes aboard several classes of ships, including *Knox* class frigates. At that time the Mk 48 was the only ship-launched weapon whose range was compatible with that of the big new SQS-26 sonar, but the project proved impracticable. It may have been abandoned partly because of the advent of LAMPS*. At present the only US application of torpedo wire guidance is aboard submarines.

*LAMPS (Light Airborne Multi-Purpose System) is the US Navy's manned ASW helicopter, armed with homing torpedoes and quite capable of attack at SQS-26 range. It carries sonobuoys and a Magnetic Anomaly Detector (MAD) to permit target localization; indeed, its ability to search for a submarine not well localized by the ship sonar makes it superior to the Mk 48.

Top left The French Navy developed its own range of ASW weapons and sensors, culminating, perhaps, in the specialized *corvette Aconit*. She is roughly the size of a US *Knox* class frigate, and has a similar performance on a single screw, which the French found disappointing. Her anchor position right forward indicates a bow sonar dome, and a big turret just abaft her 100mm gun houses the French 305mm ASW mortar/shore bombardment weapon, its four barrels being muzzle-loaded from the small glacis before it. *Aconit* was intended, too, as an air control ship and so has a three-dimensional radar (DRBV-13, in the radome) and a big air search radar aft (22A) as well as a mast atop her single funnel devoted to ECM. Amidships is a launcher for the French Malafon torpedo-carrying missile, with 13 reloads housed in the after superstructure, there are two 'catapults' for a total of eight homing torpedoes, and a VDS is fitted aft. *Aconit* was to have been the prototype for a series of French escorts, but she proved too small and lacked the desired characteristics. *(French Navy)*

Top right *De Grasse* is typical of the new French escorts, armed only with stand-off weapons: Malafon amidships, and helicopters (which consume much of the ship's length) aft; there are also two catapults for ASW torpedoes, six box launchers for Exocet surface-to-surface missiles (amidships, just visible), and a Crotale point defense SAM (not yet installed when this photograph was taken). The bow anchor indicates the usual French bow sonar, and there is a VDS on deck aft. This ship was developed from the *Aconit* design; note the deletion of the three-dimensional radar of the earlier ship. *(Official)*

ASW MISSILES

Stand-off weapons have proven far more successful. As in the case of the torpedo, the choice is between a simple unguided weapon with a relatively long dead time and a longer-range guided weapon whose effective dead time is far shorter. Since dead time equates to the area of uncertainty within which the submarine is likely to be located, the weapon system must match its dead time to the lethal volume of the homing (or nuclear) weapon it ultimately drops on the submarine.

At present ASROC, the Soviet FRAS-1, and the submarine-launched SUBROC (and perhaps the Soviet SSN-15) are the only operational unguided ASW stand-off missiles. Effective ASROC range is limited by the performance of the weapon it carries, and by the dead time associated with its own relatively low speed. Thus ASROC succeeded the very similar RAT (Rocket-Assisted Torpedo) which, however, carried the Mk 43 homing torpedo and consequently was limited to 5000yds – which was appropriate in view of the performance of the then standard SQS-4 ship sonar. The new SQS-23 promised 10,000yds under most circumstances, and the new Mk 44 torpedo offered a commensurate improvement over the Mk 43: ASROC/Mk 44 replaced RAT in the US ASW program and was mounted in many SQS-23 ships. A longer-range ASROC (18,000yds) was proposed in the early 1960s, presumably to take advantage of improvements in the new Mk 46 torpedo. It has never materialized, and now probably never will, given the success of the far more flexible LAMPS.

Command guidance for the torpedo-carrier promises longer range, since weapon course can be controlled by the ship sonar almost throughout the flight – given, however, the vital caveat that, as ranges increase, the slow speed of sound through water always gives that sonar an obsolete picture of the current stituation. Moreover, at very long ranges sonar data may be somewhat ambiguous. For example, the convergence zone is just too diffuse for convergence-zone 'pings' to be useful for fire control. Even so, several navies have adopted command guidance in the form of a guided missile which can drop a homing torpedo: Australia (Ikara), France (Malafon), and the Soviet Union (SSN-14). In each case the trade-off is weapon range vs ship-impact. ASROC is a simple ballistic rocket with small fins, but the command-guided torpedo-carrying missiles are relatively complex in themselves, requiring substantial wings – and elaborate loading systems and, moreover, almost SAM-like guidance. For example, the large French ASW frigates of the *Tourville* type carry only thirteen Malafons, whereas the much smaller US FRAM *Gearing*s carried eight weapons in the

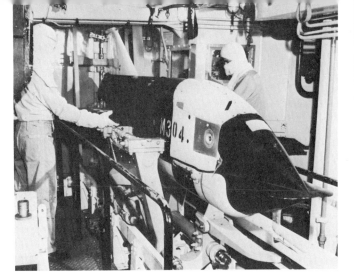

launcher plus, probably, at least as many reloads. There must be some question as to the value of such long range, given the vagaries of very long range sonar performance. For example, SSN-14 has a reported maximum range of 20nm. Ikara range is reportedly only about 10nm, and Malafon's is even less; each seems a high price to pay for so little improvement over a relatively simple weapon such as ASROC.

On the other hand, a really long range ASW weapon can be useful when detection and even localization are achieved by some means other than long-range sonar, such as detection of enemy radar and radio signals or, alternatively, the sonar of another ship or a sonobuoy field laid by an airplane.

The United States adopted an unusual command-guided ASW missile – DASH, or Drone Anti-Submarine Helicopter. DASH was conceived as a very flexible system with low ship-impact; for a time it was to have become the primary US ASW system. ASROC was retained in some ships only because it was capable of all-weather operation. This decision proved most fortunate when DASH failed; FRAM Mk II destroyers equipped only with DASH, a long-range torpedo tube (which also proved less than successful) and short-range weapons were effectively disarmed at least as regards combat with modern fast submarines. Ironically, they were the only US ASW ships equipped on a large scale with VDS, and in consequence VDS, which is most useful as a long-range sensor, was partially discredited within the US fleet.

Top left Ikara is a torpedo-carrying stand-off weapon developed by the Australian government, and currently mounted also in some British and Brazilian ships. Like Malafon and unlike ASROC, it is command-guided, and so suffers no 'dead time' from launch through water impact; indeed, Ikara can be guided by a ship other than the one which launches it, and so has (at least in theory) a very long potential reach. *(British Aerospace)*

Top right ASW weapons are not limited to what used to be called the major powers. The Brazilian frigates *Defensora* (foreground) and *Niteroi* are an ASW version of the British commercial Vosper-Thornycroft Mk 10 frigate. The small launcher aft fires Ikara (here in a version called Branik), and a single helicopter (Lynx) is accommodated above it, with a pair of Seacat point defense missiles, radar controlled, above the small hangar. The large stack and extensive intakes indicate CODAG propulsion, with the small diesel exhausts emerging from the bank of gas turbine intake louvers. Ikara is controlled using a radar under the small radome atop the bridge, as on converted British frigates. There is also a twin-barreled version of the Bofors 375mm ASW mortar in 'B' position, and a pair of triple lightweight torpedo tubes. The cut in the transom aft accommodates a VDS. In this photograph of the ship at speed, the pattern of the water around the transom stern is particularly evident; note the exposed area. *(Vosper Thornycroft)*

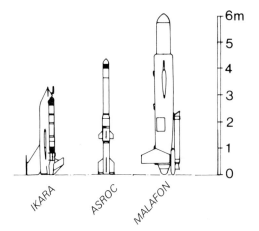

Comparative profiles of ship-launched anti-submarine missiles. ASROC (reported range about 6nm) is unguided but can carry Mk 44 or Mk 46 torpedo or depth charge payloads; the Australian-originated Ikara (10-12nm) and French Malafon (7nm) are command-guided and carry only homing torpedoes.

DASH was re-usable, and so required only a small hangar plus magazine space for its lightweight torpedoes – which were the same torpedoes the ship could fire over the side from her lightweight triple tubes. It was inherently limited in range by its ship sonar and by its line-of-sight (horizon-limited) control system: DASH was tracked by its ship's search radar, with a one-way radio link (no feedback) for control. Unfortunately it was difficult to correlate radar and sonar pictures in the CIC (Combat Information Center); proposals for longer-range DASH generally included a radar/sonar marker buoy that the helicopter could drop as a reference point visible on both radar and sonar screens. DASH failed operationally, but that appears in retrospect largely as a failure of training and maintenance due ultimately to a lack of enthusiasm in the fleet. Its more fundamental failure was that it was not an all-weather system, nor could it react quickly to a nearby submarine. Slow reaction was not too serious a problem as long as the submarine had to close the force or convoy the DASH ship was protecting before it could attack, since such an approach would be comparatively slow, given relative convoy and submarine speeds. However, it became unacceptable with the advent of long-range submarine-fired missiles, probably the underwater-fired SSN-7 in particular. Any effective counter to a Soviet 'Charlie' class submarine so armed would have to occur well outside DASH range, at the convergence zone or beyond.

THE ROLE OF THE HELICOPTER

The Royal Navy adopted what amounted to a manned DASH in its MATCH (Manned Torpedo Carrying Helicopter) system. Perhaps the greatest single advantage its manned helicopter had was that when DASH was designed and built remote control systems did not have the capacity to handle properly anything as complex as a helicopter – which is suggested by the lack of a feedback channel in the DASH control system. The manned helicopter was also more flexible, and could accept a greater range of control-ship maneuvers. MATCH was originally conceived because the Type 177 sonar introduced in the 'Tribal' class frigates (to replace the 174 of the first postwar generation) exceeded the potential of 'Limbo'; it is described unofficially, for example, as a 6600yd (in layer) sensor, whereas 174 had a range of only about 2700yds. It was probably a British equivalent of the US medium-frequency SQS-4.

Systems similar to MATCH, sometimes linked to rather more powerful sonars, can be seen aboard many Italian and Soviet ships. However, developments in helicopter design made it possible for a considerably more powerful helicopter to fit aboard platforms not too much larger than those required for MATCH. For example, although the 'Tribal', *Whitby, Rothesay,* and *Leander* classes are all limited to the single-seat lightweight Westland Wasp helicopter, the newer Type 42 *(Sheffield)* class destroyer and the new Type 21 and 22 class frigates can all accommodate the much more effective Lynx, which can carry its own sensors in addition to the usual homing torpedoes or, now, Sea Skua anti-ship missiles. The Lynx can carry either classification or localisation sensors, such as MAD (Magnetic Anomaly Detector), to confirm a submarine contact and improve accuracy to the point where homing torpedoes are most effective; or it can carry out a limited search of its own using a lightweight dipping sonar. In this sense it is similar in concept to the US LAMPS. The Lynx is an Anglo-French project, and also equips modern French ASW ships.

The US Navy has found ASROC rather heavy, so the DASH drone helicopter was developed to provide ships which could not accommodate ASROC with a stand-off capacity; at one time optimism ran so high that it was proposed that ASROC be eliminated entirely. Fortunately the latter was retained as an all-weather system. In the US Navy DASH proved very largely a failure, although its record in the Japanese Navy was better. Here one operates from the *Fletcher* class escort *Nicholas,* in February 1965.

The Royal Navy introduced a lightweight manned helicopter which performed much the same role as DASH. This is a Westland Wasp aboard a British frigate, probably *Juno.* Note the quadruple Seacat launcher with its director above the hangar. *(Ambrose Greenway)*

In practice the US solution to the stand-off problem has been a manned helicopter with some independent search capacity – LAMPS. Most Western navies adopted similar solutions, the variations being concerned chiefly with the size of the helicopter and its ability to search: some helicopters, such as the Westland Wasp, are little more than manned versions of DASH. Here a LAMPS helicopter (Seasprite) operates with the escort *Harold E Holt*, April 1972. The LAMPS data-link atop the ship's mast receives data from the helicopter, which can drop and monitor sonobuoys. A computer on board ship processes this data and assist the helicopter (which is also equipped with MAD gear) to close the submarine.

MATCH and DASH are inherently limited by the performance ambiguities of ship sonars, which is why even the MATCH-like version of the recent Lynx has its own classification and localisation sensors. In particular, as range increases, so does the difference between local sonar conditions and those at the ship. It follows that there is some considerable advantage to an ASW helicopter which carries its own sonar, even though such a helicopter is of necessity quite large. Such a system is indispensable for a convergence-zone sonar, in view of the diffuse character of the convergence zone, but it is also very useful at much shorter ranges. The Royal Navy introduced the first such helicopter in its 'County' class missile destroyers. These ships were already so large, thanks to the ship impact of the Seaslug SAM, that even the big Wessex helicopter with its dipping sonar had little additional impact on the overall design.

That was not the case in the Canadian Navy, which begain operating large helicopters from its 2700-ton frigates in the early 1960s. One peculiarly Canadian problem was that these ships had to operate in extremely rough water; the Canadians solved it by suspending a line from the helicopter, and catching it in the center of the helicopter deck by means of what they called a 'bear trap'; once the helicopter is secured in this fashion it can be winched down and then lashed on deck or moved into a hangar. Even so, it appears that the Canadian Navy considered the 2700-ton hull far too constricted; one Canadian officer remarked in the 1960s that only with the advent of helicopters did hull length begin to become critical. When the *Iroquois*

Above On a ship just about the size of the US *Dealey,* the Japanese were able to accommodate a similar gun battery (a DASH *Dealey* had only one of her twin 3in/50 mounts, and a twin 40mm gun aft, as here), the usual Mk 32 torpedo tubes – and ASROC – as well as a hull sonar, probably bow-mounted, and a VDS aft. This vessel, *Tokachi* (4 July 1976) is one of a class which is the smallest in the world to mount ASROC. *(USN Official by courtesy of Norman Polmar)*

Right The *Knox* class frigate *Pharris*, on 25 May 1978 at Portsmouth. Note her enlarged telescopic hangar, partly extended, and the VDS gear streamed from the cut in her transom stern. The US VDS 'fish' is also used to stream the new passive towed array (SQR-18). The small dish above the hangar is part of a satellite communication system; a similar dish is mounted on the ship's bridge.

Left For a small ship, the helicopter is the only acceptable very long range ASW system, here exemplified by the small Agusta-Bell AB 204B aboard the Italian frigate *Carabiniere*. The remainder of her ASW capability resides in her single Italian Menon mortar, forward, and in her pair of triple lightweight ASW torpedo tubes. Her sonar suit approximates to that of a US FRAM II destroyer: SQS-29 and the SQA-10 VDS body. The big air search radar is a US SPS-12, and the smaller (multi-purpose) radar is the Italian SPQ-2. In a ship this small, length is at a premium, and the only way to provide sufficient hangar space is to make the hangar telescopic: here it is partly extended. At 2700 tons fully loaded, this ship is midway between the US *Dealey* and the *Knox* classes. *(G Arra)*

(DDH280) class was designed, such considerations dictated a much larger hull, over 4200 tons fully loaded. Part of the problem was that the small converted ships could provide hangarage for only a single Sea King helicopter, whereas two were required to keep one operational at all times.

Helicopter size, hence ship-impact, is determined very largely by the load it must carry, ie by the performance of its sonar. Modern disposable sonobuoys are far lighter, but given sufficient signal processing a sonobuoy field can perform much the same role as a large dipping sonar. The US Navy was able to adopt a relatively small ASW helicopter, LAMPS, because it was willing to accept a combination of sonobuoys and MAD, even for searches over large areas in the convergence zone. The result has such low ship-impact that ships designed for DASH can be refitted to take LAMPS. It is essential if the very long range of the new towed arrays, or even of SQS-26, is to be exploited at all.

Most ASW ships, then, incorporate at least some helicopter facilities, but the helicopters they carry provide non-ASW potential perhaps largely unforeseen when the ships were designed. A properly equipped helicopter does extend a ship's effective horizon, eg against other ships, although by its presence it alerts those other ships to the presence of its own. It can even carry an anti-ship weapon, using its superior vantage to fire at a target for which its own ship is over the horizon.

CHAPTER EIGHT

Anti-ship Missiles

Specialized surface-to-surface or anti-ship missiles (SSMs) are a relatively recent addition to Western warships. That their role is secondary is proclaimed by the fact that in many cases a major selling point is the limited extent to which they encroach upon those functions, ASW and AAW, for which ships are primarily designed. Most SSMs appear, at least superficially, to be far more autonomous in their operation than are SAMs or even homing torpedoes; consequently it often seems that the problem of marrying a small SSM such as Exocet to an existing warship is a relatively trivial one. After all, in most cases, once the SSM is on its way the launching ship need maintain no connection with it; in fact, in the development of Harpoon this 'fire and forget' mode of operation was counted a major advantage and proponents of a data link between missile and launcher were soundly defeated.

THE PROBLEM OF TARGETING

However, the major problem in an SSM *system* is not the missile or its terminal homing but rather targeting – the recognition of suitable targets and their approximate location for fire control purposes. Almost all SSMs have ranges which bring them over the horizon, out of range of normal shipboard sensors. Many ships which carry impressive SSM batteries do not carry even helicopters, and in most cases ASW helicopters are far too busy running down submarine contacts to maintain a kind of standing patrol over an SSM ship. However, without some means of targeting for over-the-horizon combat, the range built into the SSM is useless, and indeed the missile may be unusable – particularly if an opponent has thought through the over-the-horizon problem, as the Soviets have. These problems are only exacerbated by the small size of most Western SSM batteries, which in turn is a consequence of the secondary role accorded the SSM.

An Israel Aircraft Industries Gabriel destroys the ex-British destroyer *Yaffo* with its 330lb warhead. Gabriel was the victor in several engagements between Israeli and Arab missile boats in the 1973 Middle East War; *Yaffo* was the sister of the first warship to be sunk by an anti-ship missile, the destroyer *Eilat. (IAI)*

Modern anti-ship missiles are considerably larger than the naval shells of earlier wars. They tend to strike above the waterline because they generally home on the centroid of a radar picture of the target ship. Here a Harpoon strikes the ex-destroyer USS *Haraden* in a 1976 test. This particular missile is designed to explode inside a target ship, destroying at least the compartment it enters and probably one of the bulkheads closing it off; in a small ship such damage may cause extensive flooding and may even break the vessel in half. Harpoon has a nominal range of 60nm and is credited with a 510lb warhead.

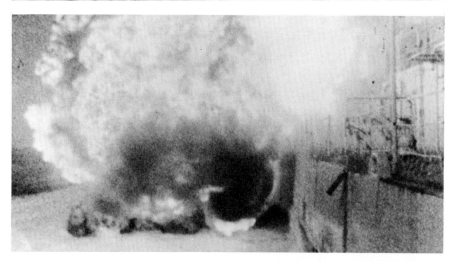

Contact explosion is an alternative fuzing mode. Here an air-launched Condor, with a 630lb linear shaped-charge warhead, bursts against the former escort USS *Vammen* in a February 1971 test. A shaped charge can generally penetrate several times its diameter in armor steel, but on the other hand its penetrating jet of hot metal may do little damage unless it meets flammable material within a ship. The big Soviet anti-ship missiles, designed to sink Western capital ships, employ large shaped-charge warheads and are liquid-fueled: generally enough fuel remains as the missile strikes to start large fires, especially where the warhead penetrates.

The *Vammen* was almost broken in half by the explosion; her single funnel vanished completely. It may be argued that modern warships are considerably larger and much tougher; they are not, after all, thirty years old. Photographs like this one are often used to prove the destructive power of modern anti-ship missiles, but it is well to keep in mind the limited radius of destruction caused even by a relatively large warhead. Condor was television-guided and so could be sent into the most sensitive part of the target, but in practice a radar-guided missile might well home on the highly reflective corners presented by a complex superstructure. Its net effect on the fighting ability of the ship would then depend, perhaps, on the extent to which subtle effects such as shock put central computers out of action, or the extent to which fragments cut waveguides and vital electrical circuits. In some cases, weapons far from the hit might well remain quite effective.

1 The Soviets were the first to employ ship-to-ship missiles on a large scale. This 'Krupny'-class 'rocket ship' fired the SSN-1 missile, codenamed 'Scrubber' in the West, and called Strella (Arrow) by the Soviets; it was a straight-winged air-breather with a maximum range of about 130nm, but was generally limited to horizon range by its command guidance system. The small helipad right aft may have been intended to take a helicopter for over-the-horizon guidance, but apparently that was not practical, and Strella was generally controlled by the standard Soviet destroyer gun director atop the bridgework. The big box magazines reportedly held ten missiles each, and the hangars atop the launch rails fore and aft, were used to warm up the missile's jet engine. The eight 'Krupnys' were the first Soviet warships built from the keel up for missile warfare; they were laid down in 1958 and 1959. SSN-1 proved less than successful, and all eight vessels have been converted into 'Kanins', with no SSMs but a twin SAM launcher aft.

2 With the advent of ship-to-ship missiles it is possible to build general-purpose frigates without large guns. This is HMS *Broadsword,* the prototype British Type 22 frigate, armed with the Exocet SSM, the Seawolf point defense missile, and (not visible) triple lightweight torpedo tubes and two Lynx ASW (and anti-ship) helicopters. Gun armament is limited to two 40mm guns for 'junk bashing' – for attacking targets too insignificant to be worth a missile. In practice a Type 22 might well work in conjunction with an Ikara-equipped *Leander,* providing anti-missile defense (Seawolf) as well as anti-ship protection. Only two of the four Exocets have as yet been installed: it is striking that, although Western naval tactics differ markedly from those of the Soviets, both blocs employ non-reloading box launchers for SSMs. However, Exocet differs from Soviet long-range SSMs in that it is autonomous: *Broadsword* fires, but the missile finds its own target. Visible on the foremast is, at the masthead, the 967/968 radar used for Seawolf search and target acquisition; a Type 1006 high definition surface search antenna is mounted below it. Radar 910, for Seawolf control, is visible atop the bridge, and a SCOT satellite communications antenna is visible abeam the foremast. Corvus is mounted at the 01 level abeam the bridge, with single Bofors guns further aft. *(Yarrow)*

3 HMS *Alacrity* shows a more typical Exocet installation, this time in conjunction with a Vickers 4.5in automatic gun forward. She is one of eight Type 21 frigates designed jointly by Vosper Thornycroft and Yarrow, and is somewhat smaller than the Brazilian Vosper Thornycroft Mk 10 frigates. These ships use an Italian fire control radar (RTN-10X) to control both the gun and the Seacat on the helicopter hangar aft; plans to fit Seawolf were abandoned in view of the topheaviness already evident – Seawolf would have required the deletion of Exocet. In this 1977 view *Alacrity* has all her radars (992Q target indication or short range air and surface search, and 978 surface search/navigation) but the two platforms just before her large (gas turbine/COGOG) funnel for SCOT antennas are empty. She reportedly has the full RN sonar fit (162, 170B, 174 and 184) but her ASW weaponry is limited to lightweight torpedo tubes and a single Lynx helicopter. *Broadsword* has two of the latter. *(C & S Taylor)*

4 Exocet must be the most successful anti-ship missile in the world, from the point of view of sales and installations. It was developed in 1970–72 by using such proven components as the aerodynamics of the AS-30 air-to-surface missile, the motor of the Martel air-to-surface television-guided missile, and the guidance of the Kormoran air-launched anti-ship missile. First firing was in July 1970. Exocet carries a 330lb hexolite/steel block warhead over a range of about 25nm; later versions will range up to 43nm. There are also air- and land-launched versions. Probably the main drawback is weight, about 1600lb compared to 1470lb for a Harpoon which has more

4

than twice the reach and a much heavier warhead. Part of the difference is that Harpoon employs a turbojet, whereas Exocet is a rocket which must carry with it both fuel and oxidizer. On the other hand, Exocet skims the sea surface at Mach 1, whereas Harpoon is subsonic (Mach 0.85). It now appears that Harpoon will capture much of the present anti-ship missile market simply because of the lower ship-impact it represents, not to mention its compatibility with existing Standard SAM (Mk 13) launchers. *(French Navy)*

Quite possibly the blind spot regarding targeting in many Western navies is a consequence of the fact that these same navies were, until recently, much more in the business of defeating SSM attacks than in mounting them. They were engaged in building up defenses, both electronic counter-measures and anti-missile guns and missiles, to make it difficult for Soviet SSMs to attack their valuable ships; surely the real problems in SSM design were problems of overcoming such terminal defenses. Since the Soviets appeared to find SSMs quite useful and did not say very much about the targeting problem, many Western naval officers never really thought it through; it was, moreover, very abstract compared to the concrete problem of making a missile fly and home properly. It is possible that analysis of warhead effects, ie of what the missile actually does at the far end of its flight, suffered a similar fate in the Western navies.

The targeting problem is threefold. First, a captain wants to be alerted when a potential target enters missile range; he needs warning. Second, he needs classification: it will not do to waste all four Exocets, for example, on a merchant ship when an enemy missile corvette is also in the neighborhood. This point is often dismissed as soft-headedness or excessive concern with the rules of warfare, a peacetime luxury. That would be so if the captain of the average Western warship had, say, forty SSMs. He usually has four or six – and they are generally mounted topside, in low-ship-impact box launchers which cannot be reloaded outside a naval base. Moreover, those SSMs are relatively small, to minimize ship-impact; it probably takes more than one to kill a big Soviet surface warship. It seems unlikely that the average captain will fire unless he is pretty sure of what he is facing. Finally, the missile itself imposes some standard of location of the target. That may not be a very stiff standard; for example, many self-homing SSMs have a homing mode in which they search continuously to either side of a line of bearing directed towards a target. Once the missile is away, the captain needs a fourth piece of information: he needs some means of evaluating the attack he has made, again because his weapons are precious and should not be wasted.

These are not trivial problems, and there is no standard textbook solution. However, there are a variety of sensors aboard many Western warships which, properly used, may help. First, sonar is in effect an over-the-horizon sensor. All sonar operators curse surface traffic because the noise of surface ships drowns out much of what they want to hear, even at great distances. However, that noise is itself a means of detecting those surface ships at great (over the horizon) ranges, a fact very well known to submariners who do it all the time. Moreover, surface ships have quite distinctive acoustic signatures, which can be collected in peacetime and then used, at least to some extent, for wartime identification. For a single ship, such passive acoustics give only a line of bearing, although knowledge of the sonar environment in the area and of the usual intensity of the ship signature being observed may make for a rough range estimate as well. However, two ships can use their sonars to triangulate a target. Probably the single greatest drawback to the use of passive sonar for target observation is that it is easy for the signature of any one ship to be drowned out by the noise of others in a busy shipping lane. In a very general sense, SSM systems are extremely vulnerable to deception by merging with non-target traffic.

The new Dutch destroyer *Tromp* illustrates just how compact Harpoon can be. In this view the surface-to-surface weapon had not yet been fitted, but the small platforms for it are visible between uptakes and bridge. *Tromp* is unusual in that she has both the Standard area defense SAM aft (visible atop her hangar) and NATO Sea Sparrow (for point defense) forward superfiring over her twin automatic 4.7in gun mount – a weapon, incidentally, salvaged from Dutch postwar destroyers now being broken up. Her 'mack' abaft the uptakes carries diesel exhausts, and the big air intakes of her gas turbines are visible below the Harpoon platform. The radome carries an elaborate three-dimensional track-while-scan radar related to one originally developed in conjunction with the Royal Navy for the abortive British carrier CVA-01 and for the *Bristol* class fast escorts. There is one Lynx helicopter and a pair of the ubiquitous Mk 32 lightweight torpedo tubes for ASW. *(C & S Taylor)*

The other major passive sensor is ESM. If a target radiates in a characteristic way, eg turns on a well-known Soviet air search radar, then at least some of that radiation generally follows the curve of the earth. High-frequency radio is even better, of course, since it generates a ground wave detectable at some distance. For example, the British *Leander*s modified to take Exocet in place of their twin 4.5in guns received extra electronic intercept gear in place of their former air search radars. However, such gear *in itself* has no great value for SSM operations unless it is built into a system for targeting rather than, as is usual, for intelligence collection: the captain cares that he is near a Soviet rocket cruiser, not that the interesting signal called Z5835555 is now on the air. Moreover, targeting by ESM runs the great risk of deception designed to cause a captain to fire his missiles at a non-target. A missile battle might resemble a Wild West shoot-out, in which one of the parties patiently counts while his enemy empties his revolver, then comes out to shoot – and many Western revolvers in this particular game hold only four bullets.

Ultimately, Western SSM doctrine will probably call for a combination of such onboard sensors as radar and various forms of ESM, including direction-finding, with shore based systems such as the big HF/DF stations and satellite terminals. The object should be to allow the captain of an SSM ship escorting other ships to know when he is about to be engaged, and by whom; he can then react. He still has the problem of assessing the effect of his fire. His problem is that his warheads are small, so that they are likely to put an opponent out of action rather than sink him. Damage assessment, then, cannot consist of waiting for the radar screen or ESM panel to go blank – it must be possible to decide that enough damage has been done at a far less catastrophic level. Proposals include careful analysis of enemy radar emissions, on the theory that no ship will turn off its warning sensors unless it absolutely must. However, any such assessment invites deception – and deception really pays in SSM warfare.

The Soviets introduced SSMs about a decade before most Western navies showed serious interest in them, and they clearly faced the same targeting problem. Their missiles are mounted only in very limited numbers, because they are quite large and because any attempt at a serious at-sea reloading system would force up the size of their SSM units unacceptably. However, there is a fundamental difference between Soviet and Western SSM missions. The Soviet SSM unit is not trying to keep some other ship from assaulting a force or convoy it is covering; it is part of a force trying to carry out a strike. Much of the Soviet naval establishment is

If the trend in the West is towards compact anti-ship missiles, that does not hold in the East. The Soviets have developed a very powerful long-range weapon – SSN-3 ('Shaddock') – specifically for anti-carrier operations, mounting it aboard their submarines and aboard eight 'rocket cruisers'. This 'Kresta I' carries two pairs of such weapons in elevating tubes alongside her bridge. No photograph of SSN-3 has at the time of writing been published, but the weapon must be a very large air-breather, and it is often credited with aerodynamic ranges in excess of 400nm.

devoted to targeting: to picking up potential targets, tracking them, confirming their character and bringing together a strike force. The Soviet captain is not an independent individual deciding on his own whether to risk his four or eight weapons; he is controlled very rigidly from above, and indeed the success of his tactics depends very much upon the extent to which he and the other Soviet officers of the strike organisation can operate as a single entity over very long distances.

Once a target has been located, the SSM has a relatively simple task. It is far faster than any target ship, and it can use either radar (passive or active) or infra-red homing, or command guidance, or any combination of the three, thanks to the ease with which the air transmits such radiation. Moreover, even the small radar which can fit into the nose of a big SSM has far more range than the kind of sonar which a homing torpedo can afford, and the slow speed of surface ships makes the design of such a radar far simpler than radar design for a SAM. The large size of the target also helps. Low target speed makes it possible for the SSM to trade missile speed for range within a missile size limited by considerations of ship-impact, as long as the missile can undertake a somewhat wider search at the end of its run out; that search is likely to be more fruitful than that of the homing torpedo because it is carried out at high missile speed (which does not degrade sensor performance) and, perhaps most importantly, because it takes place in two rather than three dimensions.

Like the homing torpedo, the radar homing missile has a finite acquisition range. However, that range is much longer – perhaps, for example, sufficient to permit an Exocet to engage a 40kt target at the end of its 38km run-out towards the target position predicted by the shipboard fire control system. The important onboard components of the Exocet system are some means of ensuring that it runs out in a straight path towards that predicted position, as well as a timer to turn on its radar seeker at the appropriate moment. Premature turn-on will warn the target without gaining very much for the missile, which is why it pays for the launch ship to have a fair idea of target range. Finally there is a radar altimeter to ensure that the missile neither flies into the sea nor rises too high: once again, the penalty for failure is warning, since missile height determines the range at which a shipboard search radar will detect Exocet. The better the altimeter, the closer the missile can fly to the sea, and the closer it will come to its target before detection. Of course missile altitude also determines missile radar range on the target, so that if the missile is too low it will not hit the target unless the target happens to be dead ahead.

As in the other weapons, missile capability is balanced off against ship-impact. For example, it is far simpler to provide a fixed than a trainable launcher, but that in turn requires either that the ship turn towards her target, or that the missile be capable of turning quite accurately on to its run-out course. Most Western SSMs are designed to be fired from fixed launchers, and so can accept large turns soon after take off (30° in Exocet, up to 90° in the US Harpoon). Harpoon is unusual in that it is designed for launch from standard US SAM launchers, which are trainable, or from fixed low-impact cannisters; its dimensions were fixed by the characteristics of the widely-used Mk 13 and Mk 26 Standard missile launchers even though, ironically, it will be carried by many missile warships in cannisters. In its SAM-launcher mode, as in the Patrol Frigate, Harpoon is unique among Western missiles in the large number which can be carried by one ship.

The combination of radar seeker and dead-time run-out permits a variety of missile operating modes. The shipboard fire control system can specify a range 'window' within which a target should be found; for example, if the missile finds nothing within this window during its straight run-out, if can follow a specified search pattern, similar in concept to the spiral search of the homing torpedo. The smaller the window (and so the better the initial fire control solution), the shorter the warning given by radar emissions from the missile. Alternatively, a fire control input consisting only of bearing can be used, with the missile seeker turned on throughout its run-out along the specified bearing.

The launch ship has no interaction with the missile after firing, which is, superficially, very attractive: it need not remain in what must surely soon become a very dangerous area, since an incoming SSM certainly defines the line of bearing back to its launcher. However, the autonomous missile has very definite limits built into its radar seeker. In particular, the seeker must have some way of deciding which ship to hit if several are present, and then where to strike the ship it chooses. Generally there are two possible ways of designing a radar seeker. If it has relatively high resolution, it will see a series of bright spots, which are reflections from corners formed in the superstructure. The effectiveness of a superstructure hit depends very much on the kind of warhead the missile carries. Many corners are high enough in the ship, for example in her masting, that a missile passing through them will miss vital areas altogether; it may not even encounter enough ship structure to cause it to explode. The principal alternative is a low-resolution radar, which sees nothing more than a blob, and which is suitable for a 'centroid homer' which goes for the center of mass of the blob, probably in the hull of the ship. However, when presented with two ships close together, the centroid homer may well steer for the center of the pattern formed by both, ie the gap between them. In general either type of missile will steer for the first suitable target it detects. However, that need not prevent it from shifting targets when presented with several close together.

For example, a missile may be unable to distinguish a small ship passing in front of the bulk of a much larger one, as in the case of a missile corvette running abeam a big freighter or tanker. In fact the captain of the missile corvette, confronted with an incoming missile, may be able to save his ship by allowing the missile to transfer its affections to the tanker (which, incidentally, will remain afloat long enough to absorb several more missiles). Once more it is the Western gun fight – the captain can count those Exocets, and he can bide his time until they have all buried themselves in that mass of shipping in which he has immersed himself.

Somewhat similarly, it is easy to envisage an SSM attack on a task force, Western or Soviet. One question rarely addressed is how the missiles distribute themselves among the available targets. It seems unlikely that initial missile settings can be made so precise that missiles can be assigned to individual ships in the task force, yet otherwise it is quite possible that all the missiles, following identical flight profiles, will home on the same ship and so let the task force as a whole escape. Even worse, it is possible that in some cases the ships worth hitting will be relatively small ones; for example, in the Mediterranean the Soviets often operate old *Sverdlov* class cruisers in conjunction with much smaller – but far more potent – missile units. The *Sverdlov* might act as a missile absorber, negating the effects of a missile strike.

The Soviets are not immune from this problem. In a mass missile strike on a carrier task force, the Soviets can never be entirely sure of which ship in the force is the carrier; even were their missiles able to distinguish large targets from small ones by the intensity of their echoes, fairly simple electronic counter-measures can make all the ships of the force appear identical. If the only worthwhile objective is the carrier, all other ships in the force are missile absorbers, wasters of incoming weapons. A pessimistic Soviet planner, convinced that it takes n missiles to disable a carrier, and faced with m ships in a task force, would have to provide at least $m \times n$ missiles in a strike, and even then he would have to control the missiles rather closely to make sure that they were evenly distributed. He would have to maintain some kind of control over the missiles to decide that they locked on to the right targets. This requirement is more obvious in the case in which the Soviet strike leader can find out which ship is the carrier, eg from a 'tattletale', a Soviet warship trailing the carrier force; but it is there even without the information provided by the 'tattletale'.

This type of problem afflicts any self-guided weapon. The two chief types of seekers are infra-red, which may carry with it some element of particular ship recognition; and anti-radiation homing, homing on a particular radar or radio signal commonly emitted by targets, which again includes some element of target recognition. Infra-red homing is inherently shorter in range than radar, and can be confused by the sun, but on the other hand it is hard to jam and a missile employing it does not announce its presence by its own radar signals. The anti-radar missile (ARM) is attractive because it can distinguish really worthwhile targets – as long as they cooperate by turning on their distinctive radars. However, the existence of an ARM weapon may be valuable because it may cause enemy warships to turn off radars which might otherwise improve its chances of defeating a missile attack. Similarly, the mixed use of ARMs and more conventional SSMs is often advocated: the ARMs either turn off (by destruction) or cause to be turned off those search radars which would locate the other SSMs on the way in.

Command and semi-command guidance comes in many forms. All SAMs have some anti-ship capability, although in some cases that capability is more claimed than real. In a few cases, such as the British Sea Dart, the capability is well advertised, to such an extent that the missile may have had its design adjusted to permit effective anti-ship fire. The Soviet SAN-3, adopted at the same time that the Soviets abandoned big anti-ship weapons aboard their rocket cruisers, may have a similar dual

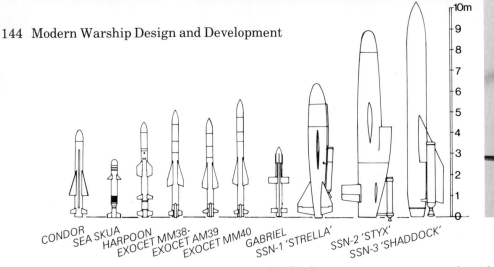

CONDOR SEA SKUA HARPOON EXOCET MM38· EXOCET AM39 EXOCET MM40 GABRIEL SSN-1 'STRELLA' SSN-2 'STYX' SSN-3 'SHADDOCK'

Comparative profiles of anti-ship missiles, showing the wide range of sizes in these weapons. Gabriel, Harpoon and Exocet are typical Western *ship-launched* missiles for combat at and beyond the radar horizon; Gabriel is unique in employing command guidance (semi-active radar homing) and has, therefore, a range effectively limited by the horizon – 12.5nm (25nm in a Mk 2 version) vs 60nm for Harpoon and 28nm for Exocet. Warhead weights are 330lb for Gabriel (total 926lb), 324lb for Exocet (1620lb) and 510lb for Harpoon (1397lb including a booster; Harpoon is turbojet-powered for long range). Condor (now defunct; 2130lb, 40-60nm range) and Sea Skua (462lb, 451 warhead, about 10nm range) are two ends of a Western *air-to-ship* missile spectrum with Condor representative of long range weapons which can be fired from heavy tactical fighters, 'Shaddock' and 'Styx' are representative of far more conservative Soviet practice and incorporate much more powerful warheads.

role. Both weapons are command-guided to some extent; Sea Dart uses semi-active radar guidance. The chief defect of such systems is that they are limited to the horizon. Talos was unusual in that it could follow a beam over the horizon, presumably with a programmed dive at the end.

Command guidance can also employ a sensor in the missile which transmits back to the launch ship The best-known example is a television camera in the missile, which the launch ship can lock on to the most appropriate target, or even the best point on the target; however, the chief Soviet anti-carrier SSM, SSN-3, reportedly incorporates a link which transmits its radar picture back, so that the launch ship can pick the target on to which the missile should lock. One consequence, of course, is that the destruction of the launch ship while the missile is in flight may well abort its mission.

Finally, command guidance can pit the large sensors on board the launching ship against the counter-measures at the target; they may have a much better chance than the small sensor in a missile limited in size by ship-impact considerations. This was the argument used by the Israelis to justify command guidance for their Gabriel missile: they felt that the ultimate answer to many forms of electronic deception was a man, not more electronics.

WARHEADS

Ultimately the effect a missile has depends upon its warhead. Warhead weight, like fuel weight and propulsion (speed) must be traded off within a missile size really determined by the size of the ship which is to carry the weapon, and not at all by operational requirements: a bigger warhead can be bought, usually, only by some advance in propulsive efficiency. However, given a warhead of fixed weight, there are several very different options beside the usual nuclear one.

Most Western SSMs are designed to attack unarmoured ships; they have *blast-fragmentation* warheads. These are intended to penetrate a ship and then explode, destroying the compartment in which they find them-selves and perhaps, by the force of their blast, tearing up a bulkhead on either side of the explosion. Fragments tear up the unarmoured interior of the ship and probably break wires and waveguides – if the missile finds itself in the appropriate compartment. At best the radius of destruction is so great that the ship structure is seriously damaged; if the missile strikes near the waterline the hole it makes in the side may cause severe flooding. However, the spectacular photographs of missile damage often released are quite misleading. They show ships with relatively weak, old hulls; and even

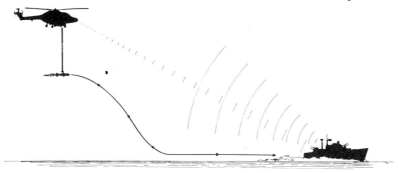

As in the case of ASW, it is deceptive to limit a list of anti-ship missiles to those fired from the ship herself. Sea Skua, shown here, is an example of a helicopter-launched missile; most modern ASW ships carry at least one and often two helicopters capable of lifting one or more such weapons. Sea Skua homes semi-actively, using the helicopter's Seaspray radar. Helicopter dimensions and power limit the size of the missile, so that it has only a 77lb warhead and a range of about 10 miles; but the announced semi-active homing system may well match up with an alternative anti-radar homer. Shrike experience against the *Worden* suggests the efficacy of even small anti-radar weapons. *(British Aerospace)*

in those cases many hits would damage a ship without eliminating her fighting capability. The problem is that the vital systems of most ships are rather widely distributed along the length of the ship, so that any weapon whose radius of destruction is small compared to ship dimensions is unlikely to put the ship out of action with a single hit – which is all that can be expected, given the small numbers of SSMs aboard most Western warships. Moreover, depending upon the efficacy of counter-measures and the details of seeker design, the missile may strike an entirely innocuous place, such as an uptake.

Two variations are more lethal. One is a *shaped-charge* warhead, which, if it penetrates a magazine, can destroy a ship. The drawback is that magazines take up very little of the length of a ship, even in the case of a large ship such as a carrier, so that statistically the shaped charge has only a small chance of doing even as much damage as does the more conventional blast-fragmentation warhead. Another variation is to spread fuel from the missile's tanks when the missile hits. This happens almost automatically when any liquid-fuel missile strikes short of its maximum range – and SSMs are the chief candidates for liquid fuel, since many of them are fuel-efficient turbojets. The liquid fuel is an *area weapon;* it can spread fire along the length of a ship, and the case of the cruiser *Belknap* shows that fire is a very lethal weapon against a modern aluminium ship. Of course, a missile designed to spray fuel over its target would be more efficient than would an SSM short of maximum range.

Neither blast-fragmentation nor some alternative point weapon exploded above water is very likely to sink a ship; the only way to do that is to get at her underwater hull. One or the more surprising discoveries of underwater explosion research is that a relatively small charge exploded in the right place well under the keel of a ship can break her in half, or at the least wipe out most of her internal systems through shock. The explosion releases a gas bubble, which expands and contracts as it makes its way to the surface. When it hits the keel of the ship, the ship acts like a girder struck in the middle: it flexes. The second flex strains the hull further, and often ships break on the third flex; everything depends upon giving the gas bubble enough time (depth) to hit the hull girder enough times with enough force. The envelope under the hull is invitingly large and would seem to make up for a multitude of minor guidance and fuzing errors, but in fact designing a missile to dive under the keel of its target appears to be relatively difficult. Such a missile would have the distinct advantage of not having to come too close (in the air) to the terminal defense weapons of its target.

The efficacy of under-the-keel charges has been known for a long time; it was just such an explosion that broke the back of HMS *Belfast* in

1939. Several navies devised magnetic torpedo exploders to achieve a similar result, but encountered severe problems. In the United States, for example, unfortunate experiences with the magnetic pistol of the Mk 14 torpedo led to a general belief that in future most torpedoes would be of the traditional type which stick to the side of a ship. However, the Germans persisted in their efforts to produce a viable under-the-keel weapon, and devised active acoustic (upward-looking sonar) and active magnetic* exploders – both of which the Soviets captured in 1945. In fact, the Soviets have published accounts of torpedo 'proximity fuzes', which suggests that they may favor just such weapons. The acceptance of such a torpedo design philosophy would strongly influence the design of Soviet warships, as compared to US types, particularly for large ships which can accommodate conventional torpedo protective systems.

Finally there is the overhead fragment weapon, usually an ARM. Modern warships are literally covered with largely unprotected waveguides and wires, without which they cannot function as fighting units. It takes very little to break enough of that wiring to disable a ship, as the US Navy found to its cost in 1972 when a 145lb Shrike was accidentally dropped on the cruiser *Worden,* disabling her completely, even though no damage at all was visible at a range of a few hundred yards. The great drawback in this type of attack is that damage assessment is very difficult; it is relatively easy for the target ship to turn off most of her electronics and so avoid another attack. However, the ARM vulnerability is so pronounced that even small warheads can be effective – which means small, hence numerous, missiles.

These warheads are useful for specially designed SSMs. They are not particularly well-suited for SAMs employed in the anti-ship role, since the SAM mission requires a warhead with a large lethal radius against a flimsy airplane. Thus most US SAMs have 'continuous rod' warheads which produce an expanding ring made out of steel rods, designed to cut apart aircraft structures. It is not clear that similar warheads would be very effective against ships, although, if they hit in the right places, they would surely destroy much of the topside electronics.

Right now it is unlikely that the blast-fragmentation warheads will be replaced by anything more, at least in the West, unless there is a war which shows that they lack the requisite lethality in the numbers available. SSMs are attractive because they impose a realtively low cost on the major ASW and AAW roles of Western warships, and at the same time appear to restore to surface ships the vital role they once had – countering enemy ships. However, unless many more are placed aboard ships, the possible salvo sizes are so small that the Western SSM is unlikely to have any great effect in battle. The Soviets know: they believe that nothing short of saturation pays. Israeli, Arab and Indian (1971) experience also favors large numbers, often of rather large weapons. It is disconcerting to reflect, for example, that the 510lb Harpoon warhead is the size of a 10in shell, and that many destroyers survived many hits of comparable size during World War II. They survived so well, in fact, that they continued to fight – which is exactly what the SSM should be able to prevent.

---

* The great problem encountered by magnetic fuzes was the possibility that a ship might have been degaussed, or that its magnetic field might be distorted by the local earth field, particularly in high latitudes. In an active system, the torpedo is fitted with several coils which set up its own magnetic field; a target ship distorts this field, and the torpedo senses the distortion. Apparently such systems can be extremely reliable, although they would probably react too slowly to be usable in a missile warhead.

CHAPTER NINE

Guns

Naval guns reached their highest stage of development just after the Second World War; the demise which followed was so precipitate that only a decade later several major US warships were designed to carry no guns at all, while other navies came close to the same conclusions: it appeared that missiles were destined to replace guns altogether. At that time most navies were all too familiar with the problems of guns, particularly the sophisticated rapid-firing types developed just after the end of World War II, whereas missiles remained largely paper promises devoid, as yet, of operational disappointments. Experience with missiles, and the discovery that there are naval tasks for which missiles are quite unsuitable, have led to a gun revival. In the process the role of the naval gun has shifted radically, so that many of the new ones are limited, in rate of fire or in elevation, in ways which might have seemed entirely unacceptable in 1945.

Compared to a missile, a gun system invests heavily in fixed shipboard equipment so that individual projectiles can be comparatively inexpensive – and small. Until very recently the shells have also been unguided after emerging from the muzzle, and their SSPK has been very low precisely because of the dead time that lack of post-boost guidance implies. Moreover, dead time increases with range, so that all naval guns are inherently far more accurate at short than at long range. Higher muzzle velocity reduces the dead time equivalent to a given range and thus in itself may improve SSPK at that range, as long as inherent gun accuracy is not lost through, for example, barrel wear. Longer range in turn gives the gun more time to engage an approaching target, so that it can make up for a low SSPK by firing many shots. Similarly, a heavier shell provides both a greater lethal radius – a greater SSPK – and more accuracy at long range, as the shell retains more of its momentum longer.

In what at the time must have seemed the last gasp of the traditional naval gun, Britain, Sweden and the United States all developed automatic cruiser guns at the end of World War II. The British cruiser *Tiger* (shown here in 1977) was originally armed with two twin 6in guns, one of which was later replaced by a helicopter platform; they were credited with a rate of fire of 20 (rather than the old 6) rounds per minute, so that – in theory – four guns could do the work previously allotted to thirteen. Unfortunately, this high rate could not be kept up for very long – a characteristic these weapons seem to have shared with many of the fast-firing medium- and heavy-caliber guns of the period. The equivalent US weapons were the 6in guns of the two *Worcesters* and the 8in of the three *Des Moines*; the latter were less ambitious and, apparently, more reliable. The Swedish automatic 6in gun was mounted in the *Göta Lejon* as well as in two Dutch cruisers, and survives today in these ships in, respectively, Chilean and Peruvian service. No account of postwar naval gun development can omit the story of the very rapid firing 3in/70, developed in collaboration by the US and Royal Navies and seen fitted in *Tiger*'s 'B' position. Both used the same barrel and the same ammunition, but otherwise the guns differed. Both were over-optimistic in their attempt to produce an extremely high rate of fire (60 rounds per minute per barrel for the Vickers Mk 6 shown, but as many as 90 for the US version); on the other hand, the successful OTO-Melara 76/62 is credited with 85 rounds per minute and has had few detractors. *(C & S Taylor)*

Both higher muzzle velocity and heavier shells impose costs in rate of fire. Any gun is limited in its rate of fire by the time it takes to recoil after each round is fired. For any given round, the longer the recoil (the lower the limit on rate of fire), the less the stress on the gun mount, and the less the loss of accuracy from round to round due to vibration. For a given length of recoil, the cost in stress and vibration is a matter of the energy the recoil must absorb – and this is the same energy which provides that muzzle velocity in the first place.

In practice most guns do not fire as rapidly as they might, given their recoil mechanisms; generally, rate of fire is determined by the ammunition feed system. Thus semi-automatic hand-loaded 4in and 5in guns appear to be limited to about 20 rounds per minute. They must recoil, eject the spent cartridge case, and accept new shells (and often, for high-velocity guns, separate cartridge cases). Power loading can double this rate of fire. However, many navies have learned to their sorrow that power loading, which approaches the limit set by the recoil cycle, can also eliminate fire altogether as the elaborate mechanism jams. For example, the British power-loaded 6in gun installed on the *Tiger* class cruisers was designed to fire 20 rounds per minute, where the previous rate had been closer to six; however, it could rarely fire for more than thirty seconds without jamming. For many years the US rapid-fire 5in/54 had a similar reputation.

THE ANTI-SHIP ROLE

These considerations balance off against the changing role of the naval gun. In 1945 it fulfilled three distinct naval functions: anti-ship, anti-aircraft, and shore bombardment. In the anti-ship role it was necessary to put a large number of rounds into a large target at considerable range; ships are hard to destroy with single hits, as users of SSMs may yet discover. Shell accuracy was quite sufficient within shell range, but that range is inherently limited. In recent years the low cost per shell, as compared to the high cost of an

Efforts were also made to automate the standard medium-caliber weapon: this is the US result, the Mk 42 5in/54, credited with about 40 rounds per minute, or twice the rate of fire of the World War II semi-automatic 5in/38. It actually replaced a proposed twin semi-automatic 5in/54. A high rate of fire is achieved partly by feeding the gun alternately from the right and left ammunition drums, shown below it in the magazine. In effect, then, there are two independent feed systems with a single breech and barrel – 1½ guns rather than 1. Rounds carried alongside the gun in the mount permit some fire even in the event of a breakdown in the automated feed system. *(FMC Corporation)*

SSM, has been an important factor in the revival of the gun: there are many targets, such as patrol craft, which can be stopped by even a single shell but which are hardly worth the cost of an SSM. Moreover, a gun can be used to warn a ship, eg by firing a shot across her bows – no one would waste an SSM that way, yet such non-lethal warnings are a very important part of the naval trade. They were eclipsed in much Western naval thinking of the immediate postwar period only because NATO assumed that its armed forces would have only one mission, the 'big war' against the Soviets.

In 1945 it was assumed that naval aircraft would provide all the anti-ship muscle required; they had, after all, been quite successful in that role during the war. What was not appreciated was that their costs would rise so dramatically that for many navies specialized aircraft would become a dream rather than a reality. The SSM is a useful replacement, but it is too expensive on a per-round basis. In this sense the airplane is more like the gun: the expensive part is re-usable, as long as the AA battery does not get it first.

THE ANTI-AIRCRAFT ROLE

The second major task for the naval gun in 1945 was anti-aircraft fire; at the time this was reckoned its only important job, and it influenced gun development for some considerable time. Anti-aircraft fire requires only one near-hit to destroy the target. However, inherent gun SSPK is so low that a very high rate of fire is necessary to place enough shells near an airplane to achieve any real chance of destruction. In fact, prewar naval AA tactics were designed to offset this lack of lethality: against the high-level bomber a ship could oppose only heavy guns, which were limited in rate of fire. They were best used to lay down a barrage, using time (ie altitude)-fuzed shells, which would deter rather than destroy a bomber: rates of fire made it impossible to put up a barrage of such density that many bombers would be destroyed. The higher the bomber and the heavier the barrage, the better the chance that its bombardier's aim would be thrown off badly enough to cause bombs to miss a maneuvering ship far below. Such tactics were useless against a diving attacker: instead, machine cannon such as the British 2pdr and the 40mm Bofors 'hosed down' the tube in space along which the dive bomber had to come; in effect their very high rates of fire made up for low SSPK. There was still a strong element of deterrence in such tactics, but they called for fire laid down against a particular attacker, rather than against a high-altitude formation. One problem in such tactics was that the lighter the gun (ie the higher its rate of fire) the shorter the range at which it would begin to have a useful net kill probability: if the gun was light enough, it might not destroy an attacker at all. Thus the US Navy abandoned first the 20mm and then even the 40mm Bofors gun when neither proved capable of stopping a Kamikaze.

The proximity (VT) fuze dramatically changed anti-aircraft tactics, by sharply improving heavy gun SSPK: now it no longer mattered whether the fire control system estimated target altitude very accurately, since the shell would explode whenever it passed near the target. Wartime advances in fire control, which amounted to early approaches to automation, reduced effective dead time, and the introduction of radar tracking improved accuracy. Taken together, these developments shifted anti-aircraft tactics towards the engagement of individual targets at long range – and at long range the SAM excels. Barrage fire was largely abandoned as a useful tactic. However, to engage targets one by one at very long range is to accept a low

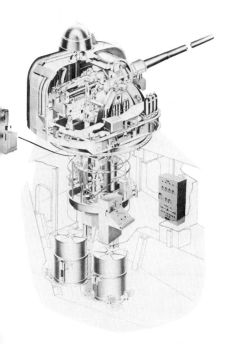

In recent years the Italian firm of OTO-Melara has produced a series of 'compact' guns of 3in and 5in caliber: this is the Italian missile destroyer *Ardito*, mounting two 5in/54 forward. Th same weapon was adopted for the Canadian *Iroquois* class. The rate of fire, 45 rounds per minute, approximates that of the US Mk 42, but the mount weighs only 34 tons compared to about 60 for the US system. Like other lightweight weapons it can be fired from outside the mount, whereas the Mk 42 requires a crew of four inside it. Besides her two 5in/54, *Ardito* is armed (aft) with the US Standard SAM and carries either two AB204 or one Sea King helicopter; her secondary AA battery consists of four OTO-Melara 76mm guns. The same weapon has been adopted by the US Navy for the Patrol Frigate (*Perry* class) and for the Missile Hydrofoil (*Pegasus*). The fore 'mack' carries a US-type SPS-12 air search radar, the aft one the US SPS-52 three-dimensional radar, with two SPG-51B missile illuminators aft. The fore topmast carries an Italian SPQ-2 surface search radar, and there are Argo dual-purpose fire control radars atop the bridge and abreast the after 'mack'. The use of 'macks' indicates steam turbine propulsion. Finally, note the banks of encapsulated life rafts abreast the bridge and helicopter hangar. Not visible in this 1977 photograph are four fixed torpedo tubes, presumably in the transom, for wire-guided torpedoes. (*C & S Taylor*)

rate of engagement and to become vulnerable to saturation. Gun rate of fire cannot counter saturation, simply because aircraft with stand-off weapons can attack from well outside gun range. However, neither can missiles, which are inherently one-on-one weapons. So far the only solutions have been specialised SAM systems with a high rate of fire and a high rate of engagement such as Aegis, and the use of area warheads (nuclear warheads) to permit a single very expensive SAM to destroy a formation of bombers – if the bombers stay close enough together for the nuclear warhead to be effective. It is conceivable that, by improving SSPK at really long ranges, laser shell guidance will make rapid-fire heavy (5in) guns an effective counter to large raids, particularly if the guns are mounted aboard ships well away from the targets of the raid.

The gun has a distinct advantage at very short range: it is simple enough to come into action much more rapidly than can a missile, and, moreover, it does not have the minimum-range problem of the missile. Thus it can be useful against targets which give very little warning time, such as low-altitude SSMs. However, such operation is very different from the classical use of naval guns for anti-aircraft purposes. What matters is not rate of fire from a gun alerted and closed-up well before the appearance of the attackers, but rather the ability to wait for months, then come into action instantly upon warning. This requirement was a major factor in the design of the Vickers 4.5in Mk 8 gun, which can fire automatically un-manned. The months of waiting require a very high level of reliability, which Vickers bought by reducing rate of fire to about 25 rounds per minute. Vickers argued that it was better to go to a relatively slow-firing heavy gun than to try for a higher rate of fire in a lighter weapon (such as the OTO-Melara Compact 3in gun) because the heavier weapon could provide a greater weight of shell in a given length of time – a consideration more appropriate for anti-ship and shore bombardment than for anti-missile defense.

In the early 1960s the US Navy abandoned the medium gun as an air defense weapon and looked for a reliable system for low-angle fire. The Mk 45 was the first result of this program: a fully automated 5in/54 whose rate of fire approximated to that of the older semi-automatic guns. Ammunition enters the breech from below, which is why elevation is limited to 65°. Proposals for a rapid-fire version and for a twin version died in the mid-1960s when the decision was made to develop the Major Caliber Lightweight Gun, which became the Mk 71. (*FMC Corporation*)

The British equivalent of the Mk 45 is the 4.5in gun Mk 8, a fully automated weapon reportedly capable of 25 rounds per minute; elevation is limited to 55°, partly on the theory that most air targets will be missiles approaching at relatively low level. (C & S Taylor)

The French equivalent of the US Mk 45 and the British Mk 8 is the 100mm/55, a weapon developed jointly with West Germany. It is a true dual-purpose gun, capable of elevating to 80° and firing 60 rounds per minute. However, the shell weighs only about 30lb, compared to about 55lb for the 4.5in and 70lb for the 5in/54. Maximum range for a surface engagement is about 18,500yds, compared to 26,000yds for the Mk 45. This March 1979 photograph shows the weapon installed aboard D'Estrées. (Stefano Cioglia)

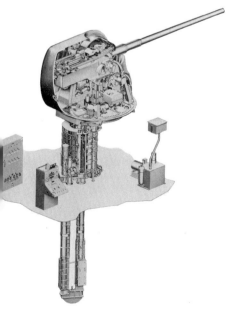

Gun development in the early postwar period went in the opposite direction. The US Navy and Royal Navy both studied the question of the ideal anti-aircraft gun, trading off shell caliber (weight), muzzle velocity and rate of fire. The ideal caliber was somewhat above 3in; both navies standardized on a 3in/70, for which each designed its own twin mount. The American version enjoyed the very high rate of fire of 90 rounds per minute – when it worked (which was apparently rarely, due to its very elaborate shell-feeding system). Nor is it clear that the British version was much better, although it was also adopted by the Canadian Navy. The fundamental defect of the 3in/70 was that, although it was a good anti-aircraft weapon, it was not powerful enough for surface fire – which, despite all the enthusiasm for air strikes, neither the US nor the Royal Navy was quite willing to abandon.

The US Navy therefore continued to develop the fast-firing 5in/54, a high-velocity replacement for its successful 5in/38. This weapon began as a fairly conventional twin mount in which a high rate of fire was to be achieved by providing two separate guns, each firing about 18 rounds per minute. As in several other fast-firing heavy guns, the US developers of the 5in/54 decided to replace two barrels by two feed mechanisms alternately feeding a single barrel. Such a design makes it possible to double the rate of fire again by placing two such guns in a single gun mount, but may also be subject to a higher rate of failure than two independent slower-firing weapons in the single mount. That may be why the French Navy never adopted the automatic 5in/54; instead it produced a new twin semi-automatic mount for its postwar destroyers and anti-aircraft cruisers. However, France did adopt the 5in/54 as a caliber and as a barrel length, in order to take advantage of the availability of ammunition from the United States*.

The Swedish Bofors company may have been unique in developing a one-sided rapid-fire medium gun, the 4.7in/50 mounted on Swedish and some Dutch destroyers in twin gunhouses. Presumably Bofors accepted the higher stresses involved in a faster single ammunition feed. Single-side operation is more common for smaller calibers, as in the case of the US 3in/70, although the older US 3in/50 did employ two separate feeds, which is one reason why the two barrels of a 3in/50 twin mount are so widely separated. The earlier gun required twin feed because the intermediate link from magazine to feed was limited in speed by the rate at which rounds could be passed by hand; that in turn greatly simplified the design of the ammunition hoist. Hand operation is unacceptable, however, in a gun mount intended to fire upon command from an unaltered (unmanned) status. In all more recent mounts, therefore, the movement of shells from magazine to breech is automated. Generally, the only hand operation is placement of the shells in ready-service stowage from which the hoist can pluck them.

The Royal Navy retained its twin 4.5in semi-automatic gun in postwar ships for the same reason which caused the United States to retain its 5in/54: a smaller gun would be better for anti-aircraft but not for anti-surface fire. No fully automatic fast-firing medium-caliber weapon came into service in the Royal Navy, although reportedly that service considered for a time adapting a fast-firing anti-aircraft gun originally developed for the British Army.

In each case large caliber implies considerable ship-impact and, for a ship of a given size, a limited number of gun mounts. In the mid-1950s France and Germany developed their own fast-firing single 3.9in/55, which fires about 60 rounds per minute, the same rate (per barrel) as the 57mm. This weapon replaced the slower-firing twin 5in/54 aboard the French cruiser *Colbert* and, indeed, the heavier gun has not been fitted since that ship was originally completed in 1959.

One might go so far as to say that in the mid-1950s all navies accepted the idea that beyond very short ranges anti-aircraft missiles would

---

*The Mk 42 5in/54 fires about twice as fast as one gun of a twin 5in/38 mount and so in effect replaces a twin semi-automatic mount. Thus the *Forrest Sherman*, listed in reference books with only three guns (and hence appearing to confirm the postwar trend towards less muscle and more ship), is actually equivalent in designed firepower to a French *Surcouf*, with six weapons in twin turrets. However, the current US lightweight 5in/54 actually does fire at a semi-automatic gun rate, albeit with no crew in the mount: the two guns on a missile cruiser (ex-frigate) are really equivalent to the two single mounts in a *Garcia*-class frigate, or to the single Mk 42 in a *Knox*. These equations, of course, omit questions of the number of targets which can be engaged simultaneously and, for that matter, of gun reliability. However, they emphasize the contrast between appearance and reality which is so striking in modern Western warships.

BRITISH 4.5IN MK 6

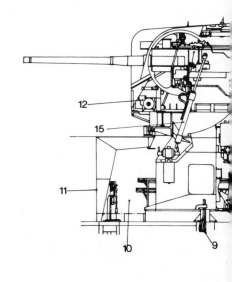

ITALIAN OTO-MELARA 76/62

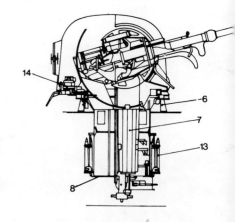

KEY		
1 Lookout hood	**11**	Ring
2 Exhaust ventilation duct	**12**	Elect
3 Firing changeover switch		train
4 Spent cartridge chute	**13**	Shel
5 Weathering seal	**14**	Train
6 Training base	**15**	Eleva
7 Shell hoist		
8 Revolving platform		
9 Electric cables		
10 Gun bay		

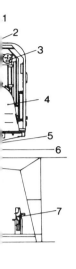

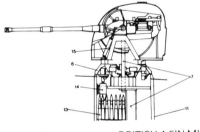

BRITISH 4.5IN MK 8

European gun mountings. Rates of fire are 85 rounds per minute per barrel for the OTO-Melara 76/62, 20-25 for the 55cal Vickers Mk 8 and 11-25 for the 50cal 4.5in Mk 6. By comparison, the Italian OTO-Melara 5in/54 fires at 45 rounds per minute per barrel and the French 100mm/55 at 60.

of gun bay anical brake for

or nder

be dominant, and that very short ranges made small calibers and high rates of fire very attractive. Anti-ship fire requirements did not justify the expense of new gun mount designs; where heavy guns were used, they were to existing designs, such as the US Mk 42 5in/54 or the British twin 4.5. In some cases NATO navies drew gun mounts from US surplus stock, which is why several Italian and Danish ships mount the World War II 5in/38, a weapon probably adequate for surface but surely not for anti-aircraft fire, and certainly not amenable to the rapid-start requirement.

Perhaps the high point of this trend was the US decision to adopt the OTO-Melara 3in/62 (Mk 75 in US service) instead of some 5in gun for the new *Perry* class frigates; previous ships in this category had the much more powerful Mk 42 5in/54. In this case short-range anti-aircraft (anti-SSM) capability was bought at the expense of anti-ship firepower, on the theory that the Mk 13 launcher could accommodate so many Harpoons that they would quite satisfy any anti-ship requirement. Such a decision runs counter to the ideas of most other navies, which mount medium-caliber guns to make up for the small number of anti-ship missiles their ships carry.

The *Perry* design was completed at the same time that the United States brought into service a new lightweight 5in/54 and also at the same time that the US, alone at least among Western navies, was developing an even larger gun, the lightweight 8in/55 Mk 71. However, these weapons were predicated on the need for shore bombardment firepower, whereas the *Perry* was a very limited design in which the choice of a smaller gun brought considerable economy – in a cost-limited ship.

The Kamikaze experience of 1945 ruined the reputation of the small fast-firing gun for air defense. Many navies continued to buy 40mm guns, but that was partly because their ships could not take anything much larger, or because they did not expect to face very severe air threats. Bofors believed so strongly that a much heavier shell was required that it developed a new fast-firing 57mm (2.25in) weapon, which in its fully enclosed twin form saw service in the French and Dutch navies as a secondary battery. The French used it as a primary gun battery in their version of the ASW escort, the E50/E52, which makes an interesting comparison with the British *Blackwood*. The latter mounted only three open Bofors guns, presumably because the British expected little serious air opposition in the central Atlantic, whereas the French had to operate much closer to Soviet air bases.

Matters have changed somewhat with the advent of the SSM. A low-flying SSM is visible for only a very short time, which, it can be argued, negates the value of the long-range medium-caliber gun and instead emphasizes rate of fire at short range. Vickers argues that heavier VT shells are still far more lethal than a stream of small projectiles which almost have to penetrate the missile to stop it – as in anti-Kamikaze warfare in 1945. On the other hand, it is now possible, as it was not in 1945, to produce a 40mm VT fuze, and companies such as Breda claim that a fast-firing, very high velocity 40mm weapon is quite effective against missiles which have penetrated longer-range defenses. Similar claims are made for weapons of even smaller caliber such as the Oerlikon 35mm, which are also effective against small craft.

Finally, there is the Gatling gun, which fires 20mm or 30mm rounds at an extremely high rate of fire. The US Phalanx employs depleted-uranium bullets, which suffer the least loss of momentum over their range, and a radar built into the gun mount observes how close the rounds come,

With the demise of the US cruiser force, it became necessary for the US Navy to develop some weapon more powerful than the destroyer 5in gun, which could be outranged by those shore defense guns standard in the Communist world. A naval version of the Army 175mm gun was developed, but in the end a lightweight 8in/55 (Mk 71) was adopted; it is shown here installed in the destroyer *Hull* for tests, April 1975. It had a rate of fire of about 12 rounds per minute, exceeding that (per gun) of the *Des Moines* class. The new *Spruances* were designed to take a Mk 71 in place of their forward 5in mounts. However, as of early 1979, it appears that the Mk 71 program has died of insufficient funding: there was general agreement that some heavy-caliber firepower would be useful in the fleet, but the priority to achieve it was far too low to compete with programs such as Aegis and ASW improvement. The only mount afloat, that aboard the *Hull*, was removed in the spring of 1979. Officially, the 8in mission is to be performed by improved (including guided) 5in ammunition. *(Drawing: FMC Corporation)*

and corrects aim automatically. The Soviets appear to employ a similar weapon, but to what extent it enjoys the sophisticated error-correcting electronics of the Gatling is not clear.

Nor is it clear whether improvements in point defense missiles will not make such last-ditch weapons obsolete. A fast enough SSM may well stand an excellent chance of surviving even Gatling fire, expecially if it is somewhat hardened against hits; inside a minimum range, hits no longer matter, since the target is within the ballistic, not the aerodynamic, trajectory of the SSM. That is why 20mm weapons were good only for warning those below to take cover as Kamikazes hit.

However, the old-fashioned 20mm does survive, for what the Royal Navy calls 'junk-bashing'. Just as the SSM was too expensive for putting a shot across the bows of a ship, the medium-caliber gun is too expensive per round to handle small craft such as junks in the Far East; what is wanted is an inexpensive way of threatening or, at a pinch, damaging such craft. The Royal Navy first learned of this requirement when it began to operate in support of Malaysia during the 1962 confrontation with Indonesia; now all British frigates mount two Oerlikons of World War II vintage.

THE FIRE SUPPORT ROLE

The third major role for the naval gun is fire support, a task which first became really prominent during World War II. It requires a shell powerful enough to disable such land targets as tanks; ideally the shipborne gun is also more powerful than standard land based artillery pieces which an enemy may use for coast defense. Most navies mount a 4.5 or 5in gun for this role, but the US Navy has developed a specialized 8in/55, on the theory that a shipborne 5in/54 may not be able to deal with such standard Communist-bloc guns as the Soviet 130/55. Development of the 8in weapon began after long-term studies as early as 1961 showed the imminent demise of the cruiser fleet which had been able to provide 8in fire; however, a projection of the US maval mission showed that if anything amphibious operations against opposition might well become more common in the context of the 'Cold War'. For a time the Navy tried to modify the Army 175/60 to achieve the economy of a common gun tube and common ammunition, but the Army gun proved unsatisfactory, and instead the existing Navy 8in/55 was adapted.

In the fire support and indeed in the anti-ship role, rate of fire is less important than reliability. In many cases it is important to be able to blanket a target, but it is not too important to be able to do so rapidly. In shore bombardment, however, it may be very important to be able to deal

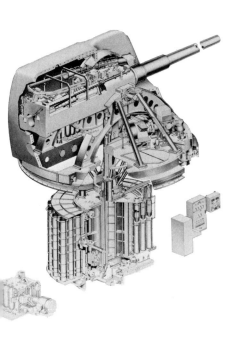

nearly simultaneously with two or more widely separated targets, such as pill boxes. Consequently Marine requirements for fire support are often stated in terms of number of guns, not rate of fire laid down. The requirement so stated in turn makes it profitable to develop relatively simple weapons which can be mounted with minimum ship-impact, hence those which can go aboard the most ships – again, as in the case of the Mk 71 8in/55.

All this discussion omits questions of gun fire control and of guided projectiles. As in the case of missiles, the ability of a gun battery to handle many disparate targets simultaneously is limited by the number of directors, no matter how many barrels it mounts: in this sense an 8in cruiser with one director is no more able to handle multiple targets than is the single 8in gun on a *Spruance*. In fact most US Navy 8in guns prior to the *Newport News* class used bagged ammunition and so were limited to about 3 rounds per minute per gun. In the *Newport News* and in the new Mk 71, brass cartridge cases permit power loading at the rate of about 10 rounds per gun per minute, which is much closer to the firing rate inherent in the gun; thus a single Mk 71 is equivalent to a triple turret and, in theory, three *Spruances* equal the shore-bombardment effectiveness of a World War II *Baltimore* class cruiser – at a rather higher price in dollars and in tons, to be sure. In fact the *Baltimore* could engage only two targets simultaneously, the *Spruances* three.

The 8in gun strains the capacity of a destroyer hull; it cannot be installed aft in a *Spruance* because it would foul the propeller shafts. As in other recent weapons, the problem is not weight but space, and in this case hull depth: automatic loading systems are great consumers of volume, and the need for high reliability consumes even more, as it is better to design large margins into parts.

FIRE CONTROL AND LASER GUIDANCE

As for gun fire directors, the main development of the postwar period has been a continual reduction in the size of their computers, so that directors have become smaller and smaller without any substantial loss of capability. In fact many modern directors have a secondary missile fire control capability, as their radar dishes can be used to illuminate targets for semi-active missile fire. The Royal Navy actually uses the same radar director to control both its 4.5in gun and its Sea Dart SAM; in some recent US ships the Mk 86 Fire Control System has a similar dual capability. As in many other cases of postwar design, such provisions have the great advantage of conserving scarce centerline space. Moreover, by buying more equivalent directors rather than fewer single purpose ones, the designer can insure against the failure or destruction of some of them.

Guided projectiles may be the next great change in naval gun fire. The larger the shell, the less lethality it must sacrifice in order to accommodate fins and the laser or other seeker in its nose. Its 'footprint', the leeway it has for maneuver, depends upon its velocity, so that a higher-velocity heavy shell has more flexibility than does a smaller one. Guidance is commonly proposed to improve accuracy for fire at ships and at small shore targets such as tanks, but it is also potentially valuable in air defense against such slowly-maneuvering but small targets as SSMs. At present it appears that the practical lower limit for laser guidance is about 5in caliber, which suggests that the choice of the 76/62 in the *Perry* may prove unfortunate.

Guns are particularly useful for close-range defense against missiles. This is the new US Vulcan-Phalanx, mounted experimentally on the fantail of the missile frigate (now destroyer) *King*, 1974. Vulcan-Phalanx differs from many other small-caliber gun systems in that its radar continuously observes the path of bursts and corrects later ones: in effect, it calculates the path that a burst will fire almost as soon as it leaves the barrel, computes an error, and then aims again. Phalanx rounds are simple solid penetrators made of depleted aluminum.

CHAPTER TEN

Some Soviet Perspectives

S oviet warships do not look like Western ones: they look a great deal tougher, and they seem to carry many more weapons per ton or per square foot of deck space. Above all, they seem to lack the bloated appearance of so many Western surface combatants, which are often described as oversized, overexpensive, and underarmed. Some analysts see in Soviet surface warships the same priorities which used to characterize our own: firepower, speed, seakeeping, in that order, rather than electronics, habitability, endurance – and only then weapons and speed.

These differences can be traced to a combination of very different naval roles, a distinctive Soviet tactical style, a distinctive economic system which has important implications for the design and production of naval weapons, and finally to the place of the Soviet Navy within the Soviet political system. It is also very important to keep in mind the vast difference in structure between the Soviet Navy and its Western counterparts: land-based Soviet naval aviation is a very different organisation than, for example, the US Navy's land-based ASW squadrons. It is, and for many years has been, the primary Soviet naval strike organisation; its mobility lies in its ability to shuttle between airfields throughout the Soviet Union, from which strikes can be mounted on Western naval forces approaching from any direction – given enough time to concentrate the bombers. In a sense the primary Soviet naval aviation airfields are almost fixed aircraft carriers.

The Soviet Navy is also much more 'submarine-heavy' than any Western navy, and it uses its submarines for many roles which in the West might fall to surface ships, such as distant-water anti-ship strike. One interesting political question is whether a navy with so large a submarine force comes, in the end, to be dominated by the submarine arm. That

certainly happened in Germany, but Admiral Gorshkov, who has shaped the modern Soviet Navy, is not a submarine man. Moreover, among the earliest consequences of Stalin's death was the demise of the massive Soviet attack submarine program. On the other hand, at present perhaps the most important task of the Soviet surface navy is ensuring the 'combat stability' of Soviet ballistic missile submarines by destroying Allied air and naval forces trying to enter their sanctuaries.

STRATEGY AND TACTICS

The Soviet Navy has always been a 'sea-denial' navy; its classical role is the destruction of particular enemy warships (now submarines, too) trying to enter waters it tries to place off limits. This mission emphasizes the targeting problem from the start: tactics begin with the discovery of the potential target, and continue through localization to the fire control data required for the final attack. Targeting and reconnaissance techniques have developed with advancing technology. For example, before World War II it appears that the Soviet Navy regarded its large submarine fleet as a means of reconnaissance; the other major distant-targeting system was radio direction-finding, supplemented by the kind of conventional intelligence for which the Soviets have always had a good reputation. At the end of World War II the Soviets captured advanced land-based HF/DF technology in Germany, and apparently that was the beginning of the sophisticated surveillance and targeting system now often termed SOSS (Soviet Ocean Surveillance System) in the West. The SOSS now also reportedly includes satellites, both passive (in effect extending the writ of Soviet land-based D/F stations) and active (radar). The latter are probably used to refine D/F data to the point where it becomes useful tactically; it is unlikely that even the Soviets have the resources to distinguish among the thousands of ships at sea that total global active radar coverage would reveal. One of the great advantages of D/F and other passive sensors is that they automatically reject signals which are not of interest.

Tactics reflect both the naval attack mission and Soviet economics. Although the Soviets produce very large numbers of missiles, tanks and tactical aircraft annually, they do not regard warships and sophisticated aircraft as expendable. Their naval tactics have always reflected this concern: many craft fire simultaneously from long range (to make counter-attack difficult) and in many cases from many different directions (to achieve saturation of any defense). The attack is controlled by an officer outside the battle. Such tactics require long-range weapons, which in turn require better targeting than do weapons fired from closer in. The character of the Soviet economy favors relatively small ships, partly because long-term economic planning favors production lines, and production lines limit the size of the ship they build.

The four 'Kynda' class 'rocket cruisers' established a Soviet reputation for heavy firepower in compact hulls, with their two quadruple launchers for SSN-3 anti-carrier cruise missiles, plus a SAM (SAN-1) launcher forward, two twin 3in AA mounts aft, multiple ASW rocket launchers forward of the SAM launcher, and triple torpedo tubes in the waist. Of the impressive-looking array of radars, the assembly atop the bridge is a 'Peel Group' for SAM control, comprising a pair of horizontally and vertically scanning radars, one large one for target tracking and one smaller one for missile tracking. The forward face of the big pyramidal mast carries a 'Scoop Pair' SSN-3 guidance antenna: the missile is command-guided from the ship, but the ship may use target data from other platforms. Atop the mast is a 'Headnet-A' air search radar; it appears that the provision for two such systems in tandem is an attempt to assure that one will always be operable. Abaft the second funnel is an 'Owl Screech' 76mm director. It is believed that the 'Kyndas' employ a pressure-fired steam plant, the type fitted in some US ocean escorts. Four vessels were built at Leningrad, probably laid down in 1957 and completed in 1961–62. *(CPL)*

Anti-carrier operations are probably the best known example of such Soviet strike tactics. The primary anti-carrier missile is the SSN-3, fired by ships and submarines from ranges of perhaps 200 miles. Many Soviet exercises, culminating in the two 'Okeans', have shown that the Soviet Navy well understands the need for coordination among widely separated units in achieving saturation with such weapons. Soviet doctrine calls for a surprise anti-carrier strike at the beginning of a war, and that element of surprise requires a simultaneous strike against all Western carriers; any failure will result in a pre-emptive attack by carrier aircraft against the relatively weakly armed Soviet missile ships, as well as an improvement in carrier defenses. The unusual character of the Soviet fleet – unusual by Western standards, that is – shows in the Soviet emphasis on combined-arms attacks (air, surface, submarine), all coordinated by a centrally located commander.

These tactics require a continual refinement of the initial target data, and the Soviets have invested very heavily in a reconnaissance/targeting organisation quite invisible to most observers and also quite alien to Western naval strategy. The consequences of poor target data can be quite serious: the relatively small Soviet surface ships and even their submarines carry no effective reloads; if their strike fails, they have no second chance, and are unlikely to survive counter-attack. The targeting organisation includes 'tattletale' destroyers which indicate to the strike leader which ship in the formation is the primary target, as all of the others will merely absorb missiles and so dilute the effect of the strike. 'Tattletale' design reflects this requirement: just before the strike, the 'tattletale' must turn away so as not to absorb missiles meant for the Western warships; she is often equipped, now, with four short-range SSMs pointed *aft*, which she can fire to add to the general effect of the strike.

Although anti-carrier warfare is the most publicized instance of Soviet concentration tactics, it is far from being the only one. Soviet ASW, for example, generally involves an operation by several ships, all of which are equipped with what by Western standards are very long-range rocket projectors (RBU) and relatively low-performance sonars, The combination would be absurd if single ships or pairs of ships were involved, but that is not the case. Rather, the sonars of the group are netted together and an area of uncertainty defined. As this area shrinks, it approaches the point at which a mass attack by the group can saturate it with rockets – at which point all of the attackers fire together. They are at maximum range, and therefore in minimum danger of counter-attack. These ASW tactics were evolved in the 1950s when the Soviets wished to be able to destroy submarines approaching within a few hundred miles of their coasts. They

Soviet warship designers did not adopt any distinctive style prior to the advent of long-range missiles: this 'Kotlin' class destroyer, photographed in October 1973, is typical of the first generation of postwar designs, with her steep sheer forward for seakeeping. Modifications since completion appear to have been limited to the elimination of the second bank of quintuple torpedo tubes and the installation of four twin 25mm automatic guns just abaft the second funnel. The quadruple 45mm gun, which (at least externally) resembles some wartime German types, was standard in Soviet warships of the mid-1950s. The main gun battery of these ships is a 130mm weapon in a stabilized twin mount somewhat reminiscent of the World War II German 105mm type. The 'Kotlins' entered service in 1955–56 and were the last conventional Soviet destroyers.

began the construction of large numbers of small, very fast ASW corvettes, such as the 'Mirkas' and 'Petyas', capable of running down a datum supplied, presumably, by an ASW equivalent of the SOSS*.

Current Soviet blue-water ASW practice seems to show similar basic concepts. The weapons, such as the SSN-14 and the FRAS-1 unguided nuclear rocket, have long ranges in comparison to the nominal ranges of the sonars their ships appear to possess. However, those same sonars, netted together, have a much better performance. For example, at a range at which one sonar has only a 20 per cent probability of detecting some target, four such sonars have a combined probability of detection of nearly 60 per cent. Homing torpedoes and nuclear depth charges have large effective lethal volumes, and the longer their ranges the lower the probability that the target submarine will be able to strike back. Soviet tactical philosophy appears to emphasize the value of surviving to fight again – not so much because individuals are valued as because it is not so easy to build replacement attack ships and aircraft.

These ideas are not new. For example, the Soviets are very proud of having developed aircraft torpedoes suitable for launch from high altitude; to all other navies such a concept seemed insane, since there would be little chance of the torpedo hitting anything once it entered the water. However, the Soviets did not intend to fire single torpedoes; their tactics emphasized group drops which would make it difficult for the distant target to evade the spread of torpedoes coming her way. In this sense the torpedo is the ancestor of the Soviet naval stand-off missile.

Long-range weapons tend to be rather large. Saturation tactics imply a relatively pessimistic view of the chance that very many warheads will hit, since many of them will be expended against defenses**. Hence any warhead which does get through must have maximum effect; moreover, the Soviets probably do not expect to make more than one attack against any one target. Hence their warheads tend to be rather large; even the short-range 'Styx' is usually credited with an 800lb warhead. It follows that in general the primary armament of Soviet warships is very large missiles, especially in proportion to the small ship size implied by production considerations. There will be few if any reloads.

*However, a recurring puzzle in Soviet ASW is the absence of any wide-area sensor, equivalent, perhaps, to SOSUS, which might provide the initial datum on which Soviet techniques appear to be based. This may, of course, be a failure of intelligence, or it may mean that the Soviets are spending a great deal to buy such a system, and prefer to plan as though all those rubles will be worthwhile. The latter might be very characteristic of Soviet society, in which the *appearance* of fulfilling the Five Year Plan is all-important.
**In ASW, saturation is not so much saturation of active defenses as saturation of the area in which the submarine may maneuver – in effect, saturation of the defense inherent in its ability to evade.

Given a radar picture of a task force at sea, it is essential that a Soviet strike commander knows which ships are his main targets: all the others act as no more than absorbers of the limited number of anti-ship missiles at his disposal. In peacetime the Soviets like to be able to shadow carrier task groups specifically to have such information constantly available; and the best visual shadowers are fast destroyers. Of course, once the attack begins, the 'tattletale' itself becomes a missile absorber: it must turn away from the target formation just prior to the attack. At that time it can add to the general destruction by firing its own SSMs backwards towards the carrier group: note that the four 'Styx' installed on this Soviet destroyer, the *Neulovimy*, point aft for just this mission. This 'Kildin' class destroyer began as one of the first Soviet SSM ships, with SSN-1 installed aft and a hangar for six reloads; she was later rebuilt, the SSN-1 system being removed and replaced by a pair of twin 3in guns and the four 'Styx'. All the other original armament was retained: four quadruple 45mm guns, and two twin torpedo tubes. The air search radar forward is unusual: it is 'Headnet-C', two two-dimensional sets mounted back to back, with one at an angle. Correlations between the returns from both give target altitude and bearing; in effect it is a three-dimensional radar with a relatively low data rate. The need for so elaborate a set in a ship without SAMs is difficult to understand.

The Soviet Navy normally conducts its operations from shore headquarters, but such tactics are not entirely satisfactory in a fast-developing battle – as Western navies have always believed. One approach to on-the-spot command has been the conversion of *Sverdlov* class cruisers into command ships; the command spaces are in the large block which replaces No 3 turret, and which carries on its roof a 'pop-up' launcher for the Soviet point defense weapon SAN-4. The two cones atop the aftermost mast are long-range microwave communications links to shore stations. Given the Soviet preference for very centralized control, it is quite possible that in practice control is still exercised from shore, the seagoing flagship actually carrying out administrative tasks only.

In fact in their earliest SSM ships the Soviets did provide reloads, but they almost certainly discovered that the simple reload systems which could fit destroyer or small cruiser ('Kynda'*) hulls were totally unworkable in rough weather; subsequent ships show no provision for reloads**. As in Western navies, the simplest way to mount an SSM was employed: a box launcher. The rotatable launchers of the 'Kynda' were probably soon found to be unnecessary, given the kind of guidance which could be built into the weapon. However, it is interesting that the 'Krivak' (though not the larger 'Kresta II' or 'Kara') has a rotatable launcher for its SSN-14 ASW missile. From the point of view of a Western observer, any large weapon in a box set on deck on a relatively small destroyer or cruiser must seem far more warlike than a small set of rails or even the small box of an Exocet or Harpoon, especially since the main battery of most Western warships is actually an air group which that ship can help control – and which is effectively invisible.

*'Kynda' is a NATO official designation rather than a Soviet one. All major Soviet surface combatants are assigned Russian-sounding names beginning with the letter K, in view of the traditional Soviet unwillingness to disclose the names of their ships. However, *Kiev*'s name is lettered boldly on her hull, and many other Soviet names are now known. Smaller surface ships also receive NATO names (eg 'Osa', 'Petya'). Submarines are given letters in a random sequence and are referred to by the standard phonetic equivalents of those letters (eg 'Whiskey' for W). These designations have no relation whatever to Soviet practice.

**The *Kiev*, which devotes large spaces to an SSN-12 (SSN-3 successor) reload facility, is both an important exception and an object lesson in the volume such a facility requires.

The Soviet 'Kashin' class destroyers have always been impressive ships: gas turbine propelled, with a reported speed of 39kts, and armed fore and aft with SAMS. This is *Obratsovy*, which visited Portsmouth in 1976. Forward, she shows a twin 76mm AA gun, and then the stabilized launcher for SAN-1, with reload hatches visible fore and aft, and a rather low blast screen abaft them; the guns are saluters temporarily mounted. The dish abaft the SAM is an 'Owl Screech' for 76mm control, with two RBU-4500A ASW rocket launchers just abaft it, and 'Peel Group' (SAM control, with the target height-finder particularly visible) atop what must be a crowded navigating bridge. (*C & S Taylor*)

In the mid-1960s the Soviet surface fleet turned away from anti-carrier contruction and towards ASW, both for the protection of the Soviet ballistic missile submarine fleet and for the destruction of Western ballistic missile submarines. For example, later units of the 'Kresta' class, such as this one, mounted quadruple SSN-14 ASW missile launchers in place of the twin SSN-3s of earlier ones; they also had a more powerful SAM, SAN-3, in place of the SAN-1 of earlier 'Krestas'. Also evident in this photograph is the big 'Top Sail' three-dimensional radar mounted atop the foremast. The large domes running down the side of that mast are for ECM. The gun battery is limited to small calibers: two twin 57mm mounts aft, controlled by 'Muff Cob' directors alongside the fat funnel, and two Gatling guns on either side abaft the SSN-14 box launcher, controlled by a centerline 'Bass Tilt' director. The rather colorful names of Soviet electronic gear are given almost entirely on the basis of external appearance and so do not reflect much information on their performance or function

However, recent Western analyses suggest that in general the Soviets prefer weapons and even sensors with a low ship-impact. They mount more such systems than do Western warships, which means that individual systems require less integration with each other than is common in the West; it also means that a ship looks far more heavily armed than would a more highly integrated Western design. It is possible that the deliberate choice of low ship-impact weapons and sensors may be more a consequence of the Soviet economic system than of any operational doctrine.

THE NAVAL INFRASTRUCTURE

The Soviet economy is planned in five-year increments, and although the Five Year Plan probably never works as intended, Soviet plant managers must think quite far in advance, as must all Soviet military and naval planners. The net effect of long-range planning is to make changes in plan very difficult and even very unpleasant politically. There is some reason to believe that in the Soviet Union decisions on production rates, which affect the operation of the industrial system and hence the fates of plant managers, are far more important than decisions as to military force levels. The art of planning is the art of designing programs so that they will suffer least from the inevitable delays and changes in those sub-programs that must feed into them. The designer of a ship has two choices. He can use weapons and other equipment already in production and hence already well-defined (but in that case the ship that he designs for inclusion in the next Five Year Plan or perhaps the one after that will be far behind the state of the art); alternatively, he can choose from a menu of systems under development, knowing that his ship had better be able to accommodate the inevitable changes in those systems as they progress towards production. The latter is practically a definition of low ship-impact: a box launcher, for example, may weigh a few hundred pounds more than it did when designed without materially affecting the design of the ship which carries it; a relatively small SAM magazine can grow a few inches in any direction without requiring a change in hull design or even in internal hull piping. Given the choice of low-impact systems, relatively poorly integrated with ship sensors, it is prudent to mount as many as possible: low-impact and small size equal, in most cases, low capability.

Soviet electronics suffers, in many instances, from an inability on the part of Soviet industry to produce sophisticated devices in very large numbers. Perhaps the best evidence of this problem is the empty platforms,

The new standard Soviet destroyer, the 'Krivak', in a way symbolizes the Soviet shift towards ASW. Her four big missile tubes forward were originally assumed to be for anti-ship weapons; only much later did it become evident that they were for SSN-10, the Soviet equivalent of ASROC. These weapons are command-guided by means of the two 'Eye Bowl' radars paired atop the bridge, with a 'Pop Group' SAN-4 control radar before them, and surface search and 'Headnet-C' air search above. The SAN-4s are the only weapons not visible; they ride below decks in what look like mounting rings for future use but are actually retractable missile launchers. These are situated on the centerline and may just be discerned, abaft the missile tubes and abaft the uptake. Two quadruple torpedo tubes amidships (covered here) and a gun battery aft complete the weapon suit; recent 'Krivaks' have heavier single-barrel weapons aft. The housing right aft conceals a variable depth sonar, and the sharply raked bow protects the bow sonar from a descending anchor. Note the two RBU-2500A ASW rocket launchers on the raised deckhouse forward. *(CPL)*

clearly intended for ECM gear, on the masts of many front-line Soviet surface warships: generally there is a high priority for the prototype equipment for the first of a class, but no one is nearly as concerned about successors. In many cases a ship has two or more identical search radars, a design practice suggesting a certain lack of confidence in the reliability of the equipment. Electronics problems also probably explain the large size of Soviet homing torpedoes: even the lightweight type is 16in in diameter, and major surface ships carry only the larger diameter type*.

Finally, the planned character of the economy favors long production runs, not merely of ships of any class but also of such sub-systems as propulsion plants, sensors and weapons. Each Soviet plant manager, at each level, receives an annual bonus based upon how close he comes to fulfilling his norm, under the Plan. He finds it infinitely easier to fulfill that norm if his output from year to year is very nearly constant, and in consequence he will resist any attempt to change model and to increase or decrease production. All changes in Plan, in fact, makes waves – and a big bureaucracy like that of the Soviet Union has as its one iron law that waves are to be avoided. Politics in the Soviet Union, as indeed in its Czarist predecessor, is the politics of the ruling class, in this case a ruling class many of whose members are plant managers and similar middle-level bureaucrats in the production machine.

Thus the character of the economy and the political structure behind it make for enormous inertia in Soviet military production. All changes are relatively difficult, and even the totalitarian government may well find it difficult to enforce priorities in a system in which any change at all requires great effort. Moreover, actual ruling power is concentrated in so few hands that the rulers find it difficult to focus their attention on any specific problem for long; inertia dominates. It follows that actual ship design may not change nearly so rapidly as naval policy, so that designs such as the 'Kashin', characteristic of much earlier periods, may remain in production for a very long time.

*In fairness, it should be admitted that the decision to use larger torpedoes may be more a matter of warhead size than of requirements for guidance electronics. Sometimes it is suggested that in the West, and particularly in the United States, there is just too much interest in miniaturizing weapons without keeping up their lethality, and that lightweight homing torpedoes are a particularly grotesque case in point.

A DIRECT COMPARISON

Perhaps most fundamentally, the reason Western warships now look unlike Westerns warships of 1945 – and Soviet warships of today – is that they require much more space for onboard command and control, while many of their most potent weapons are either rather compact (thanks to good electronics) or are aloft in naval aircraft. The Soviets, however, do not place extensive command and control facilities aboard their ships; they expect control to be exerted from some position outside the battle, such as a bunker in Leningrad. Thus they do not need the large operations rooms common in Western practice, or the kind of computer associated with NTDS. It is these developments which have displaced weapons in Western warships, not the advance of habitability standards, although of course the latter have had considerable effects.

Comparison between recent Western and Soviet warships can be instructive. For example, the Soviet 'Krivak' and the US *Knox* are both ASW frigates of similar size. The 'Krivak' is faster than the *Knox,* especially in rough water, partly because it does not have a large bow sonar, but also because its designers were willing to trade endurance for high speed in the form of a gas turbine powerplant, although just how much they traded is not clear, since, for example, it is not known (at least publicly) whether the 'Krivak' plant is a COGOG or just a simple high-power plant. The *Knox* design, on the other hand, emphasizes endurance and reliability; the latter shows as a greater volume per shp for maintenance of the plant. The 'Krivak' has both a medium bow sonar and VDS, but she has not nearly the sonar range of the SQS-26 that equips *Knox,* which may have both VDS and the towed array. This disparity may be of little consequence, given Soviet ASW tactics.

As for the weapons themselves, the 'Krivak' has three separate ASW systems: a quadruple SSN-14 (without reloads, but with two independent 'Eye Bowl' directors, which may mean no more than that standard doctrine calls for a salvo of two weapons), a pair of quadruple large-caliber ASW torpedo tubes (probably without reloads), and a pair of multiple MBU-2500A rocket launchers (with a range of over 6000yds, and almost certainly reloadable). Against this battery the *Knox* has ASROC (8 missiles plus reloads with power loading usable at sea), fixed 12.75in ASW torpedo tubes (with reloads), and LAMPS; the latter greatly extends her effective range, and has no Soviet equivalent. The 'Krivak' must operate alone or at least far from other ships of her ASW group; however, for air and surface defense she has only two SAN-4 encapsulated point defense launchers (with two directors) and two twin 76mm guns (with one director) aft. The *Knox* has Sea Sparrow, which can be controlled by a specialized director aft, but can probably respond also to illumination from her fire control radar. She also has a rapid-fire 5in/54 which can have significant effects on the 'Krivak' hull, not to mention the possibility of Harpoon fired from her ASROC launcher. To be fair, it is possible that a 'Krivak' normally carries a few conventional torpedoes for self-defense; but that reduces her already low capacity for ASW torpedoes.

Each ship carries one air search and one surface search radar; the 'Krivak's are generally less capable, which may, for example, mean that she has no significant chance of detecting a submarine periscope or snorkel, whereas the *Knox* radar has at least some capability in that direction. The 'Krivak's air search radar is a 'Headnet Charlie' incorporating two angled antennas for limited height-finding, presumably for operation with her

This view of the stern of the Soviet missile cruiser *Nikolaev* ('Kara' class) shows typical Soviet space-saving detail, with a small helipad atop the VDS housing and the hangar half-sunken into the fantail and abutting on to the after SAN-3 launcher (whose magazine capacity is probably limited by the hangar below decks – note the two rather than four reload doors, and the launcher arms in the reload position). The small control cab alongside is characteristic of many small-ship helicopter installations. The small 'fish' by the VDS housing is probably a towed anti-torpedo decoy corresponding to the US Nixie and Fanfare. One detail not visible is the extent to which the helicopter hangar extends below deck, an extent hinted at by the need for a deck opening abaft the hangar proper.

Amidships a 'Kara' shows a variety of anti-aircraft weapons, perhaps typical of Soviet unwillingness to rely on any single system. The big missile control radar on the right is 'Headlights', a pair of dishes for target track and another pair for missile track. Presumably all these, and incidentally most of the other dish fire control radars in Soviet service, are monopulse systems. Also visible at the beam is the usual pair of Gatling-type close-range defense guns, but the platform inboard of them, which is intended for the 'Bass Tilt' fire control, is as yet empty (July 1973). Forward of these weapons is the 'Pop Group' which controls the SAN-4 alongside – note the blast shield which also, incidentally, protects 'Pop Group' from the ECM radomes alongside it. Presumably the difference in size between upper and lower pairs of domes indicates different frequency ranges. Finally, there are the standard Soviet 76mm AA guns.

SAN-4s; *Knox* has no such capability but probably does enjoy a much longer radar range. This particular difference may reflect limitations on the SAN-4 as opposed to the Sea Sparrow guidance radar, or it may mean that the SAN-4 missile has somewhat greater range. Each ship carries an ECM system, details of which are not available.

The greatest difference between the two ships is in their internal volume. The 'Krivak' is a compact ship with a low superstructure, a background against which her weapons stand out impressively. The *Knox* is a much boxier ship, and some of her weapons (most notably her ASW torpedo tubes and her helicopter) are largely hidden from view. Her massive 'mack' may carry a considerable electronics load, but that too is largely invisible – a radome shows little of its contents, or, more importantly, of what those contents plus the computers and operators inside the ship can do. To some small extent the 'Krivak' may balance off her lack of internal hull volume by adopting a very compact gas turbine powerplant, but in that case she may not be able to achieve cruising economy except by running on one shaft and trailing the other – a practice not exactly popular in Western navies.

The 'Krivak' is a weapon platform well adapted to central-command tactics in which the commander and his staff are somewhere else. She is seaworthy, which is essential if she is to be able to deliver her weapons. She may not last too long in battle, since she carries few weapons, but those weapons are in the main externally stowed for minimum impact on other aspects of her design.

The 'Krivak' is typical of modern Soviet warship design. There is no evidence of any attempt to achieve a particularly ferocious behavior, as one might see in the larger Soviet missile cruisers. Instead, her design is very well adapted to the requirements of coordinated (ASW) strike warfare, within the constraints of unit cost and of large weapon size due to a need for very long range and (probably) relatively primitive and hence space-consuming electronics. Given such weapons, there is a choice between external launchers without reloads and reloadable launchers making very large internal volume demands. Moreover, very large weapons are difficult to handle aboard a small, pitching ship, as the Soviets undoubtedly learned by operating the 'Kildin', 'Krupny' and 'Kynda' classes – and, incidentally, as the German Navy learned in two World Wars by trying to mount 5.9in guns on destroyer hulls. This choice is by no means unique to the Soviets. Nearly all Western warships which carry SSMs carry them in non-reloadable external cannisters, because provisions for reloading even these relatively small weapons would impose prohibitive internal volume demands, given hulls already swollen to accept ASW and often AAW weapons.

To a Westerner, a 'Krivak' brings back memories of an age in which money went on what mattered, on weapons rather than black boxes and mysterious antennas and flashing lights in big CICs – and more and more bunk space. The reality is that much of what is aboard a Western frigate is also included in the Soviet naval establishment, except that it is accommodated either on land or aboard a specialized flagship; the Soviet Navy now has two *Sverdlov* class cruisers converted to command ships, presumably to control anti-carrier strikes. These conversions show that the Soviets can be as volume-limited as anyone else: they had to remove one turret and build up a big box aft to house their command facilities, which also seem to require many radios including what appears to be a big long-range directional link. Presumably the latter maintains the vital connection

Further forward, the 'Kara's bridge wing has the 'Owl Screech' control for the 76mm guns abaft it; the lattice foremast carries 'Headnet-C'. Note that the forward 'Headlights' are tilted aft, as they would be for tracking. Although there are two sets of dishes (to correspond, it would seem, with two missile launch arms), the fact that they are rigidly mounted together would seem to reduce them back to a single target engagement.

to the high command: Soviet tactical style cannot be unrelated to the 'top-downwards' character of their entire society, in which obedience to higher authority is prized far above individual initiative. Under most circumstances the command ship would probably function as no more than an administrative control center, but in combat, particularly at the beginning of a war, it would have the advantage of close proximity to the battle and hence of better communications. Of course it has the disadvantage that one of the best counters to Soviet tactics is to destroy the commander and his distinctive ship.

A CHANGE OF DIRECTION?

Soviet tactical style has lasted now, for at least forty years, through many radical revisions of naval role and naval technology. It seems unlikely that it will alter very much in the future, although its expression may well evolve with changes in the Soviet industrial machine. The *Kiev* and her air group may teach the Soviets that a fleet built around aircraft at sea can accomplish more than sea denial, even though clearly the *Kiev* herself is designed for classic Soviet operations. There is an even more interesting possibility. If in fact the primary decisions within the Soviet system are decisions about production rates, and if also the system favors large production runs, then the *Kiev* cannot be terribly popular within the Soviet aircraft industry. She requires a specialized small airplane and even four *Kiev*s can take only very few Yak-36s ('Forgers'). It probably follows that there is some resistance, not to a Soviet air-capable ship, but rather to one which can operate only with V/STOL aircraft. There must, in fact, be someone with authority saying that the Navy can have big ships – the Party has so decreed – but that it would be very much better if those big ships used airplanes which were already being made in large numbers. For quite some time now the Soviet Navy has been operating a squadron of conventional ground-attack jet fighters ('Fitter-C'), the first fighters (other than the Yak-36) it has had since it lost its port defense aircraft in 1960.

If such logic forces Admiral Gorshkov to build the carriers the like of which he has already built a navy to sink, then he may find that they require escorts. Ships such as the *Kiev* are nearly self-escorting, but they pay a price: they cannot operate conventional aircraft. The *Kiev* is a relatively inefficient way of deploying her particular conglomeration of weapon systems, except that she requires no elaborate ship-to-ship data links for coordination of her radars and weapons. However, any escort(s) would be quite different. Soviet style is no guide, since these ships would have to provide defensive cover rather than team up to kill one ship after another. Soviet inexperience in ship-to-ship coordination from the ships being coordinated would tend to favor construction of fewer large escorts, with weapons of sufficient range to cover both carrier and escort. Perhaps the cruiser now being built in Leningrad, about which little is known, is a harbinger of just this kind of development; by now his naval architects must have told Admiral Gorshkov that the *Kiev* is a very inefficient use of thirty or forty thousand tons – and, we can be quite sure, a very lavish slice of relatively scarce Soviet resources.

The timing of such a switch, if switch it is to be, is set largely by the sequencing of the Five Year Plans. The current Plan ends in 1980 and presumably encompasses most of the *Kiev* program, which will then have stretched over two Five Year Plans. The *Kiev* decision must have been made, at the latest, during the 1966–70 Plan, most likely before the last

'Headlights' aboard a 'Kresta II', September 1971. The very small dish between the two big ones is a microwave command transmitter. The 'Muff Cob' radar mounted on the 'mack' platform to the left of 'Headlights' controls the 57mm gun alongside the big missile control radar. Note the missile blast shield to the right.

For many years the Soviets discussed aircraft carriers only as important naval targets. In the *Kiev* and her sister *Minsk* they have gone part of the way towards their own carrier, at the same time retaining major features of classical Soviet missile cruiser design. For the first time in Soviet practice these ships have a rough-water reload capability for their large SSN-12 (improved SSN-3) missiles, in the large tubes forward; the guidance electronics for these weapons is concealed in the trapdoor right forward. These ships are practically an exhibition of the range of current Soviet naval weapons. Reading fore to aft they have two RBU-2500A ASW rocket launchers, a launcher for the SUW-N-1 unguided nuclear ASW missile (also known as FRAS-1), a twin 76mm gun, SSN-12 and an SAN-3 launcher, and two Gatling guns (with two more on a sponson to port; the electronics on the island consist of 'Owl Screech' (76mm fire control), 'Headlights' (SAN-3), 'Top Sail' (long range air search, three-dimensional), a dome presumably housing the Soviet equivalent of TACAN, 'Top Steer' (a miniature 'Top Sail'), then, symmetrically, 'Headlights' and a second 'Owl Screech'; abaft the island are another SAN-3 launcher and another twin 76mm gun; and more Gatling guns are spotted about the flight deck aft. The side of the island shows the usual array of ECM radomes, code-named 'Side Globe', and there are also navigational radars, not identified here. Also visible in these February 1979 photographs of *Minsk* are the torpedo tubes set into the side of the hull amidships, as in the earlier helicopter carrier *Moskva*. (Both photos: MoD(N))

Soviet air-capable ship, the *Moskva,* even ran her trials. If a new class is to be begun under the 1981–85 Plan, preliminary work must be going on already, as the outlines of the new Plan were probably fixed no later than 1977–78. Moreover, the plan for a new carrier most likely includes a plan for escorts – and for new long-range weapons. We may, therefore, look for a new generation of Soviet warships, perhaps much more like Western ones. If the Soviets do not go through this analysis the odds are that they will come to discover that all those unsightly boxes atop our ships are really there for a purpose, not merely to outrage our sailors, and they may be placed in the embarrassing position of having to offload many of their heavy weapons in order to add what amounts to high ship-impact command and control to their latest vessels.

That would indeed change our picture of just how tough the Soviet Navy is – at just the time it was attaining a combat capability, as a fleet, quite comparable to our own.

CHAPTER ELEVEN

Survivability without Armor

Modern warships are soft. Most are so volume-critical that their designers have been forced to build up high superstructures; topweight dictates the use of lightweight material, such as aluminum, which actually makes a ship more vulnerable; worse still, the squeeze within most hulls forces vital command and control spaces into the superstructure. Even weapon magazines are more vulnerable than they once were. Missile magazines are large and must extend far above the waterline in order to permit easy transfer from magazine to launcher; the longer the transfer path, the lower the rate of fire of the launcher – and the more vulnerable the ship to air attack.

A great part of this vulnerability is accepted because the cost of any alternative design is extremely high. In the late 1950s the then Preliminary Design Branch of the US Bureau of Ships tried to design a well-protected ship with the firepower and electronic systems of the new 'soft' frigates then being built; it came out to about three times the displacement of the frigate, because it was necessary to cover very large topside volumes with substantial armor, about four inches thick. The old standards of armor protection no longer suffice: it is not nearly enough to provide a waterline belt (to protect buoyancy and perhaps to protect the vitals against hits at the waterline), a deck to cover it, and pieces of armor around compact underwater magazines and gun turrets. The heart of a missile frigate is its combat information center and computer room, and that is both large and, worse, high in the ship. If it is moved below the waterline, the hull must be enlarged merely to provide enough volume, and that in turn requires extra power. The missile magazines themselves must project well above the waterline, and heavy armor covering them adds topweight which, again, must be balanced by a larger hull – and more power. Similar considerations

apply to waveguides and topside wiring, all of which are also essential. Even with all these points covered, the ship would remain vulnerable to damage to the radar antennas themselves, which cannot be armored. Perhaps it is indicative of the cost of protection that in recent years the only US surface combatant designed with any armor was the proposed 17,000-ton strike cruiser, which was to have had about three inches of armor to protect her CIC and computer room. Such protection was impossible on any lesser displacement.

THE CASE AGAINST ALUMINUM

There are, of course, halfway measures. Aluminium burns, and it tends to produce splinters when it is hit, as the US Navy discovered in the cases, respectively, of the *Belknap* and the *Worden*. The *Belknap*'s super-structure burned and melted after her collision with the carrier *John F Kennedy*, demonstrating that aluminum does not make for durable ships, even if it does make for good stability in a ship crammed with radars. That experience probably ended interest in aluminum hull construction, which in 1972 was advertised as a means of greatly increasing ship payload; a study of the *Belknap* showed that a saving of 41 per cent in structural weight was possible with an all-aluminum structure. That might not have precluded protection; one possibility might be a soft hull in which weight saved went partly into armored boxes surrounding vital structures within the hull.

The *Worden* case was in some ways far more sobering, since it involved a type of damage to be expected in wartime: a Shrike anti-radar missile with a fragmentation warhead was accidentally dropped on the ship off Vietnam. The fragments cut all topside waveguides and cable leads, and even damaged the wheelhouse; the ship lost all electric power for a time and for some hours was credited with less than 40 per cent of her normal fighting capacity. Her aluminum superstructure acted to multiply the fragments produced by the missile; every pellet from the missile produced two or more in the superstructure, so that instead of a shield it became a deadly instrument in its own right. The *Worden* experience was not very well known at

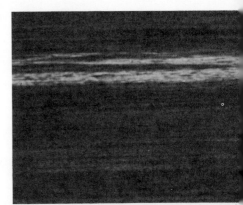

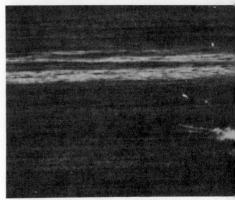

the time, but it has since been publicized; however, there has been no great effort to protect the long waveguides running up masts, upon which ships depend for their operation. Some analysts thought that the Soviet practice of enclosing their masts indicated an interest in just such protection, but the new 'Krivaks' have entirely open masts and so suggest otherwise. Generally, topweight must prohibit all but the thinnest protection at such great heights above the keel; sometimes anti-fragment materials such as Kevlar are proposed.

At least some navies prefer to accept cramping and build lower superstructures out of mild steel. It is not armor, but it is also much more protective than aluminum – and, more importantly, it does not burn. The Royal Navy adopted this practice throughout its postwar frigate program. Writing in 1974, M K Purvis, who had been responsible for all of those ships, noted that 'a visit to the wreck of the *Graf Spee* in 1940 firmly convinced the author that the fire risk inherent with aluminium was only justified by its weight saving in minor bulkheads in the superstructure. The corrosion and modulus of elasticity problems combined with the complication of construction are so costly that they do not justify the weight saving achieved, which is far less than would be anticipated at first sight if the aluminium is extended to more important structural items'. Purvis also advocated plated-in masts: 'the efficient design of a lattice mast necessitates more precise details of aerials and other weights on it than are usually available in the early stages of a design. Not only does a plated mast give design flexibility, because practical construction considerations make it over designed from a strength point of view, but it has the added advantage of providing protection to the cable runs to the aerials whereas in the case of the lattice mast those are exposed to splinter damage'.

Canada, too, demanded mild steel for her frigates, and reportedly the new Canadian frigates will have no aluminum at all topside, even over the big helicopter hangar required. In both the Canadian and the British cases, the price accepted for a more survivable hull was a lesser weapon and sensor suit on the same dimensions or, conversely, a larger hull for a given suit. In this sense lesser may include less capable, eg because radars must be lower in the hull to satisfy stability requirements.

Mild steel and Kevlar-covered waveguides are among the possible reactions to one end of the spectrum of threats a modern warship faces. Other parts of that spectrum are the threat of nuclear weapon effects and the threat of underwater damage. Just how these threats (all of which require very different protective measures) should be weighed depends upon the sort of war a ship is probably going to fight.

TOPSIDE DAMAGE

Topside damage is generally due to shellfire, which is the old way; to bombs (mainly the effects of near-misses which shower the ship with splinters); or to an SSM. The SSM is so large that no reasonable amount of armor will keep it out – which is one reason that the US Navy never even came close to building the fully protected frigate. Probably the greatest danger it presents is the possibility that it will hit a magazine and blow up the ship. Otherwise the SSM has a lethal radius which may or may not intercept some vital section of the ship; its main danger is that it may set an aluminum superstructure on fire. Ship design practice changes relatively slowly; presumably the fire danger inherent in SSMs is now beginning to be appreciated and may figure in the specifications of US warships now being designed. Weight

It has long been known that the right mixture of a fuel such as gasoline and air is highly explosive; gasoline vapor explosions were responsible for the loss of several carriers in World War II. In this sequence a gasoline cloud is formed by the fixed ejector to the left of the target ship, the old destroyer escort *McNulty*; detonators are fired into the expanding cloud, to explode it uniformly; and the detonation itself then takes place. The chief effect of fuel/air explosives is a uniform blast pressure not very different from that experienced in a nuclear blast and thus quite capable of blowing in ship structures. This series of photographs was taken in November 1972.

The *Cleveland* class cruiser *Atlanta* was converted into a test ship for one of the US Navy's most ambitious programs, an attempt to measure the effects of nuclear air blast on modern warships. She was stripped to the main deck and rebuilt with frigate and destroyer equipment topside. Nos 1 and 2 barbettes were retained to act as bases for, respectively, SPS-37 and SPS-30 (pencil-beam height-finder) radars; right forward was a typical destroyer tripod mast carrying an SPS-40 air search radar and an SPS-21 surface search antenna. The new forward deckhouse was a blast-hardened type carrying, below decks, components of the SPS-42 three-dimensional air search radar carried atop it, as well as an SPS-10D surface search set, LORAN, IFF equipment, ECM equipment, and communications gear; the 'mack' atop the deckhouse carried the SPS-42 and -10D antennas, as well as standard US ECM antennas, plus a standard pair of SPG-55 Terrier guidance radars. Alongside was a set of Mk 32 lightweight torpedo tubes; the ship also carried long fixed tubes (Mk 25, as in FRAM-II destroyers) and ASROC. Between her two deckhouses was an SPS-37A long range air search radar antenna. The after deckhouse duplicated current practice (ie, construction of the *Leahy* and *Belknap* classes), and on the fantail was an SPG-51 Tartar guidance radar. *Atlanta* was converted at the San Francisco Naval Shipyard at a cost of about $4m. No 1 engine room and fire room were activated to drive the outboard shafts only; berthing and messing accommodations for a crew of about 200 were installed, and 185 men were assigned. She was subjected to extensive underwater shock tests off San Clemente, California, in November 1964, and then tested for air blast off Kahoolawe, Hawaii, the next spring.

appears to preclude any serious armor in the superstructure, at least unless US designers adopt some more inherently stable hull form. However, it does seem absurd, as has recently been suggested, that a *Perry* class frigate (and by extension almost any modern warship) can be disabled by a rifle bullet in the right place, presumably the CIC.

During the early postwar period it appeared that, except for fast carrier task forces, most Western surface ships would be faced primarily with attack by Soviet submarines; in many navies, such as the US Navy, the danger of topside damage came to be less and less appreciated. Even within a carrier task force exposed to air attack, it appears to have become an article of faith that all efforts should be concentrated on defeating the attack by killing the aircraft or stand-off missiles, and that there was little hope of surviving the explosion of a large Soviet warhead. This may have been extremely realistic, especially if it turns out that the Soviets have always believed that carrier task forces deserve only nuclear attack, since they are potential nuclear attack systems. However, the Soviets are no longer the only potential naval adversary of any Western navy: Western naval forces may, in future, have to fight some of the smaller navies, many of which are armed with a variety of Western SSMs of relatively small size – missiles which rely on the lack of protection of most warships to make their small warheads effective.

NUCLEAR ASPECTS

Through the early 1960s it was probably US Navy doctrine to expect the free use of nuclear weapons at sea; for example, the *Leahy* class double-ended missile frigates were expected to be able to attack other ships and shore positions using nuclear versions of their Terrier SAMs. In consequences there was a recurring interest in the protection of warships from nuclear weapons. It was not that anyone ever had the idea that a ship could survive a direct hit, but rather that a bomb dropped on a formation of ships at sea would be a near miss from the point of view of most of them; and near misses can be survived. For example, at one time standard carrier formation doctrine called for the three carriers of a task group to be arranged around the perimeter of a circle; it was calculated that even a 1-megaton weapon dropped in the center of the circle would not destroy them, and a weapon dropped on any one carrier would have even less effect on the other two. If it were assumed that 1-megaton bombs were a scarce commodity in Soviet hands, it was very realistic to harden carriers against such near misses. The same held for their consorts.

A bomb produces a variety of effects, depending upon its design and where it explodes: a blast or shock wave, intense heat, underwater shock, radioactive fall-out, electromagnetic pulse (EMP) and other anti-electronics phenomena. No single nuclear explosion will produce all, but a ship must be designed against any realistic combination of nuclear attacks. For example, a bomb exploding underwater produces a shock wave which may disable equipment aboard a ship or may even break her up; in some cases the wave from the explosion may capsize a ship. An air burst produces a combination of air blast, radiation, and heat: at some ranges the heat alone may be enough to melt ship structures, especially if they are made of aluminum. About a third of the energy of the bomb goes into heat radiation, but of course relatively little of that hits a ships, as it scatters in all directions. Even beyond the range of blast and nuclear radiation, the heat may be intense enough to cause skin burns among exposed personnel.

About half of the energy of an air-burst bomb goes into a shock wave (air blast), usually categorized by the 'overpressure' (excess air pressure) it produces. For example, a 20-kiloton bomb exploded at optimum height (about 2000ft) produces an overpressure of 10 pounds per square inch (psi) at 1320yds; a 1-megaton weapon produces the same overpressure at about 5000yds. The air blast wave can tear off a ship's superstructure and wreck antennas and topside structures. Many US warships are designed to resist specific overpressures predicated on assumed attacking weapons; there is a trade-off between resistance to heat radiation and to blast, so that standards for blast have to be chosen for distances at which the ship has not already melted from heat. Protective measures include efforts to design the connection between hull and superstructure to transmit unusual stress on the surface of the latter into the hull. For example, main superstructure bulkheads are built as extensions of major hull bulkheads, which may

Atlanta's blast tests, code named 'Sailor Hat', involved the detonation of a 500-ton 'igloo' of TNS 17ft high and with a base diameter of 34ft. The white slick visible in the photograph showing the explosion is a shock wave proceeding towards and past *Atlanta*; it is reminiscent of the 1946 Bikini tests. The ship was ultimately destroyed by being blown in half.

partly account for the boxy appearance of some US warships. The protection of topside structures such as antennas and weapon launchers is more difficult.

So is protection against heat. Aluminum is once again an unfortunate structural choice, as it loses its strength very rapidly as it is heated. Searing heat also starts fires within a ship; because it can affect the whole of the ship almost simultaneously, protection against heat requires some considerable expansion of shipboard fire-fighting systems.

Any bomb exploded near, on, or under the surface of the water produces some radioactive fall-out, which must be removed from the ship. The earliest US experience, at Bikini, suggested that decontamination was the first requirement of protection against nuclear attack, since any ship which survived blast and shock would still have either to be fought or, if she were disabled, to be salvaged. The first US warship designed with nuclear attack in mind was the ASW cruiser *Norfolk*. She was designed to operate fully closed down, so that her personnel would not be directly exposed to radiation or to fall-out, and she had a wash-down system to remove fall-out as rapidly as possible. Such hull details as a sharp break between the ship's side and her deck were designed to keep fall-out from clinging to her. In addition, her funnel caps were designed to resist the kind of bomb overpressure experienced in the Bikini tests. Similar measures were taken in many later US warships; it is notable that the open bridges so well liked in World War II were abandoned. In fact at one time the US Navy considered giving up its practice of placing the helm on the bridge, and instead providing a 'cockpit' deep in the ship, near the steering gear, and connected with the enclosed CIC. In theory a ship so arranged could be operated entirely from below decks, with the aid of her radars.

US doctrine is to steer a ship out of the cloud of fall-out as rapidly as possible, relying on the wind to minimize the effects of fall-out and relying on wash-down to do the rest. Other navies have other views; many prefer to design a 'citadel' into a ship. This internal space, which includes all vital control spaces, can be completely closed down and its air supply filtered, even to the extent of providing a defense not merely against fall-out but also against chemical and biological attack – perhaps a useful measure, given the well-known Soviet interest in chemical warfare. Citadel defense can have important design implications – for example, it is necessary that weapons outside the citadel be remotely operable. The Canadians adopted the British 3in/70 for some of their frigates partly because, unlike any other gun of its time, it could be fired entirely remotely, with no one in mount or magazine.

Nuclear weapons are the mortal enemies of exactly those electronic systems which make warships so effective. Their fireballs are often opaque to radar signals, and EMP can actually burn out circuits. EMP is a powerful pulse created by the pulse of electrons released by the bomb; it is most effective over wide areas if the bomb is exploded very high in the atmosphere: a big weapon exploded at an altitude of several hundred miles might blank out electronic equipment all over an area the size of Europe. There are defenses, but they are both expensive and relatively subtle, and the effect itself is so subtle that nothing short of full-scale tests can tell how a given piece of equipment will react. Usually it is assumed that modern integrated circuits and transistors are far easier to destroy than are the older vacuum tubes, but even that is not absolutely certain. Moreover, details of the construction of a ship can be very important. For example, an enclosed

Present-generation US warships are designed to withstand a high level of underwater shock, not least because underwater nuclear weapons, such as nuclear depth charges, may be involved. New ships are generally shock-tested: here the frigate *Perry* (FFG-7) undergoes such a test, October 1978.

space is generally immune to EMP effects, but the hole cut in a bulkhead to admit a cable or a waveguide destroys that immunity. Even dents in the side of a ship may contribute.

EMP can be visualized as unwanted radio interference; it may follow that ships carefully designed to avoid mutual interference between antennas close together may have superior EMP resistance. Another anti-EMP measure is the avoidance of long wires which may act as antennas receiving the EMP pulse; for example, in some ships, lifelines along the deck are fiberglass rather than wire rope. However, this is not exclusively an anti-EMP measure: those same lifelines will tend to absorb radio signals the ship is trying to radiate and so reduce the efficiency of her own communications. Similarly, strict adherence to an enclosed superstructure is an anti-fallout measure as much as it is an anti-EMP measure.

EMP is so unreliable an effect that perhaps the best characterization is that a commander must beware of its use by an enemy, but that at the same time he cannot be sure that an EMP attack on his part will suffice to render an enemy helpless. For many years the United States has carried out extensive tests of EMP effects on equipment and even on whole ships, using elaborate non-nuclear test facilities, but the details of EMP vulnerability remain somewhat obscure, particularly as they change over the lifetime of a ship. One interesting facet of EMP strikes is that they do not kill personnel (except insofar as the failure of electronic equipment may have fatal consequences). It may follow that a commander certain of the effects of EMP on his enemies might choose to call for a 'demonstration' nuclear explosion at high altitude over a sea area in which his opponent is located, in the expectation that his opponent will be rendered helpless *without significant external damage*. The resulting retreat would look to the world like a political back-down, whereas in fact it would be the consequence of the destruction of just that invisible element of fighting strength which is so characteristic of modern warships.

Finally there is shock, which may be produced not merely by a distant nuclear explosion, but also by quite conventional mine and torpedo hits, as well as the near-misses of conventional bombs. It may also be produced by the explosion of depth charges; US interest in serious shock-hardening was probably first engendered by the consideration that US ships might well find themselves using nuclear depth charges against submarines; it would be a pity if the weapon which destroyed the submarine also disabled the attacker. Details of shock-hardening are secret; however, most warships are designed to some standard of shock-hardness, and for some time at least the United States has run a program of full-scale shock survivability tests against its warships. Similar tests are run against such new items of equipment as gas turbine modules.

UNDERWATER PROTECTION

The third category against which a modern warship may be protected is underwater attack, either under-the-keel or contact (against the side of the ship). Since World War II it has been well known that the former is a far more efficient use of the explosive in the torpedo, but it has also generally been accepted that fuzing a torpedo to explode well under a ship presents great problems; the under-the-keel threat has been limited, in Western minds, to ground mines (acoustic, pressure, or magnetic), such as those laid in Haiphong harbor. There is no great hope of surviving even a relatively small under-the-keel explosion, which is why the Germans spent a great

This is the way most torpedoed ships will probably sink in the future. The light cruiser *Wilkes-Barre* was destroyed by an under-the-keel (stand-off) explosion, which produced an oscillating, rising bubble of gas. On its first explosion, the bubble lifts the ship out of the water, straining its hull girder. Generally, the second expansion suffices to produce the result shown: the hull simply breaks. Conventional hull armor merely makes matters worse, since it makes the hull girder more rigid. This type of attack also causes severe shock damage internally, even if the bubble does not hit squarely enough to destroy the ship. This type of damage is suggested by the radar antenna askew atop the after DP director. Under-the-keel attack is particularly attractive because it is extremely efficient in terms of damage done per weight of explosive, and also because an under-the-keel weapon is lethal if it passes within a relatively wide envelope under a ship. Under-the-keel is the kill mechanism of bottom-laid mines such as the magnetic mine which broke the back of HMS *Belfast* early in World War II.

deal of time developing reliable torpedo fuzes to achieve just such effects; the products of their research fell into both Soviet and Western hands, but appear not to have been followed up in the West. One reason may be the poor performance record of Western magnetic torpedoes in World War II. The Soviets may well, unfortunately, feel otherwise.

Most torpedoes are designed to blow holes in the side of a ship, causing flooding rather than break-up. This kind of attack has been accepted as a danger for a long time, and most surface warships are designed with it in mind. Ships of the World War II period were designed to remain afloat and underway after a single torpedo hit; to this end they had unit or *en échelon* machinery arrangements. However, with the advent of anti-surface ship homing torpedoes, some experts suggested that in future most torpedo hits would be concentrated aft and that widely distributed machinery would contribute little to survivability. This type of doctrine must have been particularly welcome in view of internal hull volume problems; it is always much easier to fit one plant rather than two into a hull. In most current cases escorts such as frigates have single machinery plants, whereas fast (first-line) ships such as missile destroyers and cruisers have two separated plants.

Survivability against flooding is bought by compartmentation and by a hull design which can retain sufficient stability even after flooding. Typical US criteria call for survival after up to 15 per cent of a ship's length has been opened to the sea, or, if practicable, after rapid flooding due to an even longer break caused by a standard enemy weapon. This replaces the old two-compartment standard, in which the ship was to be designed to survive the dectruction of any one bulkhead, which would flood two adjacent compartments; it reflects the greater destructive power of modern torpedoes, as compared to those of the pre-World War II period.

This amounts to a fairly bleak picture, but then again a similar analysis of destroyer survivability written in 1939 would have been just as pessimistic, and one of the great surprises of World War II was just how tough unarmored ships could be. Much of the difference between prewar analysis and combat experience was active damage control carried out by the crew: a ship which does not sink or burn immediately can often be saved by an energetic and well-trained crew, or lost by a less effective one – as the case of the Soviet missile destroyer sunk in the Black Sea in 1974 suggests. Modern electronics can assist damage control by providing a coherent picture of the character of damage to a ship at a central damage control console from which, for example, pumps and counter-flooding pumps can be controlled, as well as fans which move air through the ship – and which, improperly handled, can spread poisonous or explosive fumes. Fire-fighting gear has also developed tremendously since World War II, in the capacity of pumps and in the variety of anti-fire foams, some of which can be released remotely to smother fires in inaccessible spaces. Recent US warships are divided into fire zones by bulkheads extending from the keel into the superstructure.

A ship's survivability in the face of guided weapons also depends upon the counter-measures it carries. Although an SSM may do enormous damage if it hits, it is far more subject than were shells and unguided torpedoes to direct counters: jammers, chaff and subtle devices such as deception repeaters. Guided torpedoes have a very high SSPK – if they are not deceived by a towed torpedo decoy such as the old Foxer or the newer Fanfare and now Nixie. In fact it can be argued that if the principal threat to a modern warship is a relatively small number of extremely lethal projectiles, then classical passive protection (armor) is not worthwhile; space, weight, and money are better spent on active defenses such as anti-missile guns and missiles, and on electronic defenses. The latter are both essentially invisible – who really notices a few extra radomes? – and very difficult to evaluate in peacetime, since in war the enemy's missile may use a radar for which the counter-measures system was not designed. On the other hand, if his radar and the deception device do fit together, then the ship emerges from an attack entirely undamaged.

In fact there is a trade-off between active defense and passive survivability. The higher the sensors are in the ship, the more distant their horizon and the more warning time they provide, for any kind of defense. Similarly, the larger and heavier these sensors, the more effective. Jammers, too, should be high in a ship to give themselves maximum time to act as a missile approaches. However, all this weight presents a stability problem, the same problem which promotes the extensive topside use of aluminum. If the jammers and the radars and perhaps the point defense missiles do their jobs, then there will be no fire in which the aluminum burns and no shower of fragments passing through it. If, however, the jammers and their ilk are just too low to counter the missile in time, then the mild steel superstructure bought by that reduction in topweight may or may not be sufficient to save those inside it.

CHAPTER TWELVE

Future Developments

Despite the developments in naval technology since 1945, present-day surface warships are very closely related to those designed in the immediate postwar period. Most current naval systems can be traced directly to projects begun either during or just after the war. For example, most US naval SAMs are direct descendants of Project 'Bumblebee'. Gas turbines went to sea for the first time in 1946. Hull forms have not changed significantly since the introduction of the big bow sonars in the mid-1950s. Even VDS dates back to experiments of the late 1940s.

'LARGE-SCALE INTEGRATION'

Possibly the most important current development is the miniaturization of electronics through 'large-scale integration' (LSI), the same development which has made it possible to build computer power into a hand-held calculator. LSI promises very high reliability and low power and cooling requirements; in theory an LSI-based shipboard computer, then, releases considerable space and weight for other purposes, even if it has to meet considerably expanded computing requirements. The same technology promises relatively inexpensive fixed-array radars which may achieve the very high data rates required to repel saturation attacks. At some cost in performance, such radars can be wrapped around curved surfaces, such as missile nose cones; in that case they promise much improved missile radar performance at little or no aerodynamic cost. Within a missile, LSI promises ECM-resistance and perhaps the ability to perform evasive maneuvers as it confronts ship or aircraft defenses. In ASW, LSI promises better performance through better signal processing; it is the key to advanced passive sonars, for example, and it may permit the installation of very large active sonars at a relatively low cost in internal hull space. Given this low cost, it becomes attractive to try to abandon the conventional sonar dome in favor of a conformal array spread out over a more conventional hull form. LSI also promises more ASW capability aboard small helicopters suitable for frigate or destroyer operation.

Inexpensive electronics may make it possible to mount advanced SAM systems such as Aegis aboard most fleet escorts. Aegis is not inherently expensive. Its cost is due to the computing power it requires, and that cost is likely to fall as technology advances – probably the only industrial item whose cost falls from year to year is the act of computation. That is a direct consequence of the advent of integrated circuits, ultimately LSI and its successors.

LSI in itself is unlikely to change the shape of surface warships. It cannot reduce the size of radars, since that is a function of radar wavelength – although a fixed array may require far less ship to support it. Nor can it reduce the size of sonars (in wavelengths), since low frequencies are chosen in view of the propagation characteristics of the sea and the noise characteristics of submarines. It does not affect the size of missiles (determined by warhead size and by propulsion technology) or the number required to defeat a raid of a given size; firing doctrine already appears to contemplate the use of no more than two SAMs per target, and it seems likely that SAM lethality and reliability will improve to the point where one will suffice. LSI can make radars, sonars and missiles far less expensive and so permit navies to capitalize on the newer low-cost ship-production techniques. It can reduce manning levels, especially among the expensive electronics technicians. It can release some superstructure volume, and permit placement of the (more compact) computers in less vulnerable spaces, until now far too small to take them. However, a great deal of the volume of even the most automatic CIC is devoted to human monitors, who are unlikely to vanish from the scene.

Moreover, as much as hull size is determined by the need to provide more and more space per man and per computer, it is also determined by the need for seakeeping performance in rough water. It will take some revolutionary development in hull form to change that equation, and so to bring about a sharp reduction in ship size in accordance with the reductions in system weight and ship-impact promised by LSI and allied technologies. Such a revolution may now be at hand.

Until very recently, the driving force in small surface ship development was the need for more and more speed. With the advent of very long range sonars and shipborne helicopters and missiles, the appetite for speed appears to have fallen off. Should that appetite not be whetted, the chances for a radical change in ship hull form are relatively small; all unconventional ships are quite expensive, in terms of ship structure and power, for the relatively small payloads they can support. However, it is not clear that the need for high speed has gone permanently, even for large ships intended for escort and sea control duties.

The key question, as always, is the relation between weapon and sensor range. In the deep ocean, at least at present, a slow or medium-speed escort can sweep a very large area with her active and passive sonars; with the towed array and a good signal processor she may be able to reach out to one or two convergence zones, ie to beyond the range at which the submarine can now fire an underwater-launched missile. However, such performance depends entirely on the state of submarine silencing and upon the character of the sea. The evolution of the towed array, then, is a contest between developers of hydrophones and signal processors on the one hand, and submarine designers on the other. At present it is the accepted wisdom that (i) Soviet submarines are relatively noisy and (ii) the Soviets appear to have little interest in silencing. Moreover, there is a very large Soviet submarine fleet consisting of noisy boats, which would be extremely expensive to silence. It is conceivable that, at least in the deep ocean, active sonars of very long range can function against even silenced submarines, by operating in the 'deep sound channel', about 4000ft below the surface, where sound travels over very long distances. Presumably enough leaks up to permit submarine detection. However, the operation of towed sonars at such depths requires a very slow platform indeed, and it may be necessary to use the sonar intermittently and then to run at high speed to catch up with the force being screened.

Matters must be considerably worse in waters whose acoustic characteristics prohibit convergence-zone or 'bottom-bounce' operation, passive or active. In such cases the sonar range of an escort is considerably shorter than the range of submarine weapons; it is conventional to observe that the submarine is just as blind as the escort, but Soviet tactics emphasize the use of external platforms (such as satellites) to gather target data, and a submarine-launched missile (such as SSN-7) can do its own homing. In this case the escort screen must be some considerable distance from the force it is protecting, and with short sonar ranges the number of escorts required may be prohibitive. One alternative, given a very fast escort, is 'sprint-and-drift': the escort uses her sonar at low (listening) speed – 'drifts' – then moves up to another listening position at high speed, to maintain a high average rate of advance without compromising sonar performance. In principle such tactics permit one or two escorts to maintain a very large screen zone around a moving force, even though their sonars may have relatively short range. The practicability of the tactic is related to the sonar range as compared to submarine and escort speed; a sonar which can detect anything within about 2000yds is far more useful against a 10kt submarine than against a 30kt one. From the submarine's point of view, a 60kt escort can effectively cover two or three escort stations at once, since the submarine cannot move fast enough to get through a temporarily uncovered zone; a 30kt escort may be far less effective. 'Sprint-and-drift' may be particularly attractive in the very bad sonar conditions of the North Sea, the Baltic and the Mediterranean.

There is, however, a definite trade-off between sonar performance and maximum speed, since radical high-speed ships are generally very limited in their load-carrying ability. It is tempting, given LSI technology, to trade in hydrofoils and surface-effect ships for a screen of big helicopters with dipping sonars; after all, the helicopters are faster than a ship, they make less noise, and it can be argued that they can fly above rough water. Given their characteristics, it is unlikely that the radical ships can employ markedly larger sonars than can the helicopters; and the latter may have the advantage that they can obtain signal processing from a remote computer aboard the carrier or large frigate on which they are based. Moreover, the helicopters can be deployed very rapidly along any direction from which a threat may come, whereas the fast surface ships are much less flexible. In this light, the fast surface ship most likely to see construction for the major navies is the Small Waterplane Twin Hull (SWATH), whose forte is good seakeeping combined with the kind of large deck area very suitable for big helicopters.

Many see the fast hydrolfoil as the warship of the future. Here the foilborne *Pegasus* makes a turn – note how she banks, like an airplane. *Pegasus* is armed with the Harpoon anti-ship missile and the OTO-Melara 76mm dual-purpose gun, but her primary defense against incoming missiles will be provided by chaff rockets (yet to be installed). The air intakes of her gas turbines are visible at the base of her tripod mast; the dome visible on the latter presumably carries her SLR-20 passive (ESM) counter-measures system. Fire control/search radar is one of the ubiquitous Dutch systems, and she has an Italian surface search set. The PHM was originally a NATO program, but cost escalation eliminated the projected non-American ships.

For quite some time the US Navy has considered hydrofoils much larger than *Pegaus*. This is a 1400-ton Deepwater Escort Hydrofoil, carrying a somewhat fanciful combat system including what appears to be a NATO Sea Sparrow on the forecastle, with illuminators atop the bridge, but the radars of a Tartar-carrying destroyer topside; aft are the usual box launchers for Harpoon. Right aft is a dipping sonar for 'sprint-and-drift' operations.

This is an artist's concept of the large 2400-tonne Hyd-2 proposed in a recent US study. This was not a serious design, in that the superstructure was essentially a redrawn *Perry* class frigate's; however, the hull form and the size of the foils and struts were realistic and suggest actual possibilities.

The radical hull forms under consideration have been known, in some cases, since early in this century: hydrofoils, surface-effect vehicles, SWATH, and a variety of hybrids. The first two differ from a conventional (displacement) hull in their mode of support; by so doing they reduce considerably the resistance offered by the water and so permit very high speed operation, often in considerable sea states. The basic logic of all three hull forms is that at high speed most resistance arises from wavemaking at the interface between air and water – the waterplane. That is also where waves interact with a ship's hull to make it pitch and roll. The smaller the waterplane, the less the resistance, especially at very high speed. If the ship is supported from well below the waterplane, a small waterplane ship should also have far better seakeeping characteristics than will a conventional one. On the other hand, the smaller the waterplane, the less buoyancy a ship gains for every inch of additional immersion; a small-waterplane ship either must operate over a very small range of displacement, or else she must employ some means of support other than buoyancy. The small waterplane may also make a ship very susceptible to underwater damage; for example, relatively little damage to foils on one side of a hydrofoil may ruin her effective stability.

HYDROFOILS

The hydrofoil supports itself primarily by the lift generated by water passing around wings (foils) held underwater. The higher the speed, the greater the lift; lift can also be increased by varying the angle of attack of the foils. One advantage of the hydrofoil is its ability to operate in rough water: as long as the waves do not reach the hull held above water by the struts, the hydrofoil is unaffected by them. Moreover, in very large waves, the hydrofoil can follow the wave counter, as long as the waves do not crest too abruptly. Properly designed hydrofoils are quite stable in high sea states, and can be quite maneuverable, thanks to steerable struts and the ability to bank into a turn. Current technology (subcavitating foil design) has demonstrated maximum design speeds as high as 60kts; newly developed, variable-geometry foils will allow operations at supercavitating speeds of 70–80kts.

It is often suggested that hydrofoils are limited to quite small sizes by the square-cube law: lift is proportional to foil area, ie to the square of hydrofoil dimensions, whereas weight is proportional to the cube. However, recent studies have shown that the length of the struts (which made up the major portion of the strut/foil system weight) does not increase in proportion to ship size. It appears that the foil system weight fraction remains relatively constant at 12 to 15 per cent of displacement from 300 to 3000 tons fully loaded, and that hydrofoils over this size range can be designed to carry useful loads (fuel and military payload) of 35 to 45 per cent of full load weight, which is comparable to the fraction carried by conventional displacement ships. For example, the 1978 US Navy Advanced Naval Vehicle Concept Evaluation (ANVCE) study included a multi-mission ship 'Hyd-2' carrying two ASW helicopters, with a payload of 335 tonnes (13.9 per cent of the 2400-tonne full load displacement) and transoceanic range. The ANVCE study suggested an upper limit, using current configurations, of about 3000–4000 tonnes, above which the square-cube law would take hold.

A second commonly suggested defect is operational: the hydrofoil is effective only over a relatively narrow range of speeds. As soon as it slows below a critical (take-off) speed, it sinks on to the sea surface: its foils no longer supply enough lift. It would then seem to be subject to all of the seakeeping problems of the small ship. However, it still retains the deeply submerged foil system with its automatic controls, and that system still provides some lift. It can act as a very potent system of stabilizing fins, incorporating a lift control with flaps underwater. Even without the automatic controls, some have judged hydrofoil seakeeping superior to a ship ten times its size, owing to the massive damping effect of the submerged foils. This kind of performance, and the claimed quietness of a hydrofoil, make 'sprint-and-drift' tactics attractive. However, a sprinting hydrofoil must cover a very long distance, and so requires frequent refueling. For example, a 40kt average speed during 'sprint-and-drift' escort of a 20kt convoy must imply that the escort covers twice the distance the convoy covers: 7200 vs 3600nm, perhaps, for an Atlantic crossing.

The hydrofoil is typical of exotic hull forms in that it is very expensive per ton. Its weight critically demands aircraft (aluminum) rather than ship (steel) structure, and such a structure is both expensive and relatively fragile in the face of anti-ship weapons, although hydrofoils in service have shown considerable ruggedness in rough water: for example, they have coped with 15ft waves at over 40kts without damage. There is some question of whether a hydrofoil's speed and maneuverability coupled with its small signature and the well-planned use of chaff will buy it a measure of immunity in the face of anti-ship missile fire. Certainly chaff will present a much larger target relative to a small Patrol Hydrofoil, Missile (PHM) than to a frigate, and the PHM will be able to remove itself from the vicinity of the chaff cloud far more rapidly. However, a frigate of similar cost may be able to carry a greater variety of counter-measures, which may defeat a missile too sophisticated to be misled by chaff. The economy of 'spirit-and-drift' may, then, prove to be a false one in the face of enemy action; moreover, the noise of drifting may well make counter-detection of the hydrofoil much easier.

Hydrofoils do appear to be ideal for the fast attack role, and for shadowing enemy ships ('tattletale'); they may also prove effective in ASW screening, but in view of their very high cost it seems unlikely that they will replace conventional surface destroyers and frigates, at least in the near future. One hydrofoil role seriously considered in the 1960s seems quite valid today – the ECM ship. A fast hydrofoil can carry considerable electronic gear to simulate a carrier or, indeed, a group of ships; moving rapidly out of a task force formation, it might turn on the equipment at some considerable distance to confuse an incoming raid. Given very early warning, which is quite possible in the face of a Soviet-style cruise missile raid, such a craft might make a major contribution to the survival of a task force.

HOVERCRAFT

The hovercraft or Captured Air Bubble (CAB) or Surface Effect Ship (SES) is another approach to the elimination of the waterplane. The ship, or most of it, is lifted clear of the water; it rides a layer of air. Most resistance to motion is due to the friction of the air cushion, although in fact the weight of the craft causes a depression in the water under it, and thus an effective very shallow draught waterplane is created. The problem of hovercraft

design is the need to feed air into the cushion to make up for leakage at the edges. The original Hovercraft floated a few inches off the surface, but later on flexible rubber skirts were added, so that the body of the craft could float several feet off the ground, with the lower edge of the skirt a few inches up to minimize air cushion loss. Such a craft can negotiate fairly large obstacles, and is effectively amphibious; hovercraft were used with considerable success in Borneo and in Vietnam, where their ability to move over swamps and in very shallow water was quite useful. However, if amphibious operation is no object, the water itself admits a much more efficient seal: the skirts of the craft can project into the water, permitting higher internal air pressures (for greater lifting capacity per square foot of lift area). Such craft are termed CAB, because the air bubble is effectively trapped (its loss rate is almost negligible), or SES; typically they have rigid side walls and flexible skirts fore and aft. Hovercraft suffer from relatively low propulsive efficiency, because they ride above the water and so cannot make contact with it; they generally employ aircraft-type propellers. An SES, however, can use propellers or waterjets, which can provide more power and so drive the larger craft which the higher air pressure supports; the SES appears to be the main hope for a really large air cushion vehicle. For example, the US Navy now has a 3000-ton SES frigate under contract, although it is by no means certain that this experimental ship will ever be built.

Unlike the hydrofoil, the SES can operate over a very wide speed range; it has a speed limit of about 80–100kts. but can also operate down to zero speed. However, it encounters seakeeping problems. In effect the SES can disregard waves up to the height of its skirts, but it tends to follow wave contours fairly closely. One solution is to adopt a considerable length to beam ratio – about 6 rather than about 2 as in fast SES designs – but that makes for lower speed, about 50kts; the long SES does, however, enjoy powering advantages at its lower speed. The short SES has to overcome a 'hump' in resistance at about 30–40kts, but at higher speeds (up to about 80kts) resistance is nearly constant, so that it can enjoy a wide range of efficient operating speeds.

All air cushion vehicles suffer severely in rough water; according to one report the hovercraft's performance degrades faster than any other known naval vehicle. Even the SES does badly compared to a hydrofoil or a

The British BH7 is a good example of current hovercraft thinking – a fast (up to 65kts), maneuvrable adjunct to a naval force, especially useful in the amphibious, fast attack or mine counter-measures role. This is the Mk 5A, showing how the wide side decks can be utilized for carrying anti-ship missiles. *(British Hovercraft Corporation)*

SWATH. However, the large SES is attractive because, due to the good seal, it can be made so large that it can retain acceptable seakeeping qualities while enjoying high speed performance. Cushion vehicles also suffer from weight problems; they must maintain lift power to overcome leakage, and the limited pressure that can be maintained limits their weight and so limits their payload and endurance; even at zero speed, the need to maintain lift power limits time endurance, but there is also considerable drag at high speeds, which requires fuel. However, as vehicle size grows, leakage (even in a hovercraft) decreases in proportion to vehicle weight. The short SES is likely to enjoy the best range performance in view of its low power requirements at very high speeds, but it is unlikely to be effective in rough water. The long SES, on the other hand, operates below the 'hump' and as such is similar in theory to a conventional displacement hull, with better overall efficiency; moreover, it can operate at a lower speed and so can trade speed for range (although its curve of power vs speed is flatter than that of a displacement hull). For example, by going from 65 to 50kts a long SES can increase its range by 25 per cent, with another 10 to 15 per cent achieved in going from 50 to 35kts. The long SES does not slow down as fast as a conventional ship in rough water – it is not as effective in this respect as the SWATH or the hydrofoil.

Surface Effect Ships are probably most effective at relatively moderate speeds; one expert suggests that the fatal disease of the 3000-ton SES is the attempt at 80kts. On the same power and with the same fans, it would be possible to build a long SES of 8000 or 9000 tons, with a speed of 50kts (hump speed would be 60–70kts, a quantity based on speed-length ratio). Cost is dominated by powerplant, so that cost per ton (and particularly per ton of payload) is far better for the 50kt large SES than for the 80kt frigate; and the big ship should be able to maintain its speed in Sea State 3 or perhaps even 4, with relatively little degradation in higher sea states.

A very fast SES is of course noisy, but compared to a displacement ship of similar power there is far less waterborne noise (since the noise tends to be fed vertically into the water) so that it does not propagate through the ocean. Similarly, semi-submerged propellers propagate their noise at the surface. Ultimately, radiated noise is proportional to power per ton, and for a long SES that quantity at 50kts might be no more than the power per ton of a conventional ship at 30kts. However, the conventional ASW ship would normally operate at a lower speed; the question of SES operation will always be the utility of high sustained speed in a ship compared to the speed of the helicopter or aircraft she can carry.

The SES does offer considerable deck area in proportion to its weight, and so is well matched to modern weapon systems, which are area-rather than weight-limited, particularly helicopters. It is also a natural user of vertical-launch missiles, again because they require large deck areas rather than much hull depth. However, there is always the problem of seakeeping. Moreover, the SES is unlikely to be particularly inexpensive. Its rationale, therefore, comes down to the need for very high speed. That is always very attractive until the bills for it become due – which is why the 3000-ton SES is in grave danger of cancellation.

Some of the problems of current SES designs may be solved in the future. For example, it may be possible to reduce vertical motion (and so greatly improve seakeeping) by adopting venting of the cushion, variable-geometry lift fans, even auxiliary stabilizing foils inserted into the water. At one point in the development of the 3000-ton SES there was a lengthy delay associated with just such a system; the current design calls for three centrifugal-flow variable-geometry fans on each side-hull, driven by a single gas turbine. However, it remains the case that an SES costs at least four times as much as a conventional ship, and that it is unlikely that the speed difference makes up for the fact that it carries a far smaller military payload.

All of this is not to deny some advantages. For example, the pressure signature of a hovercraft is far lower than that of any conventional ship, so that a hovercraft minesweeper is unlikely to set off pressure mines. Moreover, the explosion of a mine well below the surface is unlikely to affect a hovercraft or SES very severely; similarly, such a craft may well be very nearly immune to under-the-keel attack. On the other hand, like a hydrofoil, the hovercraft or SES has weight problems; it suffers from the cube-square law (although a larger SES can support a greater cushion pressure and so more weight per square foot of cushion). Hence construction tends to be lightweight, with attendant vulnerabilities. Worse, because the hovercraft or SES depends entirely on its lift engines for seakeeping, a disabling hit may subject it to fatal sea damage.

It seems likely that the hovercraft idea will be applied to minecraft and to ships for which amphibious operation is extremely useful: landing craft (as in the Soviet and US Navies) and fast attack craft which now make any convenient beach a useful advanced base. In both the latter cases speed is also a great advantage; for the landing craft, it buys some elements of surprise. In neither case is high speed likely to result in an increase in the speed required of destroyers and frigates, and so in some fundamental shift in their design.

SWATH SHIPS

The SWATH ship is another matter, because its design buys not merely better speed in a seaway, but, far more significantly, much better seakeeping for destroyer-sized ships. Even more importantly, modern destroyers are not so much weight-limited as they are 'moment-limited': it is difficult to load them with more weight *high in the ship*. Although the SWATH, like the hydrofoil and the SES, cannot tolerate large extra loads, it can easily tolerate very large amounts of topweight; it is both steady and stable, a rare combination. For example, a 200-ton US Navy prototype, the *Kaimalino*, can operate a helicopter.

Most SWATH designs envisage a pair of fully submerged torpedo-like hulls supporting a platform on tall struts. The struts must present minimal waterplane area and hence any deeper immersion of the hulls adds very little buoyancy: ballasting is quite desirable since, like a submarine, the SWATH has little reserve of buoyancy (at least up to the point where the upper box enters the water). On the other hand, the pair of widely spread hulls guarantees excellent stability and, because the buoyant support is well below the waves, the SWATH has good seakeeping.

SWATH speed performance is dominated by frictional resistance, just as is the speed performance of a submarine. Its hull area (wetted area) considerably exceeds that of a conventional displacement ship, so that at least at cruising speed a SWATH requires more power than a conventional ship. However, beyond a 'hump' speed, probably about 25–35kts, reduced wavemaking and favorable wave interference effects between the two sides of the SWATH can improve matters considerably. A great deal depends

The *Kaimalino* is the US prototype SWATH; it is shown here during helicopter compatibility trials, September 1976. The letters 'SSP' stand for Semi-Submerged Platform, an earlier SWATH designation. What was remarkable about this 200-ton platform was its dynamic stability.

One of the great advantages of the SWATH concept is the amount of clear deck area it provides, eg for helicopter operations. This is an artist's concept of a coastal surveillance (Coast Guard) cutter, with a hangar quite large enough for two Sea King helicopters – the ship-impact of which is very evident in many Canadian frigates.

upon the detailed design of the SWATH hulls. For example, in 1972 it was reported that in smooth water one design, SWATH III, required about 25 per cent more power between 30 and 40kts than a very good twin-screw destroyer of about the same displacement but 68 per cent longer and with 50 per cent less draught. However, the SWATH 7 design developed in 1977 has longer hulls of improved form: only 10 per cent more power is required between 30 and 40kts. Perhaps more importantly, either SWATH ship would show virtually no loss of speed in head seas of State 5, whereas a destroyer would require about 15 per cent more power to maintain speed in the same sea – assuming that speed were not reduced because of such ship motions as slamming, which would undoubtedly be the case.

Perhaps the single greatest problem of SWATH development is propulsion; it is necessary either to squeeze a very powerful engine into the relatively constricted hull, or else to find some efficient way of transmitting considerable power from an engine in the above-water hull down to a screw in each submerged body. The gas turbine is a very good candidate for the propulsive system: it can operate unmanned, and it may be able to utilize the struts for air intake and for exhaust. Alternatively, should liquid-cooled on superconducting electric components be developed successfully, some form of gas turbine/electric propulsion would be ideal, using the water flowing past the submerged hulls to carry away heat.

As in the other concepts, there are problems of endurance in small versions, at least partly because the SWATH may encounter greater resistance to forward motion at cruising speeds. However, a relatively small increase in full load displacement will usually suffice to solve the fuel problem, at little additional cost in resistance. In any case, the SWATH is far more economical than the hydrofoil or the SES, and it does have the potential for relatively simple construction, using materials less fragile than those in either of the other radical ship types. Moreover, its twin hulls are ideal sonar platforms for quite conventional sonar operation, since they are deeply submerged and operate in a smooth flow regime.

SWATH is limited in high-speed maneuvrability (although excellent at very low speeds), as might be expected from its broad beam, but that is not nearly as important as in earlier ships, given the range of shipboard weapons. Perhaps more importantly, it suffers from dimensions not well adapted to existing facilities, such as great beam and draught, although for the latter it may prove possible to design a SWATH which can float on its two hulls when in port. and then ballast it down to SWATH configuration for open-sea operation.

One great advantage of SWATH as compared to a conventional ship is that its hulls are relatively simple in structure and in shape; it may well be possible to mass-produce SWATH hulls without conventional shipyard facilities, which may be an important consideration in event of mobilization. The very large deck area is adaptable to a variety of current and contemplated weapons, including vertical-launch missiles; and the electronic revolution is likely to reduce manning requirements and so simplify the design of the above-water box. The new modular weapon and sensor concept is inherently more compatible with SWATH than with any other hull type.

It seems likely that SWATH will be most attractive in the range up to about 15–20,000 tons; at the upper level, conventional ships can compete in seakeeping, and it will become more and more difficult to accommodate a SWATH in conventional harbor facilities.

HYBRIDS

There are also hybrid proposals. For example, it is possible to build a single-hull low waterplane area ship, stabilized with underwater foils which act as hydrofoils (lifting surfaces) at high speed; for example, foil angle of attack can be varied with load, so that this hybrid can operate over a wide range of loads. Its unloaded weight is supported by the buoyancy of the single hull, and therefore it is far less weight-critical than a hydrofoil. However, it is unstable except above a critical speed – the speed at which the foils become effective. Below that speed, it sinks far enough into the water for the buoyancy of the upper hull to be effective.

Adopting any of the radical hull forms might mean a considerable shift in naval tactics and in the composition of fleets. It seems unlikely, then, that high-speed ships such as big hydrofoils or SES vehicles will be brought into service on a large scale unless there is some event so striking as to force major navies to invest heavily – and suddenly. On an infinitely smaller scale, the sinking of the Israeli destroyer *Eilat* by an Egyptian 'Styx' missile in 1968 was just such an event, forcing the major Western navies to take surface-to-surface missiles seriously for almost the first time. However, it seems unlikely that the adoption of very high speed missile boats will force up the speed requirements of destroyers and frigates; very high speeds may, however, cause some Western navies to build a few high speed ships if only to show their own governments that they are not hopelessly behind the times. It is possible, too, that a successful small-scale submarine campaign on the part of the part of the Soviets or their client states may force upon the Western navies so thoroughgoing a re-examination of their ASW policies as to inspire them to produce radically different types of escorts. SWATH might be a particular beneficiary of such a review.

On a more prosaic level, SWATH may be the beneficiary of the present dismal trend in warship economics. Although a SWATH ship may cost more, ton for ton, than a conventional ship, it does not cost very much more, and a relatively small SWATH has the seakeeping characteristics of a considerably larger conventional ship. It is possible that, should the US Navy be forced into a rapid build-up, SWATH would actually prove a good deal more attractive than any more conventional escort design. This hull form already has many advocates, and the US Navy is gradually moving towards a full-scale prototype. If, as seems likely, helicopters and V/STOL aircraft become more and more essential to ASW at the ranges imposed by enemy submarine-launched missiles, then escort seakeeping and stability are likely to become dominant characteristics. Merchant ship speeds are rising, and the large merchant ships can maintain those speeds in very rough water indeed. Moreover, nuclear submarines armed with medium-range missiles can intercept and attack fast merchant ships; in a future ASW war the independent routing of fast ships may become entirely impracticable. In that case there will be a premium on fast escorts capable of operating helicopters in rough water – and SWATH may be the most economical alternative.

The future for SES is probably far bleaker, unless there is some revolution in sea transportation in which substantial numbers of really large trans-oceanic SES merchant ships are built. Simply because their speed will not buy them immunity from attack, these ships will require escort by ships with similar speed characteristics, and it will be necessary for a navy to build a class of SES frigates. Short of such a development, SES is probably too expensive to be built in a period of generally tightening fiscal resources. Its main asset is strategic mobility, the ability to provide some minimal naval power at a distant point twice or three times as fast as a conventional task force can reach that point. Thus it is sometimes argued that an SES aircraft carrier might be an extremely valuable asset in a convoy battle extending, as future battles well may, over the whole of the North Atlantic, simply because it could multiply the effect of carrier-borne ASW aircraft, refuelling them far from their carriers. Quite possibly cost will restrict the SES to wargame boards unless there is some massive naval rearmament under which funds will become much more freely available.

THE LONG-TERM VIEW

The radical hull forms represent current or short-term technology. However, ships last from twenty to thirty years, and quite conventional ships now on the slip will probably still be in service past the year 2000, unless there is a war in the interim to use them up. By then naval technology may have evolved in far more radical directions. A caveat is necessary here: had these words been written in 1945, the naval world of 1980 would be described in terms of all-nuclear fleets, using nuclear-missile weapons, and probably directed by satellite – if ships were required at all. Probably the greatest surprise of naval development since 1945 is the relative absence of radical change. Navies tend, for excellent reasons, to be fairly conservative. They must deal with an unchanging sea, the physical character of which is far stronger than any new technology. Moreover, by far the bulk of the world's military research and development funds has gone into a combination of nuclear research (power and weapons), aerodynamics (missiles and high-speed aircraft), and sensors (radar and sonar, much more the former, which benefits from Army and Air Force as well as Navy

An artist's impression of the 3000-ton Surface Effect Ship on order from Rohr Marine Inc for the US Navy. It is to be about 270ft long and to achieve over 80kts on a combination of four LM 2500 propulsion engines and two LM 2500 lift engines, a total of about 120,000hp. The weapon system shown includes a frigate (FFG-7) fire control system but no missile launcher or OTO-Melara gun; it is presumably not the one which will be fitted should the SES actually be built. That is in question, as the Navy and the Department of Defense have found it difficult to define the SES mission very clearly. (Rohr Marine Inc)

With the rise of the smaller navies and the ageing of the World War II destroyers and frigates which initially equipped them, there is now a very large market for new surface warships, from corvettes through missile destroyers, with an emphasis on low unit cost (including manning), firepower, and speed, in ships which will spend a good part of their time near their bases. Gas turbines have been a particularly important development, in that they promise great power at a low investment in personnel, space, and weight. In about 1962 Vosper began a series of studies of light surface ships, initially corvettes but later light destroyers, particularly after the merger with Thornycroft early in 1966. Mark numbers were initially assigned on the basis of tonnage: Mk 1 for the 500-ton corvette, Mk 3 for the 650-tonner, Mk 5 for a 1300-ton destroyer, and Mk 7 for a 1500-ton destroyer. Mark numbers were also applied to designs not brought to the point of production. However, the recent Mk 9 (not built) is a 740-ton corvette, somewhat modified (and enlarged to 840 tons) for the production version for Nigeria; Mk 10 is a large frigate built, so far, for Brazil. This series has probably had the greatest success of any purely commercial frigate so far. Each outline design is offered with a variety of machinery configurations and with alternative weapon suits; for example, Brazil bought both ASW and general-purpose versions of the Mk 10.

1 The first two Vosper corvettes were built for Ghana as a joint venture with Vickers and were designated Mk 1; this is *Kromantse*. She displaces 440 tons (standard) and is impressively armed for that size: a 4in gun forward, a 40mm mount aft, and Squid for ASW. The air search radar is the commercial Plessey AWS-1, and there is a keel sonar. She is diesel driven at 20kts. This type made a considerable impression at the time, as an indication of just how inexpensive a small ASW ship could be, both in hardware and in personnel (total complement was limited to 54). (*Vosper Thornycroft*)

2 Libya bought the Mk 1 (*Tobruk* is shown) in somewhat modified form, with four 40mm guns, surface search radar only, and no Squid. A suite of State apartments was included in this version of the basic design. (*Vosper Thornycroft*)

3 The Mk 3 was an enlarged Mk 1, with far more sophisticated fire control (the Dutch HSA M-20 in the forward radome) as well as a separate surface search radar (Decca TM 626). There is no ASW battery, only a standard Royal Navy twin 4in dual purpose gun forward, two 40mm and two 20mm guns. There is design provision for sonar and an ASW weapon, but these have not been fitted. As in the Mk 1, propulsion is by diesel, with speed increased to 23kts. Design requirements included operation in long Atlantic swells (note the bulwark and freeing ports abreast the gun) as well as in the tropical coastal environment (living spaces are air conditioned). The success of these units led directly to a Nigerian order for two Mark 9s. A Mk 3, *Dorina*, is shown here. (*Vosper Thornycroft*)

4 The 850-ton Mk 9 corvette was essentially an enlarged Mk 3 with provision for air, surface, and subsurface warfare. As in the earlier ships, she employs a full-width superstructure to gain internal volume, and a considerable flare forward (as well as a knuckle) both for seakeeping and to increase forecastle area. In fact this photograph of the Nigerian *Erin'mi*, taken in a Force 7 gale, gives some idea of just how seaworthy these craft are. The weapon and electronic suit is international, and far more sophisticated than that of the Mk 3: an OTO-Melara 3in/62 dual purpose gun forward, with a two-barreled Bofors 375mm ASW rocket launcher superfiring above it; a 40mm/70 Bofors gun aft with a high rate of fire (and proximity-fuze shells); and a new triple Seacat launcher right aft. There are also two single 20mm guns for dealing with small craft; they had not yet been mounted, nor had the two chaff launchers, when this photo was taken. The main sensors are a Plessey PMS 26 sonar (which also warn of approaching torpedoes), a Dutch HSA WM-24 fire control system, a Plessey AWS-2 air search radar, and a Decca TM 1226 surface search radar. The M-24 is designed to track one air and two surface targets for fire control, and at the same time to provide data for manual tracking of four targets (air or surface); this is not anything like the capabilities achieved by automated combat data systems aboard major Western (or, presumably, Soviet) warships, but it does suffice for the kinds of threat that Nigerian Navy is likely to encounter. Finally, the Mk 9, like the earlier Vosper corvettes, is diesel driven; however, the coupling developed for the Mk 10 frigate permits the use of two engine per shaft, and speed therefore rises to 27 kts. (*Vosper Thornycroft*)

5 Work on a light destroyer development of the Vosper corvettes began in 1964; design requirements included small size (the original target was 1000 tons but that had to be relaxed) and the ability to carry a 4.5in gun, a point defense weapon such as Seacat, and a smaller automatic gun; versions were to include one to carry a small ASW helicopter such as the Westland Wasp, or an ASW mortar, or perhaps a surface-to-surface missile. Speed was set at 40kts, achieved by a CODAG plant. The four units built for Iran (this is *Faramarz*) were armed with a single 4.5 gun forward, a triple Seacat before the bridge, an Italian Sea Killer surface-to-surface missile aft, and a twin 35mm Oerlikon AA gun right aft, as well as 'Limbo' in an after well – an impressive performance on only 1110 tons (standard). The radar suit included an AWS-1 for air search and there were two Contraves Sea Hunter fire control systems. Sea Killer is a beam-riding (Sea Hunter beam) anti-ship missile with a range of about 15nm; it is apparently unique to this class. (*Vosper Thornycroft*)

6 The Mk 7 was an enlarged Mk 10 which could equipped with a large fixed-dome keel sonar such as the British Type 184, as well as a small ASW helicopter in a collapsible hangar. A weapon and sensor suit comparable with that in much larger Royal Navy frigates could be accommodated on the basis of much reduced spare parts and stores stowage, as the ship would operate at a relatively short distance from a base. The Mk 5 powerplant would drive this larger ship (1325 tons) at 37.5kts. In fact the single unit built, the Libyan *Dat Assawari*, was designed primarily for surface and air warfare, with a single 4.5in gun forward, two single 40mm, and a twin 35mm right aft, plus 'Limbo' in a well, with the three muzzles visible. (*Vosper Thornycroft*)

5

6

7 With the six Mk 10 frigates, Vosper-Thornycroft passed over to the construction of ships fully as large as contemporary Western types, and indeed rather larger than the contemporary British Type 21 design. Propulsion is CODAG. The battery is not nearly so much more powerful than that of a Mk 7 as one might imagine from the difference in displacement, but much of that difference comes from the fact that the Mk 10 must operate in the conventional manner, far from its base. Note that speed is no longer a vital consideration in this warship. The Royal Navy, faced with the obsolescence of many of its frigates and delays in the Type 22 design, chose to purchase eight frigates (Type 21) designed by Vosper-Thornycroft and Yarrow in collaboration; the ships thus reflect experience gained in the construction of many foreign corvettes and light destroyers.

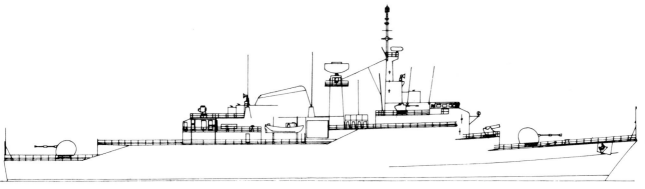

7

interest); other military and civilian money has gone into computers. That leaves very little for radical new hull forms or unconventional engines or even for new kinds of communications nets.

Possibly the most radical future development would be a wide-area ASW sensor, which could turn the ocean into a more or less murky kind of glass. SOSUS is one approach; a worldwide SOSUS network linked together by effective communications and feeding very fast computers might actually be able to detect submarines in almost any part of the world. It would be blinded in areas of high shipping density and it might be defeated by many ocean thermal conditions, as well as by rough (noisy) surface weather, but it would fundamentally change the balance between convoy and HUK in ASW. A variety of non-acoustic sensors is often advertised in a similar connection; for example, a submarine churns up the cold water of the deep ocean and so leaves a thermal wake, perhaps visible to a very sensitive thermocouple – even one in space. The wake is a very weak effect, and there is a great deal of 'noise' on the ocean surface, but it is the kind of effect which just might be visible from space – as one popular movie has suggested. There are other phenomena as well, and several navies are willing to spend a great deal of money in the hope of rendering the world ocean essentially transparent. Should this objective be realized, the value of speed will rise very suddenly, since a wide-area locator requires very fast HUK forces to capitalize on its detections. Long-range maritime aircraft may well supplant most ASW escorts, and submarines may lose much of their present significance. Shipping warfare may become the province of surface ships capable of defending themselves against air attack, and therefore unconcerned that any ship on the ocean surface is already (in theory) detectable.

Of course, the advent of a wide-area submarine detector would have other implications as well, probably the most important of which would be the end of the sea sanctuary for ballistic missiles. Such a development would probably affect the West far more than the Soviets, since it is already Soviet doctrine to maintain submarines in coastal sanctuaries under the cover of other Soviet naval and land-based forces. Western ballistic missile submarines, on the other hand, are maintained in attack positions in peace-time as a deterrent; they are, therefore, out of range of friendly forces. The advent of later versions of the US Trident is likely, however, to make a US sanctuary worthwhile. In that case there might be a requirement for US barrier maintenance forces comparable to those now operated by the Soviet Union.

Finally, it is possible that with the advent of nuclear parity between the United States and the Soviet Union, minor warfare between the two and between their proxies will become far more common than has been the case. Amphibious operations may also become more common, and there may be a revival of shore-bombardment ships, such as the abortive American LFS fire support ship. Western interest in anti-ship operations may continue to increase as missile-firing fast patrol boats become more and more common in Third World navies, and as intervention against those navies seems more and more likely. Carrier aircraft are probably the most economical way to deal with fast attack craft firing medium-range missiles such as 'Styx' or Exocet; it remains to be seen whether the Western navies will return to carrier operations after having abandoned them as too expensive. In that case the current trend towards missile-armed general purpose escorts may well reverse in favor of pure carrier escorts. The future evolution of vertical

One of the major influences on ship design – at least in the Western world – is that of spiralling costs; in an attempt to meet this problem, a number of radical designs have been proposed. One such is the 'Flower' class multi-role corvette, a collaborative project involving Britain (Three Quays Marine Services) and West Germany (Thyssen Nordseewerke and Bremer Vulkan). On a common 282ft hull, three basic variants are proposed: the offshore protection version (armed with a single 40mm); the anti-submarine version (one OTO-Melara 76/62, two 40mm, four torpedo tubes); and the strike version (eight Exocet or Harpoon missiles, two 40mm, four torpedo tubes). In addition, up to two Lynx helicopters can be accommodated. The plan views illustrate the basic layouts of each version; the profile depicts the ASW version.

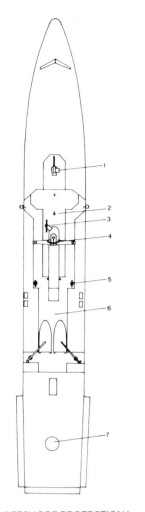
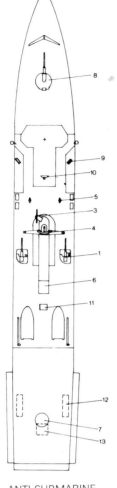
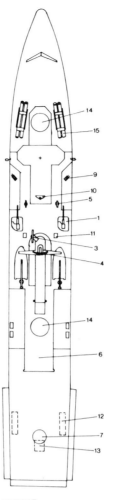

OFFSHORE PROTECTION/ PATROL   ANTI-SUBMARINE   STRIKE

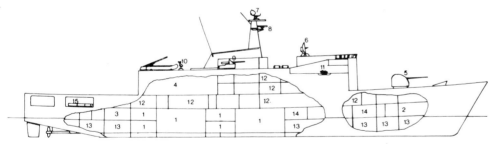

KEY (PLAN VIEWS)

 1 40mm gun mounting
 2 Fire monitor
 3 Navigation radar Type TM 1226
 4 Surveillance radar Type AWS4 or -5
 5 Flare projector
 6 Hangar for Lynx helicopter(s)
 7 Deckload
 8 OTO-Melara 76/62 gun mounting
 9 Hycor chaff launcher

10 Tracker radar RTN 10X
11 Optical radar
12 ASW torpedo tubes Type PM W
13 Towed acoustic array
14 BPD missile system
15 MM40 or Harpoon missile launchers

KEY (PROFILE)

 1 Machinery compartments
 2 OTO magazine
 3 Torpedo magazine

 4 Hangar
 5 OTO-Melara 76/62 gun mounting
 6 Tracker radar
 7 Surveillance radar
 8 Navigation radar
 9 40mm gun mounting
10 Optical tracker
11 Chaff launcher
12 Accommodation areas
13 Fuel
14 Stores
15 Torpedo tubes

take-off (and, far more important, vertical landing) aircraft will have a great deal to do with the future of carrier aviation and hence, by extension, with the future shape of surface warships. All of these developments are of course less radical than the shifts in the shape of warships possible should SES or SWATH come to be widespread.

There is, after all, a great deal of new technology available, and one can sketch a great variety of radical new naval concepts. However, the same sketches could be – were – drawn two decades ago, and they have not yet been translated into steel. New ideas cost little, but radical shifts in strategy and in basic technology are extremely expensive. No navy is so willing to give up its existing plant that it will easily shift; shifts generally come when there is no other way out of some existing problem, or when all navies uneasily realize that a shift is coming. That was the case with HMS *Dreadnought*: Sir John Fisher knew that the all-big-gun battleship was coming, and resolved to meet the new age head-on. Carrier aviation was devised to meet the immediate problems of World War I, but its exploitation after the war was certainly encouraged by the knowledge that aviation was already present in naval affairs in land-based form; there was no alternative. There is no comparable revolution on the naval horizon, but that proves relatively little.

One reason for the lack of revolutionary developments is probably that there has been no great naval war to test the systems built up since World War II. Exercises do not have nearly the effect of the test of battle, which is why even wars clearly unlike the major scenarios drawn by the great navies can have disproportionate effects: the sinking of the *Eilat,* the Indo-Pakistani War of 1971, the Arab-Israeli War of 1973. None exercised modern command-and-control systems, which are the heart of US naval tactics. The United States learned a great deal during its naval operations off Vietnam, but those operations were so atypical of navy-on-navy warfare that they will probably have few long-lasting effects. This situation recalls the period from the Crimean War through 1914, when quite minor naval wars in South America had major effects on European warship design, and when conflicting attaché reports from the Russo-Japanese War were major-caliber ammunition in the *Dreadnought* debate. Then, as now, no one had the slightest idea of how the most modern fleets would behave in battle, or even, for that matter, of what their principal problems would turn out to be.

We can only hope that the Western navies will not find a new Jutland at the end of that period of peace.